Paramagnetic Resonance

Frontiers in Physics

A Lecture Note and Reprint Series

DAVID PINES, *Editor*

N. Bloembergen **NUCLEAR MAGNETIC RELAXATION:** *A Reprint Volume*

Geoffrey F. Chew **S-MATRIX THEORY OF STRONG INTERACTIONS:** *A Lecture Note and Reprint Volume*

R. P. Feynman **QUANTUM ELECTRODYNAMICS:** *A Lecture Note and Reprint Volume*

R. P. Feynman **THE THEORY OF FUNDAMENTAL PROCESSES:** *A Lecture Note Volume*

Hans Frauenfelder **THE MÖSSBAUER EFFECT:** *A Collection of Reprints with an Introduction*

Robert Hofstadter **NUCLEAR AND NUCLEON STRUCTURE:** *A Reprint Volume*

Leo P. Kadanoff and Gordon Baym **QUANTUM STATISTICAL MECHANICS:** *A Lecture Note Volume*

George E. Pake **PARAMAGNETIC RESONANCE:** *An Introductory Monograph*

David Pines **THE MANY-BODY PROBLEM:** *A Lecture Note and Reprint Volume*

L. Van Hove, N. M. Hugenholtz, and L. P. Howland **PROBLEMS IN THE QUANTUM THEORY OF MANY-PARTICLE SYSTEMS:** *A Reprint Volume*

PARAMAGNETIC RESONANCE

An Introductory Monograph

G. E. PAKE

Washington University
Saint Louis

W. A. BENJAMIN, INC. New York 1962

PARAMAGNETIC RESONANCE

Library of Congress Catalog Card Number 62–15643
Manufactured in the United States of America

The manuscript was received on January 20, 1962, and was published on September 1, 1962

The publisher is pleased to acknowledge the assistance of William Prokos, who produced the illustrations

W. A. BENJAMIN, INC.
2465 Broadway, New York 25, N.Y.

Editor's Foreword

The problem of communicating in a coherent fashion the recent developments in the most exciting and active fields of physics seems particularly pressing today. The enormous growth in the number of physicists has tended to make the familiar channels of communication considerably less effective. It has become increasingly difficult for experts in a given field to keep up with the current literature; the novice can only be confused. What is needed is both a consistent account of a field and the presentation of a definite "point of view" concerning it. Formal monographs cannot meet such a need in a rapidly developing field, and, perhaps more important, the review article seems to have fallen into disfavor. Indeed, it would seem that the people most actively engaged in developing a given field are the people least likely to write at length about it.

"Frontiers in Physics" has been conceived in an effort to improve the situation in several ways. First, to take advantage of the fact that the leading physicists today frequently give a series of lectures, a graduate seminar, or a graduate course in their special fields of interest. Such lectures serve to summarize the present status of a rapidly developing field and may well constitute the only coherent account available at the time. Often, notes on lectures exist (prepared by the lecturer himself, by graduate students, or by postdoctoral fellows) and have been distributed in mimeographed form on a limited basis. One of the principal purposes of the "Frontiers in Physics" series is to make such notes available to a wider audience of physicists.

It should be emphasized that lecture notes are necessarily rough and informal, both in style and content, and those in the series will prove no exception. This is as it should be. The point of the series is to offer new, rapid, more informal, and it is hoped, more effective ways for physicists to teach one another. The point is lost if only elegant notes qualify.

A second way to improve communication in very active fields of physics is by the publication of collections of reprints of recent articles. Such collections are themselves useful to people working in the field. The value of the reprints would, however, seem much enhanced if the collection would be accompanied by an introduction of moderate length, which would serve to tie the collection together and, necessarily, constitute a brief survey of the present status of the field. Again, it is appropriate that such an introduction be informal, in keeping with the active character of the field.

A third possibility for the series might be called an informal monograph, to connote the fact that it represents an intermediate step between lecture notes and formal monographs. It would offer the author an opportunity to present his views of a field that has developed to the point at which a summation might prove extraordinarily fruitful, but for which a formal monograph might not be feasible or desirable.

Fourth, there are the contemporary classics—papers or lectures which constitute a particularly valuable approach to the teaching and learning of physics today. Here one thinks of fields that lie at the heart of much of present-day research, but whose essentials are by now well understood, such as quantum electrodynamics or magnetic resonance. In such fields some of the best pedagogical material is not readily available, either because it consists of papers long out of print or lectures that have never been published.

"Frontiers in Physics" is designed to be flexible in editorial format. Authors are encouraged to use as many of the foregoing approaches as seem desirable for the project at hand. The publishing format for the series is in keeping with its intentions. Photo-offset printing is used throughout, and the books are paper bound, in order to speed publication and reduce costs. It is hoped that the books will thereby be within the financial reach of graduate students in this country and abroad.

Finally, because the series represents something of an experiment on the part of the editor and the publisher, suggestions from interested readers as to format, contributors, and contributions will be most welcome.

David Pines

Urbana, Illinois
August 1961

Preface

This small book grew from my lecture notes for a special-topics graduate course given at Stanford University during the winter, or middle, term of the 1960–1961 academic year. The academic quarter offers but ten weeks of lecture period, and in the interest of accuracy it must be said that the book represents what I had *hoped* to accomplish during the term. Those who attended the lectures will find fewer omissions of important topics as well as, if my efforts have succeeded, improved treatment of others.

The readers to whom my writing is directed are students or scientists in any specialization who possess in their background the equivalent of the usual one-year graduate course in quantum mechanics. In some instances these readers will be graduate students beginning research in some branch of physics—e.g., low temperature or solid state—for which paramagnetic resonance is a useful research tool. In other instances they will be physicists, chemists, biologists, or engineers already established in their fields, who are desirous of understanding a new and powerful technique for exploring or applying the electronic magnetic properties of matter. The book is in no sense a treatise, but it does attempt to provide a coherent and comprehensible introduction to the fundamentals of paramagnetic resonance. Study of the book should enable the reader to turn successfully to any paper on the subject in the periodical literature. References encountered as one proceeds will introduce the periodical literature to date, but no claim of completeness can be made for the list of references cited.

This book was conceived just prior to the expected appearance of Abragam's masterful treatise, "Principles of Nuclear Magnetism" (Oxford University Press, New York, 1961). Casual examination will show frequent reference to Abragam, and it might be asked why the present book was written at all. The first reason, of course, is that electronic magnetism possesses certain complicating features not found in nuclear magnetism and therefore not treated in Abragam's book. The most fundamental of these features is the influence of the crystalline electric field, which may be strong enough to suppress substantially all of the orbital angular momentum of the paramagnetic ion. Generally speaking, the hierarchy of interactions for paramagnetic ions is both more heavily populated and less well segregated in magnitude than that for nuclear magnets, with the consequence that perturbation procedures in electron resonance often are either strained or not applicable at all. On the whole, electronic paramagnetism is less precisely understood than nuclear magnetism. Some day in the near future, electronic paramagnetic resonance will doubtless benefit from a treatise such as Abragam's. The present volume is quite obviously in *no* sense a pretender to that role—neither in completeness nor in sophistication. In fact, the aim is to impart that initial physical understanding upon which the student can base a more sophisticated and complete comprehension.

The elegance of group theory is missing from Chapter 3, which deals with the crystalline electric field. In my judgment, both for the lectures and for this resulting volume, use of group theory is precluded by the fact that the overwhelming majority of those in the anticipated audience are not conversant with it. Doubtless the physics graduate curriculum of the immediate future must include group theory as a standard element, inasmuch as physicists are aware that it is the symmetries of nature upon which our understanding ever more heavily relies. For the present, group theory is not available, and our treatment lacks its compactness. I dare to suspect that this defect in a first introduction to paramagnetic resonance is less serious than many would suppose, for my teaching experience at various levels from freshman to graduate does not convince me that compactness of treatment always provides maximum understanding.

Chapter 7, on the general theories of relaxation, is again anything but a complete and elegant discussion, and it perhaps needs a word of explanation. Graduate students in experimental physics, as well as experimental physicists with more experience, generally find heavy going in the papers applying the density-matrix formalism to assemblies of elementary magnets. I have written Chapter 7 in an effort to introduce the topic with emphasis on the rationale and the physics rather than the formalism. On the other hand, certain computational procedures, such as trace calculation, are carried through in detail for a particular illustrative example. The emphasis on exchange narrowing, which was not foremost in the presentation by Kubo and Tomita of their theory, is especially suited to this volume. I hope the chapter will prove genuinely useful, and I shall be disappointed if it only adds to the "heaviness" of the going or, worse yet, if it confuses.

The book is definitely limited to a discussion of the fundamentals of the subject. Applications of several kinds are sketched ever so briefly in Chapter 8, which serves chiefly as a bridge to the literature on these topics.

It had been my intention from the outset to include within this volume reprints of the Bleaney–Stevens and Bowers–Owen articles (References 6 and 7 of Chapter 1), with a view to providing historical perspective concerning paramagnetic resonance as well as numerical data on a representative group of paramagnetic crystals. Initial announcements of this book, which indicated that the reprints would be included, were based upon early permission from the Physical Society of London. However, unanimous permission of the authors could not be obtained. I deeply regret that we were not able to reproduce the review articles in their entirety, but I am grateful that permission to reproduce excerpts enables us to provide an appendix giving numerical data on a reasonably large sample of paramagnetic crystals.

I should like to acknowledge many profitable discussions over recent years with Professor James H. Burgess, who has probably influenced my view of paramagnetic resonance more than we both realize. I am deeply indebted to Professor Joseph F. Dreitlein and to Dr. Theodore G. Castner, both of whom read carefully the entire manuscript and suggested a number of substantial improvements in accuracy and clarity. Finally, for cheerful willingness to work long, back-breaking hours on manuscript typing to meet a deadline, I owe an incalculable debt of gratitude to Miss Catherine Rieser.

G. E. Pake

Los Altos, California
June 25, 1962

Contents

Paramagnetic Resonance

[1]

Introduction

1-1 What Is Paramagnetic Resonance?

The confusion in magnetic resonance terminology leads us to begin on a somewhat pedantic note. Our subject is sometimes called electron paramagnetic resonance or electron spin resonance. Paramagnetic resonance, strictly speaking, refers to the magnetic resonance of permanent magnetic dipole moments and it encompasses not only the magnetic resonance of electrons but also nuclear magnetic resonance (NMR), a topic that is touched upon but is not the central theme in this book. Electron spin resonance is more specific, but it is perhaps inaccurate in its implications because orbital angular momentum as well as spin angular momentum contributes in general to the electronic magnetic dipole moment. Even the famous quenching which occurs for the iron group ions does not stamp out altogether the orbital angular momentum contribution to the magnetic moment.

Our decision simply to refer to paramagnetic resonance throughout the book is perhaps justifiable on the grounds that the extensive contributions of the Oxford workers have earned for them the right to name the subject. Fundamentally, even the all-encompassing feature of the term should not be misleading, as it is easy in principle to transform the theory of electronic paramagnetic resonance for use with nuclear moments, which in general have interactions of the same or simpler form but of considerably smaller magnitude.

We shall denote by $\boldsymbol{\mu}$ the total magnetic moment, arising from all contributions, of the paramagnetic entity that endows the substance of interest with its paramagnetism. Throughout the study we shall find ourselves concerned with the energy E_i of interaction of the ith paramagnet with the magnetic field $\mathbf{H}_i$ in which it exists:

$$E_i = -\boldsymbol{\mu}_i \cdot \mathbf{H}_i$$

Since the magnetic field $\mathbf{H}_i$ may arise from neighboring paramagnets within the substance of interest, as well as from external laboratory magnets and currents, it is clear that the magnetic energy of the substance will involve a many-body Hamiltonian in which the paramagnets are at least coupled in pairs through magnetic dipole–dipole interactions.

The greatest simplification occurs when the paramagnets may be considered independent and noninteracting. Then, since each paramagnet has a moment $\boldsymbol{\mu}$ proportional to the total angular momentum $\mathbf{J}$ of the ion, atom, or molecule,[1] a sample placed in a uniform field $\mathbf{H}_0$ will have for each of its constituent paramagnets a ladder of $2J + 1$ accessible levels (see Fig. 1-1). Thermal excitation lifts fractions of the total number of these paramagnets into the upper levels, and we shall see shortly (Sec. 1-2) that classical Boltzmann statistics predicts the resulting magnetization for this case.

Magnetic resonance is the phenomenon of inducing transitions among the $2J + 1$ energy levels, although we shall find magnetic resonances experimentally for many materials that do not admit a single particle model or uniformly spaced energy levels. Indeed, the great interest in paramagnetic resonance lies in the information we can glean from it concerning interactions involving the individual paramagnet with its neighbors and the "crystalline" environment (whether ordered in a truly crystalline form or not). Much of what we do in these studies will consist of treating these interacting particles by perturbation procedures designed to handle weak couplings. However, even weak interactions are not readily taken into account for a many-particle system.

[1] This is a special case of the Wigner–Eckhart theorem. It follows from the quantum mechanical properties of angular momentum, as indeed it must, because there is no vector other than $\mathbf{J}$ in the problem. For more formal discussions, see, e.g., E. Feenberg and G. E. Pake, "Notes on the Quantum Theory of Angular Momentum," Stanford University Press, Stanford, Calif., 1959 (reprinting of the 1953 Addison–Wesley edition), or A. R. Edmonds, "Angular Momentum in Quantum Mechanics," Princeton University Press, Princeton, N.J., 1957, or M. E. Rose, "Elementary Theory of Angular Momentum," Wiley, New York, 1957.

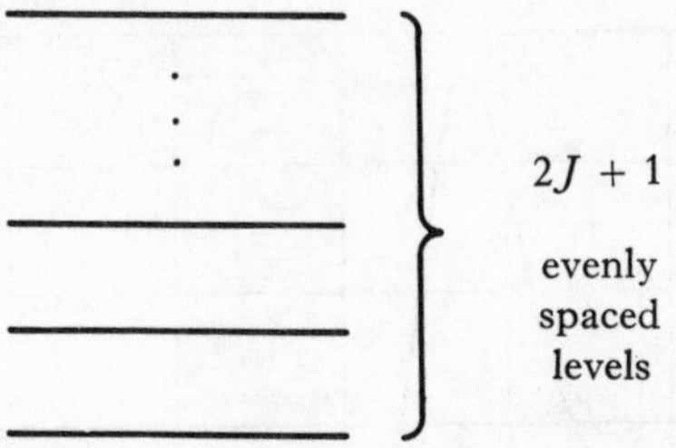

Fig. 1-1 The levels of a free ion of angular momentum J in an external magnetic field. Because the interaction is that responsible for the Zeeman effect in optical spectroscopy, these are often called the Zeeman levels.

The first experimental observations of laboratory-induced transitions among the Zeeman levels of electrons were those of Zavoisky[2] reported in 1945. The initial experiments used a 25-meter wavelength to observe absorption as a function of magnetic field in substances whose line widths were ~ 50 gauss or larger, and a resonance line was scarcely discernible at such low frequencies, which correspond to a resonance "peak" at about 4 gauss. The second series of experiments found a maximum for Cu^{++} ion at 47.6 gauss, using a frequency of 133 Mc sec^{-1} (still not in what we would call the microwave range) and allowed Zavoisky to conclude in effect that $g = 2$. Subsequently Zavoisky[3] pushed into the microwave region and observed clearly resolved resonances of 200 to 300 gauss width in fields of about 1000 gauss. Cummerow and Halliday[4] in the United States published a nicely resolved resonance of Mn^{++} in 173 g of $MnSO_4 \cdot 4H_2O$ placed in a microwave cavity excited at 2930 Mc sec^{-1} (see Fig. 1-2). To interpret such a curve properly, we shall, of course, have to develop in considerable detail the relationship of the power absorbed to the magnetic moment of the sample.

In 1947 Bagguley and Griffiths[5] performed an experiment at the Clarendon Laboratory observing the Cr^{3+} resonance in a chrome alum crystal at 3.18 cm wavelength. There followed at the Clarendon Laboratory an important and fruitful period of paramagnetic resonance researches in which the subject was extensively explored and much of

[2] E. Zavoisky, *J. Phys. USSR*, **9,** 211, 245 (1945).
[3] E. Zavoisky, *J. Phys. USSR*, **10,** 197 (1946).
[4] R. L. Cummerow and D. Halliday, *Phys. Rev.*, **70,** 433 (1946).
[5] D. M. S. Bagguley and J. H. E. Griffiths, *Nature*, **160,** 532 (1947).

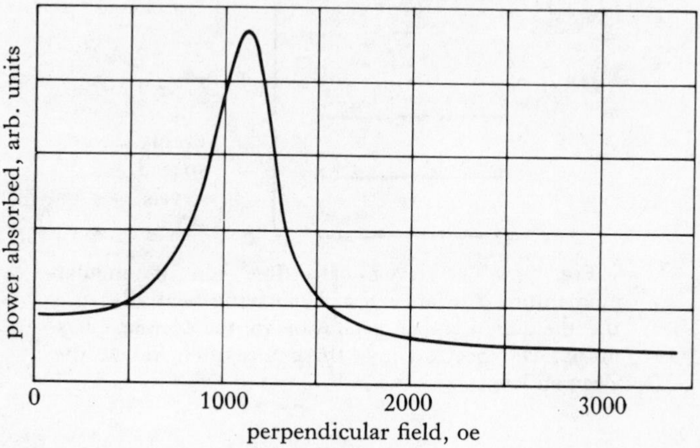

Fig. 1-2 Paramagnetic resonance of Mn^{++} ion in $MnSO_4 \cdot 4H_2O$ observed at 2930 Mc sec^{-1} by Cummerow and Halliday in early experiments.

our present-day understanding was established. This development of the field is chronicled up to 1955 in two reviews by members of that Oxford group contained in *Reports on Progress in Physics*.[6,7]

What motivated these experiments? In part it was an obvious game one could play with the microwave techniques developed during World War II. But, far more fundamentally, there had been earlier interest among low-temperature physicists in the very important question of the thermal contact between an assembly of electronic magnets and the vibrational degrees of freedom of the crystal lattice. The method of cooling by adiabatic demagnetization raises the question of such contact. A sudden demagnetization of the electrons means a corresponding disordering, and the entropy increase ΔS will soak up an amount of heat energy

$$\Delta Q = \int_{S_0}^{S_0+\Delta S} T\, dS$$

from the lattice vibrations. An important experimental question clearly

[6] B. Bleaney and K. W. H. Stevens, *Repts. Progr. in Phys.*, **16,** 108 (1953).

[7] K. D. Bowers and J. Owen, *Repts. Progr. in Phys.*, **18,** 304 (1955). A number of the tables from this review are contained in an appendix at the end of this volume. Supplementary tables to these, without discussion, are presented by J. W. Orton, *Repts. Progr. in Phys.*, **22,** 204 (1959).

is: How much time will this heat exchange require? We shall learn that resonance experiments tell us much about this so-called *spin–lattice relaxation time*.

A second relaxation time of importance measures the rate at which the magnet assembly comes to internal equilibrium at a temperature, whether or not it be the lattice temperature. It is called the *spin–spin relaxation time*. The study of both paramagnetic relaxations, prior to 1946, was in the almost-exclusive custody of physicists of The Netherlands. What they learned was by nonresonant absorption measurements, to be discussed in Chapter 6. Because the resonance experiments are so much easier to visualize and understand, we shall depart here from the strict historical development. One should not, however, let this pedagogical tactic minimize the great debt of gratitude that the subject of paramagnetic resonance owes to the Dutch pioneers. In another respect we shall necessarily be historical; the static paramagnetic properties must be familiar to us when we take up resonance studies.

1-2 Static Paramagnetism

Let us consider an assembly of particles each having total angular momentum $\mathbf{J}\hbar$ and assume them to be noninteracting—which is, as stated earlier, the greatest possible simplification. The magnetic moment operator for one particle will be $\boldsymbol{\mu}$. Then, by the Wigner–Eckhart theorem of quantum mechanics,[1]

$$\boldsymbol{\mu} = (\text{const})\mathbf{J}\hbar$$

We write this also as

$$\begin{aligned} \boldsymbol{\mu} &= -g(|e|\hbar/2mc)\mathbf{J} \\ &= -g\beta\mathbf{J} = -\gamma\hbar\mathbf{J} \end{aligned} \tag{1-1}$$

where $\beta = |e|\hbar/2mc$, the Bohr magneton; g is the spectroscopic splitting factor, or "g factor," or just "g"; and γ is the "magnetogyric" ratio or gyromagnetic ratio. In these definitions we treat the various physical constants as positive and incorporate the negative moment of the electron through the sign in (1-1). When corresponding definitions are given for nuclei, the minus signs of (1-1) do not appear.

The potential energy of a dipole in an external field $\mathbf{H}_0$ is

$$E_i = -\boldsymbol{\mu}_i \cdot \mathbf{H}_0 \tag{1-2}$$

and the probability that a dipole within the assembly at temperature T

has a potential energy E_i is, according to Boltzmann,[8]

$$p_i = \text{const}\exp(-E_i/kT)$$

Taking $\mathbf{H}_0 = H_0\mathbf{k}$,[9] we have the magnetic energy as

$$E_i = -\boldsymbol{\mu}_i\cdot\mathbf{H}_0 = g\beta H_0 J_{zi} = g\beta H_0 m_i \tag{1-3}$$

where m_i is the magnetic quantum number ($m_i = J, -J+1,\ldots,J$). Then

$$p_i = \frac{\exp(-g\beta H_0 m_i/kT)}{\sum_{m_i=-J}^{J}\exp(-g\beta H_0 m_i/kT)} \tag{1-4}$$

Our experiments observe a macroscopic property of the sample, conveniently the magnetization $\mathbf{M}$, which is defined as the magnetic moment per unit volume:

$$\mathbf{M} = (1/V)\sum_i \boldsymbol{\mu}_i \tag{1-5}$$

The measurable component of $\boldsymbol{\mu}_i$ along z is

$$M_z = (1/V)\sum_i \mu_{zi}$$

$$= \frac{N\sum_{m_i=-J}^{J} -g\beta m_i\exp(-g\beta H_0 m_i/kT)}{\sum_{m_i=J}^{J}\exp(-g\beta H_0 m_i/kT)} \tag{1-6}$$

[8] Electrons obey Fermi–Dirac statistics, and the student should not thoughtlessly acquiesce in the use of Boltzmann statistics here. We suppose that the electrons in Cu^{++} ion, for example, definitely obey the Pauli exclusion principle in so far as they compete with each other for quantum states within the ion. Once the paramagnetic properties of the ion are so determined, however, our assumption of independent noninteracting Cu^{++} ions implies a spatial separation and, in effect, a spatial distinguishability of particles. This spatial distinguishability means that Boltzmann statistics are appropriate (cf. R. C. Tolman, "Statistical Mechanics," Oxford University Press, London, 1938, Chap. 10, especially p. 367).

Later on, in Sec. 4-1, we shall consider the reality that the electrons of closely spaced ions or atoms in the lattice do indeed have electrostatic interactions with each other, which, although weaker than the intraatomic electrostatic interactions, manifest themselves as the exchange couplings so important to magnetism. Then the Fermi statistics of the electron must necessarily be invoked.

[9] Throughout we use **i**, **j**, and **k** as unit vectors respectively along the x, y, and z axes.

Here we understand N to be the number of paramagnets per unit volume. In the high-temperature approximation $g\beta H_0/kT \ll 1$, the exponentials may be expanded. But $H_0 = 7000$ oe, for example, gives

$$g\beta H_0/k \approx 1°\text{K} \qquad (H_0 = 7000 \text{ oe})$$

and the approximation using the first term in the expansion is too restrictive. Thus we collect terms and obtain the magnetization proportional to the Brillouin function $B_J(x)$:

$$M_z = NgJ\beta B_J(x) \tag{1-7}$$

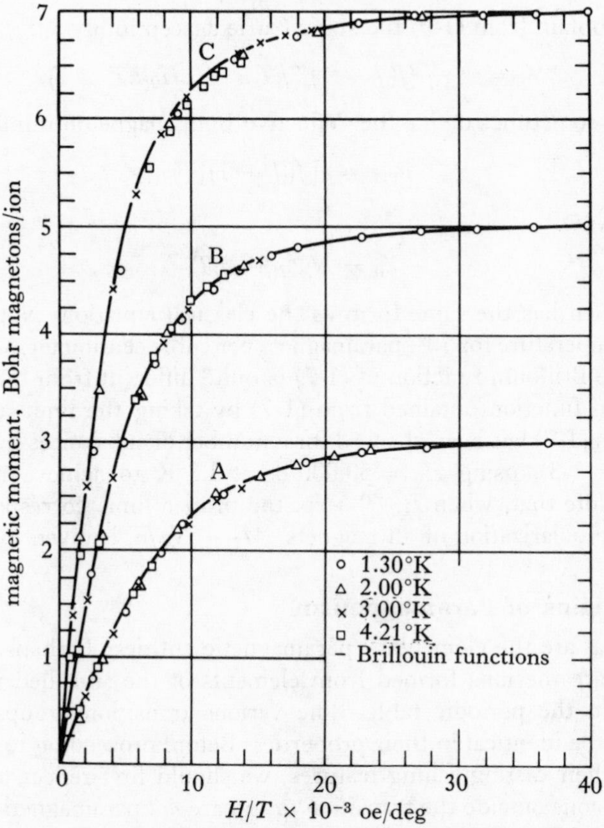

Fig. 1-3 Experimental tests[10] of the Brillouin function for the magnetization of three different ions: (A) Cr^{3+} in potassium chrome alum ($S = \frac{3}{2}$), (B) Fe^{3+} in iron ammonium alum ($S = \frac{5}{2}$), and (C) Gd^{3+} in gadolinium sulfate octahydrate ($J = S = \frac{7}{2}$).

where $x = gJ\beta H_0/kT$ and

$$B_J(x) = \frac{2J+1}{2J}\coth\frac{(2J+1)x}{2J} - \frac{1}{2J}\coth\frac{x}{2J} \tag{1-8}$$

For $x \ll 1$, being careful in the expansions of the hyperbolic cotangents, we find that

$$M_z = NJ(J+1)g^2\beta^2H_0/3kT \tag{1-9}$$

The magnetic susceptibility χ is defined as

$$M_z = \chi H_0$$

and we obtain from (1-9) the static Curie susceptibility χ_0:

$$\chi_0 = Ng^2\beta^2J(J+1)/3kT \qquad (\beta H_0/kT \ll 1) \tag{1-10}$$

Authors sometimes define the "effective Bohr magneton number"

$$\mu_{\text{eff}} = g[J(J+1)]^{1/2} \tag{1-11}$$

so that

$$\chi_0 = N\mu_{\text{eff}}^2\beta^2/3kT \tag{1-12}$$

which then has the same form as the classical equation. Note that, at room temperature for 10^{22} paramagnets per cubic centimeter, $\chi_0 \sim 10^{-5}$.

The Brillouin function of (1-7) is quite different from the classical Langevin function obtained from (1-7) by taking the limit as $J \to \infty$. Equation (1-7) has been checked for a number of substances by Henry[10] (see Fig. 1-3), using $H_0 = 50{,}000$ oe at 1.3°K to achieve maximum H_0/T. Note that, when $H_0/T \to \infty$, the proper limit corresponding to complete polarization of all magnets, $M_z \to NgJ\beta$, is given by (1-7).

1-3 Origins of Paramagnetism

What are the elementary paramagnetic entities? Perhaps the most studied are the ions formed from elements of the so-called transition groups in the periodic table. The various transition groups are not found to be identical in their properties. Before proceeding to a discussion of their distinguishing features, we should first reflect upon why it is that ions outside the transition group are *not* paramagnetic.

Consider a crystal of NaCl, for example. Its structure is ionic, but the transfer of an electron from each Na atom to each Cl atom assures an inert rare gas configuration for the electrons of each ion; there is

[10] W. E. Henry, *Phys. Rev.*, **88**, 559 (1952).

zero resultant angular momentum (whether spin or orbital in nature) and, by (1-1), zero magnetic moment.

Of course, not all compounds are ionic. The water molecule, for example, is covalent. In chemical combination, two hydrogen atoms and one oxygen atom have their electrons so arranged that, apart from rotation of the molecule as a structural unit, no net electronic orbital or spin angular momentum exists, and again no paramagnet exists.

Although we surely expect any atom without a rare gas configuration to be paramagnetic by these considerations, a little reflection leads us to the conclusion that isolated atoms are chemically quite reactive and not easily kept in the laboratory. The very act of their chemical combination cancels out the paramagnetism we are about to study!

The significance of the transition groups for paramagnetism is now readily seen. These groups occur at regions of the periodic table where *inner* electron shells are growing from one inert configuration to a larger one. Along the way, we shall certainly encounter inner shells with an odd number of electrons, for which spin angular momentum, if nothing else, simply cannot be zero. It also happens that such transition configurations with an even number of electrons have in general magnetic moments, a fact which can be seen by consideration of Hund's rules for the sequences of atomic energy levels.[11]

These rules for an electron shell follow:

1. Assign maximum S consistent with the Pauli principle.

2. Assign maximum L consistent with the S. (Recall, of course, that L is the maximum value of M_L for the group of electrons.)

3. $J = L - S$ when the shell is less than half full, and $J = L + S$ when the shell is more than half full.

The first transition group encountered in the periodic table is the iron group, but we postpone it briefly to discuss the rare earth group, which is, in one sense, simpler to understand. The $4f$ shell in the rare earth transition is building up to its full complement of 14 electrons.

[11] For a discussion of Hund's rules in relation to the paramagnetism of electron shells, see, e.g., the classic book by J. H. Van Vleck, "Electric and Magnetic Susceptibilities," Oxford University Press, New York, 1932. Although it is thirty years old, this book is an excellent reference for many topics we shall discuss. Hund's rules were originally essentially empirical, but simple physical and quantum mechanical considerations give them theoretical justification (R. B. Leighton, "Principles of Modern Physics," McGraw-Hill, New York, 1959, Chap. 8; V. Heine, "Group Theory in Quantum Mechanics," Pergamon, New York, 1960, p. 97).

The ions resulting from chemical combination have outer electronic configuration $5s^2 5p^6$ after losing three electrons to become trivalent. Table 1-1 lists these ions in order, giving the electron-shell configuration. Next is given the spectroscopic term as determined from Hund's rules. (The student should check several of these terms to be sure he understands application of the rules and the cryptic term-code to which physicists insist upon clinging.)

If one assumes *LS* coupling, the Landé *g*,

$$g = 1 + \frac{J(J+1) + S(S+1) - L(L+1)}{2J(J+1)} \tag{1-13}$$

may be used in conjunction with (1-11) to give μ_{eff}(calc) as tabulated in Table 1-1. The final column gives μ_{eff}(exp) as obtained from the experimental χ_0 and (1-12). It is clear that, with one or two exceptions, of which Eu^{3+} is the most outstanding, the *LS* coupling model accounts well for the static paramagnetism of rare earth ions.

Table 1-1

Trivalent Rare Earth Ions

Element	Config.	Term	μ_{eff}(calc)	μ_{eff}(exp)
Ce^{3+}	$4f^1 5s^2 5p^6$	$^2F_{5/2}$	2.54	2.4
Pr^{3+}	$4f^2$	$^3H_4$	3.58	3.5
Nd^{3+}	$4f^3$	$^4I_{9/2}$	3.62	3.5
Pm^{3+}	$4f^4$	$^5I_4$	2.68	
Sm^{3+}	$4f^5$	$^6H_{5/2}$	0.84	1.5
Eu^{3+}	$4f^6$	$^7F_0$	0	3.4
Gd^{3+}	$4f^7$	$^8S_{7/2}$	7.94	8.0
Tb^{3+}	$4f^8$	$^7F_6$	9.72	9.5
Dy^{3+}	$4f^9$	$^6H_{15/2}$	10.63	
Ho^{3+}	$4f^{10}$	$^5I_8$	10.60	10.4
Er^{3+}	$4f^{11}$	$^4I_{15/2}$	9.59	9.5
Tm^{3+}	$4f^{12}$	$^3H_6$	7.57	7.3
Yb^{3+}	$4f^{13}$	$^2F_{7/2}$	4.54	4.5

Table 1-2 returns to the iron-group ions, in which the 3*d* shell is in transition from $3d^1$ through $3d^9$, inclusive. Similar quantities appear in the various columns of the table, with one notable change. Since $g[J(J+1)]^{1/2}$ does not agree with experiment, an additional column gives $2[S(S+1)]^{1/2}$, in which the factor 2 is the spin-only *g* factor. The close agreement of the new column with μ_{eff}(exp) forces us to conclude that the iron-group ions behave much as if only their spin—

not their orbital—angular momentum is effective in generating the paramagnetism. As will be discussed in more detail in Chapter 3, this is a consequence of the electric field at the ion arising from the crystal lattice in which it resides.

One may well inquire why such fields have no effect for the rare earth ions of Table 1-1. In a qualitative sense it is clear that the electric fields arising from sources external to the ion are relatively less important for the rare earth ions, not because they are necessarily weaker but because the $4f$ shell lies deep within the ion and feels a much stronger nuclear coulomb field. The iron group, in contrast, has its paramagnetic shell effectively at the surface of the ion, where it is screened more effectively from the nucleus.

Table 1-2

Iron-Group Ions

Ion	Config.	Term	$g[J(J+1)]^{1/2}$	$2[S(S+1)]^{1/2}$	μ_{eff}(exp)
Ti^{3+}, V^{4+}	$3d^1$	$^2D_{3/2}$	1.55	1.73	1.8
V^{3+}	$3d^2$	$^3F_2$	1.63	2.83	2.8
Cr^{3+}, V^{++}	$3d^3$	$^4F_{3/2}$	0.77	3.87	3.8
Mn^{3+}, Cr^{++}	$3d^4$	$^5D_0$	0	4.90	4.9
Fe^{3+}, Mn^{++}	$3d^5$	$^6S_{5/2}$	5.92	5.92	5.9
Fe^{++}	$3d^6$	$^5D_4$	6.70	4.90	5.4
Co^{++}	$3d^7$	$^4F_{9/2}$	6.63	3.87	4.8
Ni^{++}	$3d^8$	$^3F_4$	5.59	2.83	3.2
Cu^{++}	$3d^9$	$^2D_{5/2}$	3.55	1.73	1.9

Consider the Cu^{++} ion, for example. Its electron configuration is $1s^2 2s^2 2p^6 3s^2 3p^6 3d^9$ after giving up a $3d$ and a $4s$ electron to form the ion. (It is evident why cuprous compounds are diamagnetic, as $3d^{10}$ is a closed shell.) The electrostatic potential "seen" by the $3d^9$ electrons in a cupric crystal has a lower symmetry than the essentially spherical symmetry provided by the nucleus and core electrons for a bare ion, because the disposition of atoms or ions in the crystal lattice about the ion is necessarily of lower symmetry than spherical. In a nonspherical potential there will in general be absence of invariance of the Hamiltonian with respect to spatial rotations about an arbitrary direction. Since such orbital rotations are generated by the component of **L** in the direction of the rotation axis, it is apparent that $\mathbf{L}\cdot\mathbf{n}$ (where **n** is a unit vector) will not in general commute with the electrostatic Hamiltonian, and thus M_L will not be a good quantum number.

Without presenting a derivation now, we may illustrate the kind of eigenstate which may be encountered for a crystalline potential. For example, a ^2D state ion in a crystalline potential of cubic symmetry has for one of its eigenstates

$$\psi = (1/\sqrt{2})\left[\phi_{L=2}^{M_L=-2} + \phi_{L=2}^{M_L=+2}\right]$$

This state has $\langle \mathbf{L}^2 \rangle = 2(3)$ but has $\langle L_z \rangle = 0$.

The jargon used to denote this effect of the crystalline field on the components of orbital angular momentum is "quenching," and it prevails in the iron group. On the other hand, it is apparent that we get away with LS coupling for the rare earths, because the incomplete $4f$ shells are more deeply buried.

The theory of these effects—in all its group-theoretical splendor—is called *crystal field theory*. It is the only "field theory" in which we shall have much interest in this book. There is a further question of the magnitude of the spin-orbit coupling. The crystal field theory, including spin-orbit effects, is a big subject in its own right and will not be treated herein in real detail. Nonetheless, we must find ways to take into account the symmetry of the crystal, and our limited discussion will occur in Chapter 3.

Other transition groups are the palladium group, $_{39}$Y through $_{46}$Pd, in which the $4d$ shell fills, and the platinum group, $_{71}$Lu through $_{79}$Au, in which the $5d$ shell fills. Both these groups of ions have g near, but not precisely, 2. Finally there is the actinide group, beginning with $_{89}$Ac and going up, in which various combinations of partially filled $6d$ and $5f$ shells provide the paramagnetism.

Not all objects of investigation by electronic paramagnetic resonance are transition ions, by any means. We list some other very important categories of paramagnets below:

Triplet-state molecules. The common oxygen molecule, O_2, happens to have $S = 1$ for the ground state instead of $S = 0$. This is a rare occurrence but evidently not totally absent in nature.

Odd-electron molecules. A number of molecules are "chemically happy" with an odd number of electrons, elementary valence rules notwithstanding. Examples are NO and NO_2. Clearly one cannot cancel off spin angular momentum by pairing all the electron spins in a collection of an odd number of electrons.

Also in this category are the stable free radicals, many of them organic, which exist with an odd number of electrons. Examples are triphenyl methyl, $C(C_6H_5)_3$, or naphthalene negative ion, $C_{10}H_8^-$ (Secs. 4-3 and 5-3).

Damaged molecules or crystals, achieved by irradiation or heating or by imperfect chemical combination, are often characterized by what we may call broken bonds, which contain odd electrons with unpaired spin. Paramagnetic resonance is a powerful tool for studying such damage.

Metals. It is well known that a paramagnetism is associated with the conduction electrons of metals. These electrons have a paramagnetic resonance which has been observed for a few metals (see Sec. 8-2).

Donors, acceptors, and other impurities in solids. Although similar to odd-electron molecules, such impurities are listed separately. The odd electron gained or lost may be associated with an energy band of the crystal. Again, paramagnetic resonance is a powerful tool for study of these impurity centers (see Sec. 8-3).

[2]

The Phenomenon of Magnetic Resonance

2-1 The Gyromagnetic Top

Consider a top with total angular momentum $\mathbf{J}\hbar$. Its motion is governed classically by

$$(d/dt)(\mathbf{J}\hbar) = \textbf{torque} \tag{2-1}$$

If the top carries a negative electric charge, then

$$\boldsymbol{\mu} = -\gamma\hbar\mathbf{J} \tag{2-2}$$

and the torque is $\boldsymbol{\mu} \times \mathbf{H}$ if the top is placed in a magnetic field $\mathbf{H}$. Multiplying (2-1) by $-\gamma$ gives

$$(d/dt)\,\boldsymbol{\mu} = \gamma\mathbf{H} \times \boldsymbol{\mu} \qquad \text{(negative moments)} \tag{2-3}$$

A simple, well-known solution of this equation for $\mathbf{H}$ equal to a constant vector $\mathbf{H}_0$ is the precession of a vector $\boldsymbol{\mu}$ of constant magnitude at a fixed angle with $\mathbf{H}_0$ and at frequency

$$\boldsymbol{\omega}_0 = \gamma\mathbf{H}_0 \qquad \text{(Larmor precession)} \tag{2-4}$$

For free electrons, $\gamma = 17.6 \times 10^6$ (sec oe)$^{-1}$ and (2-4) corresponds to $\omega_0/2\pi H_0 = 2.80$ Mc(sec oe)$^{-1}$. In a field $\mathbf{H}_0$ of approximately 3600 oe, $\omega_0/2\pi = 10^{10}$ sec^{-1}, corresponding to 3-cm microwaves.

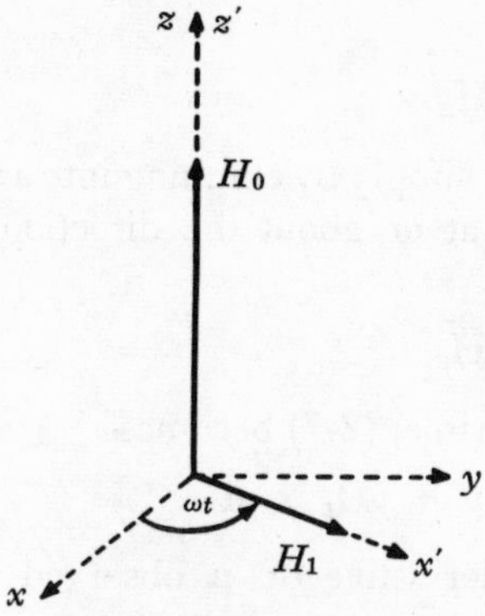

Fig. 2-1 Definition of rotating (primed) coordinate system.

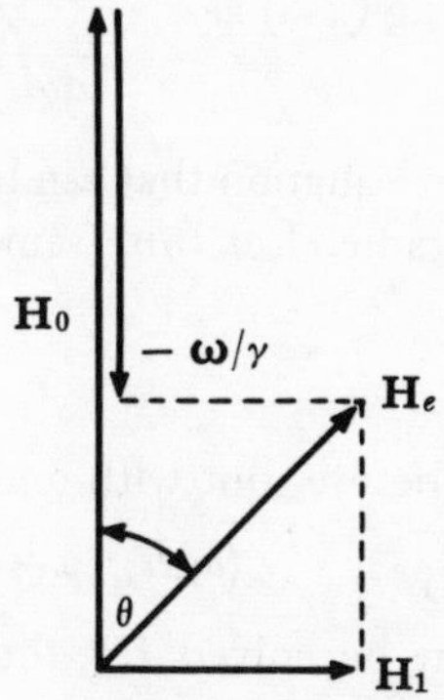

Fig. 2-2 Diagram of the effective field in the rotating frame, defining the angle θ.

Magnetic resonance experiments do not use a constant **H** field but employ a time-dependent field obtained by adding to the constant component a small precessing one at right angles. The situation is treated most simply by use of a rotating coordinate system. Consider the magnetic field sketched in Fig. 2-1 and given by $\mathbf{H} = \mathbf{i}H_1 \cos \omega t + \mathbf{j}H_1 \sin \omega t + \mathbf{k}H_0$. The $\mathbf{H}_1$ field is thus perpendicular to $\mathbf{H}_0$ and rotates about it at frequency $\boldsymbol{\omega} = \mathbf{k}\omega$. The rotating coordinate system of most use to us will be one in which $\mathbf{H}_1$ is constant, i.e., one rotating at $\boldsymbol{\omega}$. From the classical mechanics of tops, we know that

$$(d/dt)\,\boldsymbol{\mu} = (d/dt)'\,\boldsymbol{\mu} + \boldsymbol{\omega} \times \boldsymbol{\mu} \tag{2-5}$$

where the prime signifies differentiation with respect to the rotating frame. Substituting (2-5) into (2-3) gives

$$(d/dt)'\,\boldsymbol{\mu} + \boldsymbol{\omega} \times \boldsymbol{\mu} = \gamma\mathbf{H} \times \boldsymbol{\mu}$$

from which

$$(d/dt)'\,\boldsymbol{\mu} = (\gamma\mathbf{H} - \boldsymbol{\omega}) \times \boldsymbol{\mu} \tag{2-6}$$

is the equation of motion of $\boldsymbol{\mu}$ as viewed from the frame rotating at $\boldsymbol{\omega}$. We define $\mathbf{H}_e = \mathbf{H} - \boldsymbol{\omega}/\gamma$, which is, by comparing (2-6) with (2-3), the effective magnetic field in the frame rotating at $\boldsymbol{\omega}$. Figure 2-2 shows a vector diagram of the effective field, pictured in the $\mathbf{H}_1,\mathbf{H}_0$ plane or the $x'z'$ plane of the primed (rotating) coordinate system.

Writing (2-6) as

$$(d/dt)'\,\boldsymbol{\mu} = \gamma \mathbf{H}_e \times \boldsymbol{\mu} \tag{2-7}$$

gives us an equation that can be solved simply by climbing into a second rotating frame. Let this frame rotate at $\boldsymbol{\omega}'$ about the direction of $\mathbf{H}_e$ with

$$\boldsymbol{\omega}' = \gamma \mathbf{H}_e \tag{2-8}$$

Then, as before, but with one more prime, (2-7) becomes

$$(d/dt)''\,\boldsymbol{\mu} + \boldsymbol{\omega}' \times \boldsymbol{\mu} = \gamma \mathbf{H}_e \times \boldsymbol{\mu}$$

which can be solved for the time derivative of $\boldsymbol{\mu}$ observed in the doubly rotating frame:

$$(d/dt)''\,\boldsymbol{\mu} = (\gamma \mathbf{H}_e - \boldsymbol{\omega}') \times \boldsymbol{\mu} = 0 \tag{2-9}$$

The vanishing follows from our definition of ω' in (2-8).

Equation (2-9) says that, whatever the initial value of $\boldsymbol{\mu}$ may be, it remains unchanged with time in the doubly rotating frame. To find that frame, visualize yourself on a merry-go-round rotating about $\mathbf{H}_0$, with $\mathbf{H}_1$ clearly painted on the platform of the merry-go-round. Figure 2-2 shows the magnitude and direction of $\mathbf{H}_e$ relative to $\mathbf{H}_1$ and the axis of merry-go-round rotation. In a frame rotating relative to the moving merry-go-round with $\boldsymbol{\omega}' = \gamma \mathbf{H}_e$, $\boldsymbol{\mu}$ is constant. The same can be said of the motion of $\mathbf{M} = \Sigma_{\text{unit vol.}}\,\boldsymbol{\mu}_i$, provided each $\boldsymbol{\mu}_i$ sees the same $\mathbf{H}_0$ and $\mathbf{H}_1$.

Figure 2-3 is an attempt to picture this state of affairs, but it may also be used to calculate a result of quantum mechanics. To see this, we should first note that quantum mechanical considerations lead to (2-3) as the equation of motion for the expectation value of the operator $\boldsymbol{\mu}_{\text{op}}$. The quantum mechanical equation of motion is

$$i\hbar(d/dt)\,\boldsymbol{\mu}_{\text{op}} = [\,\boldsymbol{\mu}_{\text{op}}, \mathscr{H}\,] \tag{2-10}$$

where, after (1-1), $\mathscr{H} = -\boldsymbol{\mu}_{\text{op}} \cdot \mathbf{H}$. Recalling (2-2) and the commutation rules for angular momentum yields, from (2-10),

$$(d/dt)\,\boldsymbol{\mu}_{\text{op}} = \gamma \mathbf{H} \times \boldsymbol{\mu}_{\text{op}}$$

and the observable expectation value $\langle \boldsymbol{\mu}_{\text{op}} \rangle$ is

$$(d/dt)\langle \boldsymbol{\mu}_{\text{op}} \rangle = \gamma \mathbf{H} \times \langle \boldsymbol{\mu}_{\text{op}} \rangle \tag{2-11}$$

the classical equation.

Returning to Fig. 2-3, we see the $\boldsymbol{\mu}$ vector at an angle α with $\mathbf{H}_0$ having started, for example, at $\boldsymbol{\mu}_0$ along $\mathbf{H}_0$. As viewed from a frame

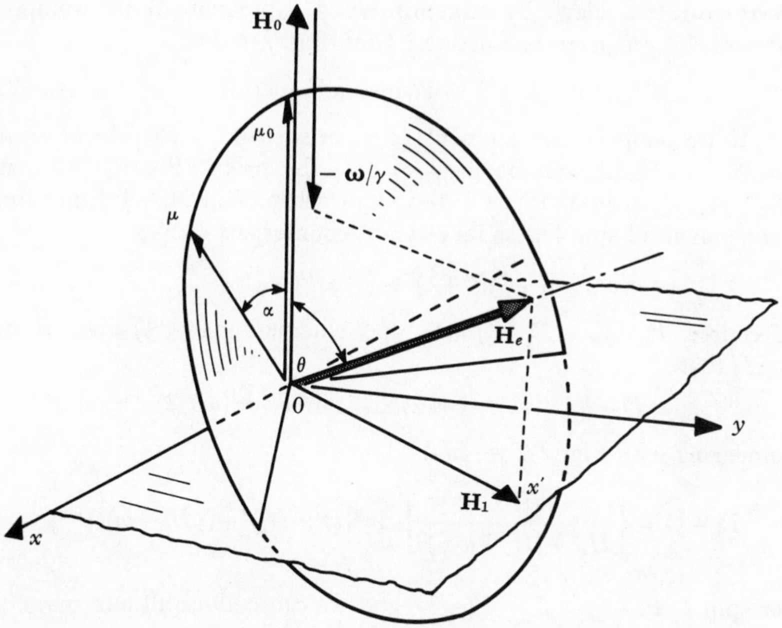

Fig. 2-3 Sketch showing the "coolie hat" generated by the tip of the vector $\boldsymbol{\mu}$ as it precesses about $\mathbf{H}_e$ in the rotating frame. The complete motion is then obtained by rotating the x' axis about $\mathbf{H}_0$ at the velocity $\boldsymbol{\omega}$.

(the merry-go-round) in which $\mathbf{H}_e$ is constant, $\boldsymbol{\mu}$ precesses about $\mathbf{H}_e$ at frequency $\boldsymbol{\omega} = \gamma\mathbf{H}_e$, thus generating a conical "coolie hat," of which the rim is shown and the vertex is at 0. To obtain the complete motion, the motion just described must of course be rotated about $\mathbf{H}_0$ at $\boldsymbol{\omega}$. As viewed from the laboratory, the motion of $\boldsymbol{\mu}$ will not generate the closed circle rim of the coolie hat, because $\mathbf{H}_1$ and therefore $\mathbf{H}_e$ in Fig. 2-3 both rotate about $\mathbf{H}_0$ at a rate $\boldsymbol{\omega}$ which is, near resonance, far more rapid than $\boldsymbol{\omega}'$. The vector $\boldsymbol{\mu}$ will appear from the laboratory to tip down slowly during a large number of Larmor precessions.

However, we shall find it more convenient to view life from the merry-go-round, and the coolie hat will arise for us so long as θ is constant. We can be content with this vantage point because the z component of $\boldsymbol{\mu}$ determines the energy [Eq. (1-2)], which means that only $\cos \alpha$ is needed. It is more readily obtained from Fig. 2-3, the merry-go-round view. By straightforward expression of the components of the vector $\boldsymbol{\mu}$, one deduces from Fig. 2-3 that

$$\cos \alpha = 1 - 2 \sin^2 \theta \sin^2 (\omega' t/2) \tag{2-12}$$

If we suppose the moment $\boldsymbol{\mu}$ to arise from a particle of spin $J = S = \frac{1}{2}$, (2-12) can be used to give the probability $P(-\frac{1}{2})$ that $\langle S_z \rangle = -\frac{1}{2}$, given that at $t = 0$ we know that $\langle S_z \rangle = +\frac{1}{2}$. Since the z component of spin has as its classical counterpart $\frac{1}{2} \cos \alpha$,

$$\tfrac{1}{2} \cos \alpha = (+\tfrac{1}{2})P(+\tfrac{1}{2}) + (-\tfrac{1}{2})P(-\tfrac{1}{2})$$

Of course, $P(+\frac{1}{2}) + P(-\frac{1}{2}) = 1$, and eliminating $P(+\frac{1}{2})$ gives from (2-12) that

$$P(-\tfrac{1}{2}) = (1 - \cos \alpha)/2 = \sin^2 \theta \sin^2(\omega' t/2)$$

Comparing with Fig. 2-2 we find

$$P(-\tfrac{1}{2}) = \left[\frac{H_1^2}{H_1^2 + (H_0 - \omega/\gamma)^2}\right] \sin^2\{\tfrac{1}{2}t[(\gamma H_1)^2 + (\gamma H_0 - \omega)^2]^{1/2}\} \tag{2-13}$$

For spin $\frac{1}{2}$, $P(+\frac{1}{2}) = 1 - P(-\frac{1}{2})$, and we can deduce all our answers from (2-13).

It is informative to consider the special situation when $\boldsymbol{\omega} = \gamma \mathbf{H}_0 \equiv \boldsymbol{\omega}_0$. A glance at Fig. 2-2 shows that $\mathbf{H}_e = \mathbf{H}_1$, since $\theta = \pi/2$. From Fig. 2-3 we see that the coolie hat has degenerated into a plane. The

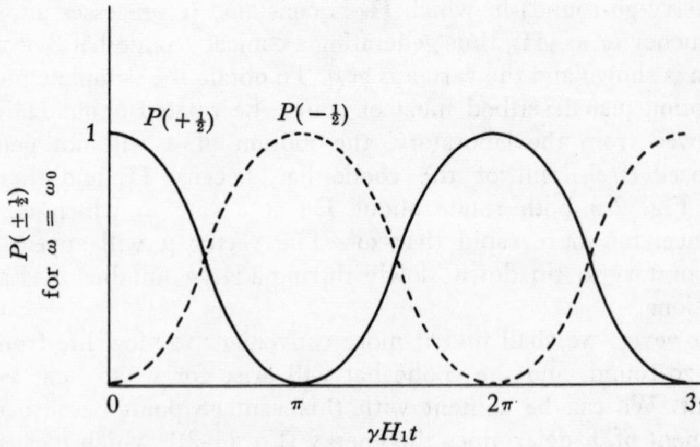

Fig. 2-4 Curves of the probabilities $P(+\frac{1}{2})$ and $P(-\frac{1}{2})$ at resonance, $\omega = \omega_0$, if it is known that $m_S = +\frac{1}{2}$ at $t = 0$.

magnetic moment now oscillates (see Fig. 2-4) between $+z$ and $-z$ directions according to

$$P(-\tfrac{1}{2})|_{\theta=\pi/2} = \sin^2(\gamma H_1 t/2) = \tfrac{1}{2}(1 - \cos \gamma H_1 t)$$

We see that the angular velocity of $\boldsymbol{\mu}$ around the circle of which H_1 is the axis is simply $\gamma \mathbf{H}_1$. This situation, which may be variously described by $\theta = \pi/2$, $\omega = \omega_0$, or $\mathbf{H}_e = \mathbf{H}_1$, is called magnetic resonance. If these conditions are not met, the gyromagnetic top is off resonance. We may say that magnetic resonance occurs when $\boldsymbol{\omega}$ equals the Larmor precession frequency (2-4) that an isolated moment would have in the field $\mathbf{H}_0$.

Throughout all the discussion of this section we have used classical mechanics and geometry to obtain answers that could be obtained quantum mechanically, according to our earlier argument about the equations of motion. We have done this to provide the maximum "physical feel" for the situation. However, to make his understanding complete, the student should derive (2-13) quantum mechanically. Starting with the Schroedinger equation and $\mathscr{H} = -\boldsymbol{\mu}\cdot\mathbf{H}$, where $\mathbf{H}$ is the vector sum of $\mathbf{H}_0$ and $\mathbf{H}_1$, he should perform the unitary transformation on the wave functions corresponding to the rotating frames we have discussed. From these he can deduce[1] the form of $\mathbf{H}_e$ quantum mechanically, as well as the result (2-13).

The solution obtained in this section is easily visualized, and the reader should be warned against overconfidence at this stage. The calculation has been simple because we have used a single-particle model. A first attempt at accounting for interactions among many paramagnets is taken up in Sec. 2-2.

2-2 The Phenomenological Equations of Bloch

In 1946 Bloch[2] proposed a set of phenomenological equations to describe the dynamic magnetic behavior of interacting nuclear paramagnets. These equations introduce the relaxation times, which in general will have for electrons different magnitudes from those Bloch

[1] The student not familiar with the operators generating the unitary transformations corresponding to rotations should see Ref. 1 of Chapter 1 and then proceed to I. I. Rabi, N. F. Ramsey, and J. Schwinger, *Revs. Mod. Phys.*, **26,** 167 (1954), where most of the exercises suggested in this paragraph are carried out. Also useful in expressing $\mathbf{H}_e$ is a paper by J. Schwinger, *Phys. Rev.*, **51,** 648 (1937).

[2] F. Bloch, *Phys. Rev.*, **70,** 460 (1946).

used to typify nuclei. However, the physical considerations underlying the equations apply to both nuclei and electrons.

Bloch supposed that the interactions cause the magnetization $\mathbf{M} = \Sigma_{\text{unit vol.}} \boldsymbol{\mu}_i$ to tend exponentially toward its thermal equilibrium value (1-9), which we denote by $\mathbf{M}_0$ and write here in terms of χ_0 from (1-10):

$$\mathbf{M}_0 = \chi_0 \mathbf{H}_0 \tag{2-14}$$

One imagines that somehow a nonequilibrium magnitude and orientation of **M** have been achieved. This can be accomplished in a number of experimental ways, one of which pulses the rotating $\mathbf{H}_1$ field and applies it to a sample in which $\mathbf{M} = \mathbf{M}_0$ initially. As can be seen from Fig. 2-3 with the macroscopic magnet **M** replacing $\boldsymbol{\mu}$, turning off the $\mathbf{H}_1$ field after a short period of time will in general leave **M** pointing in a nonequilibrium direction (although it will still have its initial magnitude M_0) to some general point on the coolie-hat rim.

When the nonequilibrium situation is achieved and the $\mathbf{H}_1$ field is turned off, **M** will tend to precess at $\boldsymbol{\omega}_0 = \gamma \mathbf{H}_0$, except for the effects of interaction between the spins, i.e., effects of relaxation. Two relaxation processes may be distinguished. The z component of **M** will grow as individual moments $\boldsymbol{\mu}_i$ making up **M** flip to bring M_z toward M_0. This process requires the moments to give up energy to the lattice and is called spin-lattice relaxation.

A second process—not requiring energy exchange with the lattice and therefore often faster—can destroy the component $M_\perp$ of **M** perpendicular to $\mathbf{H}_0$. For example, the individual moments $\boldsymbol{\mu}_i$ each "see" a local dipolar field from their neighbors which adds vectorially to $\mathbf{H}_0$ in such a way as sometimes to add and sometimes to subtract from $\mathbf{H}_0$. Thus each $\boldsymbol{\mu}_i$ in general precesses in a slightly different field, and the coherence in the individual components making up $M_\perp$ is lost, causing $M_\perp$ to decay.

Viewed from a frame rotating with $M_\perp$, we have

$$\begin{aligned} (d/dt)'M_z &= (1/T_1)(M_0 - M_z) \\ (d/dt)'M_\perp &= -(1/T_2)M_\perp \end{aligned} \tag{2-15}$$

in which we have introduced phenomenologically the time constants of exponential decay as T_1 and T_2, following Bloch.

Transforming back to the laboratory we have the Bloch equations (for a system with a negative magnetic moment):

$$\begin{aligned} dM_x/dt &= \gamma(\mathbf{H} \times \mathbf{M})_x - M_x/T_2 \\ dM_y/dt &= \gamma(\mathbf{H} \times \mathbf{M})_y - M_y/T_2 \\ dM_z/dt &= \gamma(\mathbf{H} \times \mathbf{M})_z + (M_0 - M_z)/T_1 \end{aligned} \tag{2-16}$$

Although we reasoned to these equations by describing relaxation after the $\mathbf{H}_1$ field was turned off, we shall normally use these equations even when a time-varying field $\mathbf{H}_1$ small compared to $\mathbf{H}_0$ is present. The equations (2-16), in fact, give incorrect results when $|\mathbf{H}_0|$ is not appreciably larger than $|\mathbf{H}_1|$. In low $\mathbf{H}_0$ fields it has been found[3] that a better description is provided if the equations are constructed so that $\mathbf{M}$ relaxes toward the direction of the total instantaneous $\mathbf{H}(t)$.

In order to discuss solutions of (2-16) we shall have to be careful in defining *adiabaticity*. We begin by discussing what we shall call *Ehrenfest adiabaticity*. The problem is this: Consider a magnetic field $\mathbf{H}$, initially constant, with a magnetization $\mathbf{M}$ making some definite angle relative to it. Neglecting for the moment any relaxation terms, $\mathbf{M}$ will, according to

$$d\mathbf{M}/dt = \gamma\mathbf{H} \times \mathbf{M} \tag{2-18}$$

precess forever about $\mathbf{H}$ at the same angle. If now we change the direction of $\mathbf{H}$ the question arises: How slowly must we make $\mathbf{H}$ change in direction so that $\mathbf{M}$ preserves its angle with respect to $\mathbf{H}$ and thus preserves its energy of interaction with $\mathbf{H}$?

We can answer this question by means of our rotating coordinate formalism if we turn $\mathbf{H}$ slowly at angular frequency $\mathbf{\Omega}$. Then, as viewed from a frame rotating with $\mathbf{H}$, the equation of motion in the rotating frame will be

$$(d/dt)'\mathbf{M} = (\gamma\mathbf{H} - \mathbf{\Omega}) \times \mathbf{M} \tag{2-19}$$

[3] Codrington, Olds, and Torrey, *Phys. Rev.*, **95,** 607A (1954), describe this procedure for constructing the modified Bloch equations and present in an unpublished technical report the following form (also written for negative moments, with $\gamma > 0$):

$$d\mathbf{M}/dt + \mathbf{M}/T_2 - \chi_0\mathbf{H}/T_1 + (1/T_1 - 1/T_2)(\mathbf{M}\cdot\mathbf{H})\mathbf{H}/H^2 + \gamma\mathbf{M} \times \mathbf{H} = 0 \tag{2-17}$$

Note that the total instantaneous field $\mathbf{H}$ appears throughout. Garstens [*Phys. Rev.*, **93,** 1228 (1954)] and Garstens, Singer, and Ryan [*Phys. Rev.*, **96,** 53 (1954)] obtain solutions for low fields that agree with those Codrington et al. find for (2-17) without, however, writing down explicitly the modified Bloch equations.

We shall say that the angle between **M** and **H** is preserved when the motion as viewed from the slowly rotating frame is the same as the initial motion (2-18). This is clearly true in (2-19) if

$$|\mathbf{\Omega}| \ll \gamma|\mathbf{H}| \tag{2-20}$$

which simply states that $|\mathbf{\Omega}|$ must be very much less than the Larmor frequency ω_0 if the angle is to be preserved. In this simple situation of slowly rotating a fixed magnitude **H**, $d\mathbf{H}/dt = \mathbf{\Omega} \times \mathbf{H}$, and we may write (2-20) as

$$|\mathbf{H} \times d\mathbf{H}/dt|/H^2 \ll \gamma|\mathbf{H}|$$

or, less precisely for our special case,

$$H^{-1}|d\mathbf{H}/dt| \ll \gamma|\mathbf{H}| \qquad \text{(Ehrenfest adiabaticity)} \tag{2-21}$$

Next we return to a field of the form

$$\mathbf{H} = \mathbf{i}H_1 \cos \omega t + \mathbf{j}H_1 \sin \omega t + \mathbf{k}H_0 \tag{2-22}$$

and consider what we shall call *adiabatic passage* through the resonance condition $\omega = \omega_0 \equiv \gamma H_0$. By passage we mean here a variation or slow sweep of the magnitude of $\boldsymbol{\omega}$ from $\omega < \omega_0$ through $\omega = \omega_0$ to $\omega > \omega_0$. Figure 2-5 pictures the successive positions of $\mathbf{H}_e$ in the plane of $\mathbf{H}_0$ and $\mathbf{H}_1$ for these conditions.

It is clear from Fig. 2-5 that such a sweep of ω corresponds to a turning of $\mathbf{H}_e$ in the $x'z'$ plane of the rotating frame. (Alternatively, of course, one can turn $\mathbf{H}_e$ by holding ω constant and sweeping H_0 through $\omega = \gamma H_0$.)

Suppose we find our sample initially at thermal equilibrium with $\mathbf{M} = \mathbf{M}_0 = \chi_0\mathbf{H}_0$ pointing along $\mathbf{H}_0$, and therefore approximately along $\mathbf{H}_e$, since $H_1 \ll H_0$ and $\omega \ll \gamma H_0$ (see Fig. 2-5a). The initial motion viewed from the frame rotating at $\boldsymbol{\omega}$ is precession of **M** about $\mathbf{H}_e$. Now we can raise, from our viewpoint in the rotating frame, the same kind of question we raised in the laboratory frame when discussing Ehrenfest adiabaticity: How slowly must we turn $\mathbf{H}_e$ so that **M** will follow? Our result (2-21) can be carried over into the rotating frame since the equation of motion analogous to (2-7),

$$(d/dt)'\mathbf{M} = \gamma\mathbf{H}_e \times \mathbf{M} \tag{2-23}$$

simply replaces (2-18), with $\mathbf{H}_e$ now playing the role of **H**. Therefore, the condition for adiabaticity in the rotating frame is

$$H_e^{-1}|d\mathbf{H}_e/dt| \ll \gamma H_e \tag{2-24}$$

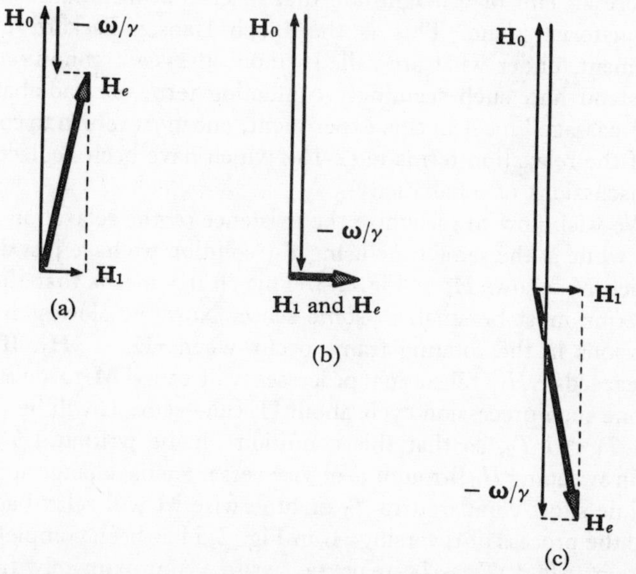

Fig. 2-5 Successive positions of $\mathbf{H}_e$ as ω is swept through γH_0. By the argument following (2-25), the magnetization vector **M**, if initially along $\mathbf{H}_0$, can be made to follow $\mathbf{H}_e$ from (a) $\omega < \gamma H_0$ to (b) $\omega = \gamma H_0$ to (c) $\omega > \gamma H_0$ under certain conditions.

But $\mathbf{H}_e = (H_0 - \omega/\gamma)\mathbf{k} + H_1\mathbf{i}'$, and for a given rate $d\omega/dt$ the left number of (2-24) is greatest when $H_e = H_1$ at $\omega = \omega_0$. Hence a condition at least as strong or stronger than (2-24) is

$$H_1^{-1}|(d/dt)(\mathbf{H}_0 - \boldsymbol{\omega}/\gamma)| \ll \gamma H_1 \qquad \text{(adiabaticity in the rotating frame)} \tag{2-25}$$

Physically, these adiabatic conditions state that the magnetic field in question turns imperceptibly during the period of a Larmor precession about it.

If one now proceeds through the steps of Fig. 2-5, always satisfying (2-25), the **M** vector viewed in the rotating frame will follow $\mathbf{H}_e$. Viewed from the laboratory, the **M** vector tips down from being along $+\mathbf{H}_0$ and sweeps out in ever-widening near-circles on a sphere of radius M_0 until Fig. 2-5b is achieved, and thenceforth it spirals in decreasing circles to a position essentially antiparallel to $\mathbf{H}_0$ (Fig. 2-5c). A coil placed around or near the sample and having its axis in the equatorial plane will thus experience a harmonically varying flux linkage and therefore an emf of a magnitude that reaches a maximum with **M** in the equatorial plane. This is the Bloch–Hansen–Packard induction experiment, under what are called "rapid passage" conditions.[2,4] To understand how such seemingly conflicting terms as "adiabatic" and "rapid passage" meet in this experiment, one must return to consideration of the relaxation terms in (2-16), which have been neglected in all our discussions of adiabaticity.

We wish now to recognize the existence of the relaxation terms in (2-16) while at the same time using the solution we have just described in which **M** follows $\mathbf{H}_e$ in Fig. 2-5. This clearly means that the relaxation terms must be small in some sense. Now the slowest important precessions in the rotating frame occur when $\gamma\mathbf{H}_e = \gamma\mathbf{H}_1$. If $1/T_1$ or $1/T_2$ exceeds γH_1, relaxation processes will cause **M** to decay before even one such precession cycle about $\mathbf{H}_e$ can occur. It will be seen later that $1/T_1 \leqslant 1/T_2$, so that this condition can be written $1/T_2 \ll \gamma H_1$. Also, in sweeping H_0 through ω or vice versa, θ must change appreciably in a time short compared to T_1 or otherwise **M** will relax back to $\mathbf{M}_0$ before the process of reversing $\mathbf{H}_e$ in Fig. 2-5 has been completed. This condition, $(d\theta/dt)T_1 \gg 1$, may be written approximately from Fig. 2-2 as

$$H_1^{-1}|(d/dt)(\mathbf{H}_0 - \boldsymbol{\omega}/\gamma)| \gg 1/T_1 \qquad \text{(rapid passage)} \qquad (2\text{-}26)$$

Collecting these conditions together we have the following:

$$\left.\begin{aligned} &H_1^{-1}|(d/dt)(\mathbf{H}_0 - \boldsymbol{\omega}/\gamma)| \ll \gamma H_1 \\ &H_1^{-1}|(d/dt)(\mathbf{H}_0 - \boldsymbol{\omega}/\gamma)| \gg 1/T_1 \\ &\gamma H_1 \gg 1/T_2 \end{aligned}\right\}\text{(adiabatic rapid passage)} \qquad \begin{aligned}&(2\text{-}27\text{a})\\&(2\text{-}27\text{b})\\&(2\text{-}27\text{c})\end{aligned}$$

These are the conditions that, whatever the initial relative angle between **M** and $\mathbf{H}_e$ when the field (H_0) or frequency (ω) sweep begins, the angle remains the same as **M** precesses about $\mathbf{H}_e$ while $\mathbf{H}_e$ turns. The particular example treated above (**M** initially at its equilibrium value $\mathbf{M}_0$ and $\mathbf{H}_e$ initially parallel to $\mathbf{M}_0$) is one of the more useful cases experimentally.

In performing an experiment, one first takes T_1 and T_2 as nature gives them. Choosing H_1 large enough to meet (2-27c), one then selects a sweep rate rapid enough to satisfy (2-27b). If this sweep rate crowds the adiabatic condition (2-27a) then H_1 will have to be made larger so as to meet this condition. So it is that "adiabatic rapid passage" is a meaningful term.

[4] F. Bloch, W. W. Hansen, and M. Packard, *Phys. Rev.*, **70,** 474 (1946).

Before we leave the discussion of adiabatic rapid passage, it is essential to emphasize an inadequacy of the treatment we have given. In Bloch's original discussion[2] of rapid passage, he required $H_1^{-1}dH_0/dt \gg 1/T_2$. This is extremely stringent for substances that have $T_2 \ll T_1$, and it is in fact not necessary for observation of the rapid-passage response in solids. There is as yet no rigorous theory for the effects of strong H_1 fields in solids. Agreement with experiment can be obtained, however, by postulating the existence of a spin temperature in the rotating frame; i.e., a definite temperature is assumed to describe the excitation of the degrees of freedom that the spin system appears to have when viewed from the rotating frame. Discussion here of this novel assumption and its implications would take us far afield. Fortunately, the postulate and its application to rapid-passage experiments have received excellent and detailed treatment in the book by A. Abragam, "Principles of Nuclear Magnetism" (Oxford University Press, New York, 1961). Rapid-passage conditions are introduced in Abragam's Chapter III, spin temperature is discussed in Chapter V, and rapid passage in solids is taken up in detail in Chapter XII. It may be noted that our condition (2-27c) appealed to considerations of precessions about $\mathbf{H}_e$, and thus it was really based upon the rotating frame. However, as discussed by Abragam, even (2-27c) is more restrictive than experiment shows to be necessary, as much weaker H_1 fields will still lead to adiabatic rapid-passage responses from solids.

Next we turn to the "slow-passage" solutions. We suppose that H_0 and ω are essentially constant and that we have waited for a steady-state condition $dM_z/dt = 0$. We still use the rotating $\mathbf{H}_1$ field,

$$\mathbf{H}_1 = \mathbf{i}H_1 \cos \omega t + \mathbf{j}H_1 \sin \omega t \tag{2-28}$$

but we may as well note now that we consider it to arise as the properly rotating component of an oscillating field

$$H_x = 2H_1 \cos \omega t \tag{2-29}$$

of which the counterrotating part is $\mathbf{i}H_1 \cos \omega t - \mathbf{j}H_1 \sin \omega t$. From our rotating-coordinate analysis, it can be seen that the counterrotating part is far off resonance if the part (2-28) is anywhere near resonance, since the effective field in the counterrotating frame would be $(H_0 + \omega/\gamma)\mathbf{k} + \mathbf{H}_1$, which is very large and essentially along the $+z$ direction.

Although numerous references exist for the slow-passage solution, we repeat it hastily here, as we wish to obtain it for electrons with their negative moment, and certain sign changes are necessary.

In carrying forward the solution, we shall find that M_x has components in phase and out of phase with H_x; complex numbers are useful to handle this. Think of H_x as the real part of $2H_1e^{i\omega t}$, and take the magnetization M_x to be the real part of

$$\mathscr{M}_x = \chi \cdot 2H_1e^{i\omega t}$$

where χ is the complex susceptibility,

$$\chi = \chi' - i\chi'' \tag{2-30}$$

Then

$$\mathrm{Re}\,\mathscr{M}_x = M_x = \chi' \cdot 2H_1 \cos \omega t + \chi'' 2H_1 \sin \omega t \tag{2-31}$$

With the rotating field (2-28) added to $\mathbf{H}_0$, the phenomenological equations are

$$\begin{aligned} dM_x/dt &= \gamma(M_zH_1 \sin \omega t - H_0M_y) - M_x/T_2 \\ dM_y/dt &= \gamma(H_0M_x - M_zH_1 \cos \omega t) - M_y/T_2 \\ dM_z/dt &= \gamma(M_yH_1 \cos \omega t - M_xH_1 \sin \omega t) + (M_0 - M_z)/T_1 \end{aligned} \tag{2-32}$$

Defining $\mathscr{M}_\pm = M_x \pm iM_y$, we have from the first two equations (2-32) that

$$d\mathscr{M}_\pm/dt = \gamma(\mp iM_zH_1e^{\pm i\omega t} \pm iH_0\mathscr{M}_\pm) - \mathscr{M}_\pm/T_2 \tag{2-33}$$

The time dependence in each of equations (2-33) can be removed by defining $\mathscr{M}_\pm = e^{\pm i\omega t}\mathscr{N}_\pm$:

$$\pm i\omega\mathscr{N}_\pm = i\gamma(\mp M_zH_1 \pm H_0\mathscr{N}_\pm) - \mathscr{N}_\pm/T_2 \tag{2-34}$$

Now we impose the condition $dM_z/dt = 0$ and seek a solution compatible with it. Since

$$M_y \cos \omega t - M_x \sin \omega t = (1/2i)(\mathscr{M}_+e^{-i\omega t} - \mathscr{M}_-e^{+i\omega t})$$

the term dM_z/dt in (2-32) becomes

$$(\mathscr{M}_z - M_0)/T_1 = (\gamma H_1/2i)(\mathscr{N}_+ - \mathscr{N}_-) \tag{2-35}$$

Rearranging (2-34) gives

$$\mathscr{N}_\pm = \frac{\gamma H_1 M_z}{\omega_0 - \omega \pm i/T_2} \tag{2-36}$$

Since $\mathscr{N}_+$ and $\mathscr{N}_-$ are complex conjugates, we see immediately from (2-35) that M_z is real.

$$M_z = \chi_0 H_0 \frac{1 + T_2^2\,\Delta\omega^2}{1 + T_2^2\,\Delta\omega^2 + \gamma^2H_1^2T_1T_2} \tag{2-37}$$

where

$$\Delta\omega = \omega_0 - \omega \tag{2-38}$$

The solution $M_x = \frac{1}{2}(\mathscr{M}_+ + \mathscr{M}_-) = \frac{1}{2}(\mathscr{N}_+ e^{i\omega t} + \mathscr{N}_- e^{-i\omega t})$ is

$$M_x = \tfrac{1}{2}\chi_0(\gamma_0 H_0 T_2)\frac{T_2\,\Delta\omega\,2H_1\cos\omega t + 2H_1\sin\omega t}{1 + T_2^2\,\Delta\omega^2 + \gamma^2 H_1^2 T_1 T_2} \tag{2-39}$$

Comparing with (2-31) we identify immediately the complex susceptibility:

$$\begin{aligned}\chi' &= \tfrac{1}{2}\chi_0\omega_0 T_2\frac{T_2(\omega_0 - \omega)}{1 + T_2^2(\omega_0 - \omega)^2 + \gamma^2 H_1^2 T_1 T_2}\\ \chi'' &= \tfrac{1}{2}\chi_0\omega_0 T_2\frac{1}{1 + T_2^2(\omega_0 - \omega)^2 + \gamma^2 H_1^2 T_1 T_2}\end{aligned} \tag{2-40}$$

The average rate A at which energy is absorbed per unit volume by the sample from the H_1 field depends, of course, on the out-of-phase component. We have

$$A = (\omega/2\pi)\int_0^{2\pi/\omega} \mathbf{H}\cdot(d\mathbf{M}/dt)\,dt = 2\omega\chi'' H_1^2 \qquad (\text{erg sec}^{-1}\ \text{cm}^{-3}) \tag{2-41}$$

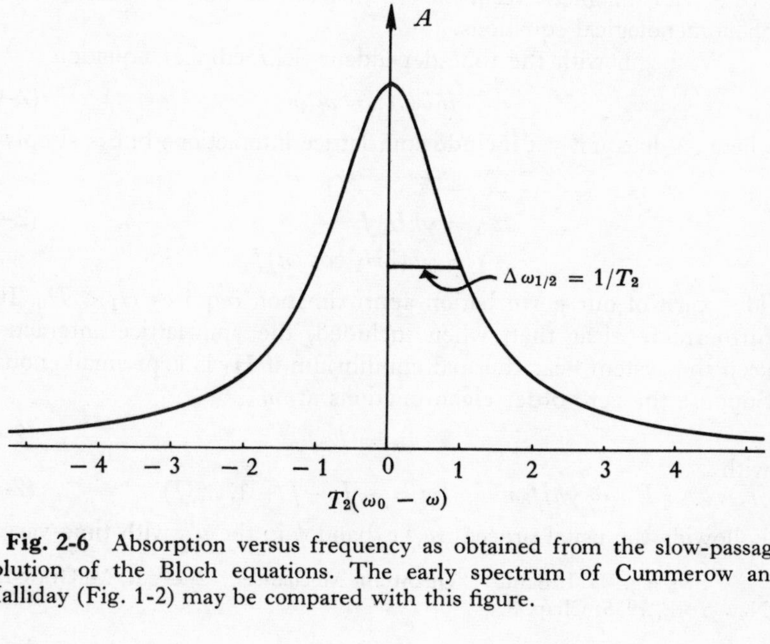

Fig. 2-6 Absorption versus frequency as obtained from the slow-passage solution of the Bloch equations. The early spectrum of Cummerow and Halliday (Fig. 1-2) may be compared with this figure.

For H_1 small and a sharp resonance ($\omega_0 T_2 \gg 1$), we obtain

$$A = \frac{\omega_0(\omega_0 T_2)\chi_0 H_1^2}{1 + T_2^2(\omega_0 - \omega)^2} \tag{2-42}$$

which can be plotted as a function of either ω or ω_0, supposing the other to be constant (see Fig. 2-6).

Absorption plotted as a function of slowly varying $\omega_0 = \gamma H_0$ defines a resonance curve with maximum at $\omega_0 = \omega$ having a half-width at a half-maximum of $\Delta\omega_{1/2} = 1/T_2 = \gamma \Delta H_{1/2}$. Thus $1/\gamma T_2 = \Delta H_{1/2}$ is the half-width expressed in units of the external field, which is slowly varied through resonance. [Note that the rapid-passage condition (2-27c) can thus be written $H_1 \gg \Delta H_{1/2}$.]

2-3 Perturbation Theory and More General Line Shapes

The line shape in Fig. 2-6 has a functional form found in simple theories of any kind of damped oscillator. It is often referred to as the Lorentz line shape in magnetic resonance, and it occurs mathematically in consequence of our assumed exponential decays. More general line shapes are found experimentally, and they are perhaps more readily treated using a perturbation-theory approach. In any case it is instructive to view magnetic resonance in this way as well as in terms of the phenomenological equations.

We begin with the time-dependent Schroedinger equation

$$i\hbar \partial\psi/\partial t = \mathcal{H}\psi \tag{2-43}$$

where $\mathcal{H}$ does not yet include spin-lattice interactions but is simply

$$\begin{aligned} \mathcal{H} &= \mathcal{H}_0 + \mathcal{H}_1 \\ \mathcal{H}_0 &= \gamma\hbar H_0 J_z \\ \mathcal{H}_1 &= \gamma\hbar(2H_1 \cos \omega t)J_x \end{aligned} \tag{2-44}$$

The spirit of our perturbation approximation requires $H_1 \ll H_0$. It is furthermore clear that, when included, the spin-lattice interactions keep the system near thermal equilibrium if $\mathbf{H}_1$ is kept small enough. Suppose the zero-order eigenfunctions are u_m,

$$\mathcal{H}_0 u_m = E_m u_m \tag{2-45}$$

with

$$E_m = \gamma\hbar H_0 m \qquad (m = -J, -J+1, \ldots, J) \tag{2-46}$$

Following the usual procedure,[5] expand ψ in the u's with time-varying

[5] See, e.g., L. I. Schiff, "Quantum Mechanics," 2nd ed., McGraw-Hill, New York, 1955, Chap. 8.

coefficients,

$$\psi = \sum_{m''} a_{m''}(t) u_{m''} \exp(-iE_{m''}t/\hbar) \tag{2-47}$$

and substitute into (2-43). Using (2-45), multiplying by $u^*_{m'}$, and integrating gives

$$i\hbar \dot{a}_{m'} \exp(-iE_{m'}t/\hbar) = \sum_{m''} a_{m''}(u_{m'}|\mathscr{H}_1|u_{m''}) \exp(-iE_{m''}t/\hbar) \tag{2-48}$$

If we suppose initially that the system is known to be in state m, then $a_{m''}(0) = \delta_{mm''}$ and (2-48) gives to first order in $\mathscr{H}_1$ that

$$\dot{a}_{m'} = (i\hbar)^{-1}(u_{m'}|\mathscr{H}_1|u_m) \exp(i\omega_{m'm}t) \tag{2-49}$$

where $\omega_{m'm} = (E_{m'} - E_m)/\hbar$.

For our problem,

$$\mathscr{H}_1 = \hbar\gamma[H_1 \exp(i\omega t) + H_1 \exp(-i\omega t)]J_x \tag{2-50}$$

and we wish to know how $|a_{m'}(t)|^2$ increases from $t = 0$. Using (2-50) in (2-49) we integrate to find

$$a_{m'}(t) = -\gamma H_1(m'|J_x|m)\left[\frac{\exp[i(\omega_{m'm} + \omega)t]}{\omega_{m'm} + \omega} + \frac{\exp[i(\omega_{m'm} - \omega)t]}{\omega_{m'm} - \omega}\right]_0^t \tag{2-51}$$

Keeping only the larger term in which the denominator tends to vanish at resonance, we find

$$|a_{m'}(t)|^2 = \gamma^2 H_1^2 |(m'|J_x|m)|^2 \xi(\omega_{m'm} - \omega, t) \tag{2-52}$$

where

$$\xi(\omega_{m'm} - \omega, t) = \frac{4 \sin^2[(\omega_{m'm} - \omega)(t/2)]}{(\omega_{m'm} - \omega)^2} \tag{2-53}$$

which is the famous function plotted against $\omega_{m'm} - \omega$ in Fig. 2-7.

Next suppose that there is a distribution of magnetic locales, whether because of dipolar interactions between the electrons or because of possible spatial inhomogeneity of the $\mathbf{H}_0$ field. Let the normalized distribution function for the values of $\nu_{m'm} = (E_{m'} - E_m)/h$ be $g(\nu_{m'm})$. Then the number of electrons having resonance frequency $\nu_{m'm}$ in interval $d\nu_{m'm}$ is

$$dN = N_0 g(\nu_{m'm})\, d\nu_{m'm} \tag{2-54}$$

where N_0 is the total number of paramagnets in unit volume which initially are in state m. We may couple (2-52) with (2-54) and calculate

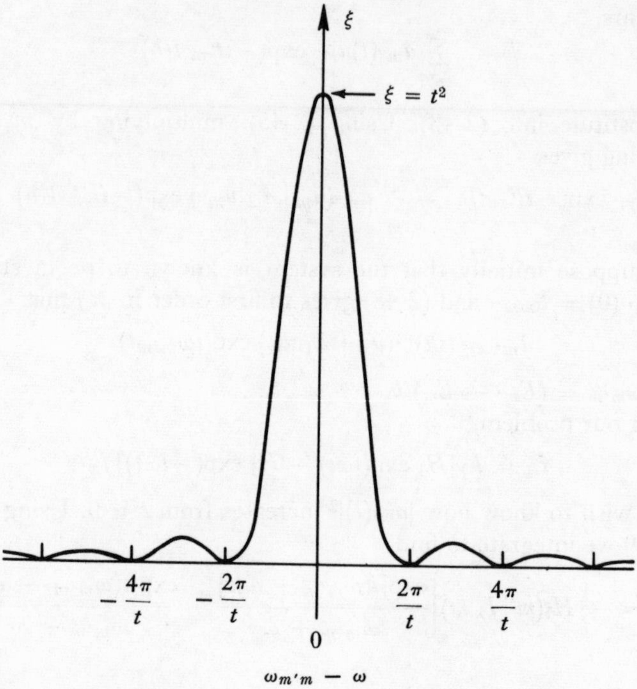

Fig. 2-7 The function $\xi(\omega_{m'm} - \omega; t)$ against $\omega_{m'm} - \omega$ for a particular value of t.

the number of paramagnets, initially in state m, to be found in m' at time t:

$$\Delta N_{mm'} = \int_0^\infty \gamma^2 H^2 |(m'|J_x|m)|^2 \xi(2\pi\nu_{m'm} - 2\pi\nu; t) N_0 g(\nu_{m'm})\, d\nu_{m'm} \tag{2-55}$$

Here we have shifted from angular frequencies ω to numerical frequencies $\nu = \omega/2\pi$. The integral can be evaluated simply if t is long enough so that ξ is a sharper function of $\nu_{m'm}$ than is g, for then

$$\xi(\omega_{m'm} - \omega; t) \to 2\pi t\delta(\omega_{m'm} - \omega) = t\delta(\nu_{m'm} - \nu)$$

and (2-55) assumes a form integrable by inspection:

$$\Delta N_{mm'} = \int_0^\infty \gamma^2 H_1^2 |(m'|J_x|m)|^2 t\delta(\nu_{m'm} - \nu) N_0 g(\nu_{m'm})\, d\nu_{m'm}$$

Calling $\Delta N/N_0 t = w_{m'm}$ the probability per unit time that a paramagnet initially in m will be found in m', we obtain from the integration that

$$w_{mm'} = \gamma^2 H_1^2 |(m'|J_x|m)|^2 g(\nu) \tag{2-56}$$

Here $\int_0^\infty g(\nu)\, d\nu = 1$ and $g(\nu)$ is expected to peak near $\nu_0 = \omega_0/2\pi$.

There are conditions on t implicit in (2-56), for ξ is a sharp-enough δ function only if $t \gg T_2$ (cf. Figs. 2-7 and 2-6). On the other hand, our assumption that all but one of the $a_{m''}$ in (2-48) vanish will be untrue unless $t \ll 1/w_{mm'}$.

We wish to use $1/T_2$ as a general measure of the width of the resonance peak. Since $g(\nu)$ is normalized to unity, this clearly implies that $g(\nu)]_{max} \approx T_2$, at least for bell-shaped curves with a single maximum. Bloembergen et al.[6] have established the convention that $T_2 = \frac{1}{2} g(\nu)]_{max}$, which combines with the normalization and the functional form of $g(\nu)$ to determine just how high on the sides of the $g(\nu)$ peak the points $g(\pm 1/T_2)$ fall.

Sometimes we shall wish to use a normalized shape function on the $\omega = 2\pi\nu$ scale. We shall denote it as $f(\omega)$, where

$$\int_0^\infty f(\omega)\, d\omega = 1$$
$$2\pi f(\omega) = g(\nu) \tag{2-57}$$

In principle it would be possible to distinguish different functions $g_{m'm}(\nu_{m'm})$ describing a different distribution for each initial state m and final state m'. This refinement is generally unnecessary for the usual experimental techniques and theoretical approximations.

When the spin-lattice relaxation mechanisms keep an excess of spins in the lower states, the net absorption A from the excess of absorptive transitions will have the shape $g(\nu)$ from (2-56). Comparison with the Lorentz form (2-42) gives the Lorentz shape function

$$g(\nu) = \frac{2T_2}{1 + T_2^2 (2\pi)^2 (\nu_0 - \nu)^2} \tag{2-58}$$

for which $\int_0^\infty g(\nu)\, d\nu = 1$, provided $2\pi\nu_0 T_2 \gg 1$; i.e., the resonance is sharp compared to ν_0. The parameter T_2 is clearly deducible from an experimentally observed profile of $g(\nu)$.

[6] N. Bloembergen, E. M. Purcell, and R. V. Pound, *Phys. Rev.*, **73**, 679 (1948).

When the term $\gamma^2 H_1^2 T_1 T_2$ is much less than unity, (2-40) and (2-31) provide a linear response of **M** to $\mathbf{H}_1$. Under these conditions the assumption that the response $M(t)$ to the field $H(t)$ cannot antecede it in time leads[7] to the Kronig–Kramers relations between $\chi'(\nu)$ and $\chi''(\nu)$:

$$\chi'(\nu) - \chi'(\infty) = \frac{2}{\pi} \int_0^\infty \frac{\nu' \chi''(\nu')\, d\nu'}{\nu'^2 - \nu^2}$$

$$\chi''(\nu) = -\frac{2\nu}{\pi} \int_0^\infty \frac{[\chi'(\nu') - \chi'(\infty)]\, d\nu'}{\nu'^2 - \nu^2} \tag{2-59}$$

(use Cauchy principal values)

For our purposes we shall usually be able to take $\chi'(\infty) = 0$. The relations (2-59), which hold very generally for complex quantities used to describe the response of physical systems to harmonic stimuli, enable one to determine the form of $\chi'(\nu)$ corresponding to any given frequency dependence $g(\nu)$ of $\chi''(\nu)$.

2-4 Saturation and the Rate Equations for Spin $\frac{1}{2}$

The condition $\gamma^2 H_1^2 T_1 T_2 \ll 1$ can be assured with small enough H_1. However, as the amplitude of the rotating or oscillating field increases, the external radiation field begins to put energy into the electronic paramagnets at a rate comparable to the ability of the spin-lattice relaxation processes to carry it off. That $1/T_1$ determines the maximum energy absorption is readily observed by coupling (2-41) and (2-40) and evaluating the limit as $H_1 \rightarrow \infty$.

$$A_{\max} = \lim_{H_1 \to \infty} 2\omega H_1^2 \chi''$$

$$= \lim_{H_1 \to \infty} 2\omega H_1^2 \frac{\frac{1}{2}\chi_0 \omega_0 T_2}{\gamma^2 H_1^2 T_1 T_2}$$

$$= \chi_0 H_0^2 / T_1 \tag{2-60}$$

[7] More accessible than the original references of Kronig or Kramers, as well as more suitable for our purposes, is the treatment by A. Abragam, "Principles of Nuclear Magnetism," Oxford University Press, New York, 1961, p. 93.

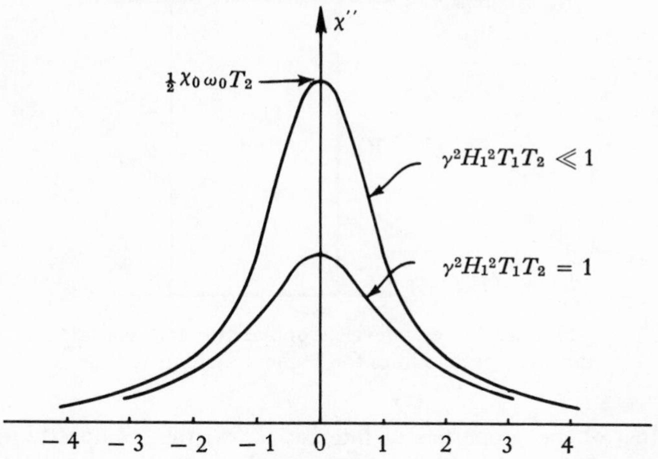

Fig. 2-8 Saturation illustrated by plotting χ'' of (2-40) for two values of $\gamma^2 H_1^2 T_1 T_2$.

Evidently the peak in the $\chi''(\omega)$ curve drops as H_1 increases. Figure 2-8 compares χ'' for $\gamma^2 H_1^2 T_1 T_2 \ll 1$ with χ'' for $\gamma^2 H_1^2 T_1 T_2 = 1$. It is clear that the possibility of measuring T_1 rests with this effect, which is called *saturation* because the paramagnetic system (or spin system, in more conventional jargon) is saturated with power to the extent that the spin-lattice relaxation processes cannot carry it off to the lattice without disturbing the equilibrium of the paramagnets.

Our discussion of the approach to equilibrium of the paramagnets will be carried forth for the special case $J = S = \frac{1}{2}$. This is an important one experimentally and, in any event, more compactly illustrates the physical nature of the saturation process. In this discussion we shall frequently adopt the widespread convention which refers to the paramagnets as "spins" and ignores the fact that the paramagnetism arises in general from orbital plus spin angular momentum.

Figure 2-9 defines the situation we have in mind. Subscripts + and − denote the states with $m_S = +\frac{1}{2}$ and $m_S = \frac{1}{2}$. N_+ and N_- are their respective populations. W_a and W_e are transition probabilities per unit time induced by whatever interactions with the lattice enable spins to flip and to create or inelastically scatter phonons. From the direction of the arrows one sees that W_a is an absorption process for spins and W_e a corresponding emission process.

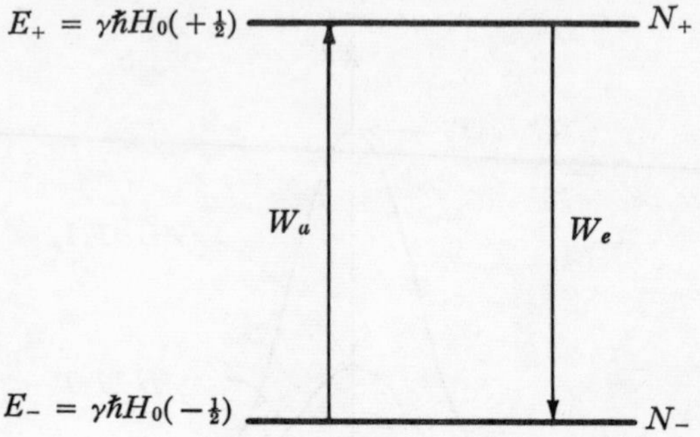

Fig. 2-9 Energy levels, populations, and relaxation transition probabilities for a spin ½ system.

Most of the properties of interest are written compactly in terms of the population excess n of the spins in the lower level, which leads us to change variables to n and N.

$$\left.\begin{aligned} N_+ + N_- &= N \\ N_- - N_+ &= n \end{aligned}\right\} \rightarrow \quad \begin{aligned} N_- &= \tfrac{1}{2}(N + n) \\ N_+ &= \tfrac{1}{2}(N - n) \end{aligned} \tag{2-61}$$

Thermal equilibrium is characterized by

$$N_-^0/N_+^0 = \exp(\epsilon/kT) = W_e/W_a \tag{2-62}$$

where $\epsilon = E_+ - E_-$, because thermal equilibrium is the steady-state population distribution determined by the W's for the lattice at temperature T. If we think in terms of phonons at frequency ν, we can express W_e/W_a in terms of the mean phonon number $\overline{n(\nu)}$ with $h\nu = \epsilon$:

$$W_e/W_a = \overline{n(\nu) + 1}/\overline{n(\nu)} \tag{2-63}$$

In terms of the Einstein A and B coefficients,[8] this ratio is $(A + B\rho)/B\rho$, where ρ is the phonon energy per unit volume and unit frequency interval. This gives, of course, the Boltzmann factor of (2-62), if the oscillators are in equilibrium at temperature T.

Transient adjustments of nonequilibrium $n = N_- - N_+$ toward equilibrium occur in consequence of the simple rate equations which follow from conservation of the number of spins and from the definition of the W's:

$$\begin{aligned} dN_+/dt &= N_-W_a - N_+W_e \\ dN_-/dt &= N_+W_e - N_-W_a \end{aligned} \tag{2-64}$$

[8] W. Heitler, "Quantum Theory of Radiation," 3rd ed., Oxford University Press, New York, 1954, pp. 178–179.

By subtraction,

$$dn/dt = 2(N_+W_e - N_-W_a) = 2(N_+W - N_-We^{-\epsilon/kt}) \quad (2\text{-}65)$$

where we define $W_e = W$ and use (2-62) to express W_a. From (2-61) we can rearrange (2-65) to give

$$dn/dt = W[1 + \exp(-\epsilon/kT)]\left[N\frac{1 - \exp(-\epsilon/kT)}{1 + \exp(-\epsilon/kT)} - n\right] \quad (2\text{-}66)$$

After a long-enough wait, $dn/dt \to 0$, and

$$\begin{aligned} n &\to N\frac{1 - \exp(-\epsilon/kT)}{1 + \exp(-\epsilon/kT)} = n_0 \\ n_0 &\cong N\epsilon/2kT = N\gamma\hbar H_0/2kT \qquad (\text{for } \epsilon < kT) \end{aligned} \quad (2\text{-}67)$$

If we are treating unit volume of sample, then $M_z = n\gamma\hbar\frac{1}{2}$ and we can compare

$$dn/dt = W[1 + \exp(-\epsilon/kT)](n_0 - n) \quad (2\text{-}68)$$

with (2-16) for $\mathbf{H} = \mathbf{H}_0$ along z:

$$dM_z/dt = \gamma(\mathbf{H}_0 \times \mathbf{M})_z + (M_0 - M_z)/T_1 \quad (2\text{-}69)$$

Thus we observe

$$\begin{aligned} 1/T_1 &= W[1 + \exp(-\epsilon/kT)] \\ &= 2W \qquad (\text{for } \epsilon < kT) \end{aligned} \quad (2\text{-}70)$$

The emission probability per unit time for one spin fixes T_1.

Clearly the effect of applying an oscillating $\mathbf{H}_1$ field perpendicular to $\mathbf{H}_0$ is to alter the rate equations by introducing a second transition-producing agent. For $J = S = \frac{1}{2}$, (2-56) gives us a reversible[9] transition-probability rate, either upward or downward in Fig. 2-9, which we denote as V:

$$V = w_{1/2,-1/2} = w_{-1/2,1/2} = \tfrac{1}{4}\gamma^2 H_1^2 g(\nu) \quad (2\text{-}71)$$

Including V in addition to W_a and W_e transforms (2-68) into

$$dn/dt = (1/T_1)(n_0 - n) - 2nV \quad (2\text{-}72)$$

[9] The question why V is reversible when the W's are not is one that we really should not duck. In fact, V_a and V_e are not precisely equal, being given by a ratio $[n(\nu) + 1]/n(\nu)$ for photons, which is quite analogous to (2-63) for phonons. However, typical microwave fields H_1 will make the photon number $n(\nu)$ so very large that this ratio is, for practical purposes, unity compared to the ratios (2-62) and (2-63). See, e.g., J. P. Lloyd and G. E. Pake, *Phys. Rev.*, **94,** 579 (1954).

from which the steady-state solution is

$$n_{ss} = n_0/(1 + 2T_1V)$$
$$= n_0T/T_s \qquad (2\text{-}73)$$

We sometimes call $(1 + 2T_1V)^{-1}$ the *saturation factor* and $2T_1V$ (which we shall see is $\gamma^2H_1^2T_1T_2$) the *saturation parameter*. The quantity T_s is called the spin temperature, analogous to the temperature T appearing in (2-67) for the steady state n corresponding to thermal equilibrium at temperature T. We see that the effect of saturation is to raise the spin temperature T_s, a thermodynamically consistent conclusion. For a discussion of the validity of this concept, see Abragam's book.[7]

It is instructive to consolidate the ideas of Sec. 2-3 and the present section by obtaining the χ'' solution (2-40) of the Bloch equations using only the considerations of the present section with an assumed Lorentz shape function. Equations (2-58) and (2-71) give us

$$V = \tfrac{1}{2}\gamma^2H_1^2T_2/(1 + T_2\,\Delta\omega^2) \qquad (2\text{-}74)$$

as the expression for the transition probability as a function of frequency. The form of the expression V as we have derived it should depend in no way upon the populations of the levels + and − in Fig. 2-9, yet we wish to obtain from it (2-40) including the saturation term, which means that populations have become disturbed. We do so by writing an expression for the rate of energy absorption in terms of the steady-state population difference n_{ss} of (2-73). Since the transition rate is V for both absorptive and emissive transitions, the rate of energy absorption depends only upon the steady-state excess number of spins in the lower level, n_{ss}:

$$A = n_{ss}\cdot V\cdot\hbar\omega \qquad (2\text{-}75)$$

From (2-74) and (2-73),

$$A = n_0\frac{1}{1 + T_1[\gamma^2H_1^2T_2/(1 + T_2^2\,\Delta\omega^2)]}\,\frac{\tfrac{1}{2}\gamma^2H_1^2T_2}{1 + T_2^2\,\Delta\omega^2}\hbar\omega \qquad (2\text{-}76)$$

To obtain the form of (2-40) one now must use (2-67) to eliminate n_0 in favor of quantities that contribute to form the χ_0 of (1-10) for $J = \frac{1}{2}$, giving finally,

$$A = \frac{2H_1^2\frac{1}{2}(N\gamma^2\hbar^2/4kT)\omega_0T_2}{1 + T_2^2\,\Delta\omega^2 + \gamma^2H_1^2T_1T_2} \qquad (2\text{-}77)$$

Equation (2-77) is precisely (2-42) for the special case of spin $\frac{1}{2}$ and a Lorentz χ''.

It is an interesting exercise to invert the above procedure, using (2-71), (2-73), (2-75), and (2-41) to express χ'' for any shape function $g(\nu)$:

$$\chi'' = \frac{1}{4}\frac{\chi_0\omega_0 g(\nu)}{1 + \frac{1}{2}\gamma^2 H_1^2 T_1 g(\nu)} \tag{2-78}$$

However, the Kronig–Kramers relations *cannot* be used to find the corresponding χ' because of the nonlinearity inherent in (2-78).

For systems that have higher spin than $\frac{1}{2}$, or for multilevel systems whether evenly spaced or not, rate equations are often (but not always) applicable, and saturation of a transition involving any pair of levels is, in general, possible experimentally. Lloyd and Pake treat this situation,[10] finding that there is always a saturation factor such as that of (2-73). However, the quantity $(2T_1)^{-1}$ is replaced by a function of transition probabilities between the various pairs of levels, which cannot in general be related to time constants of transient response of the spin system.

There are serious limitations to the rate-equation approach. In particular, when $\gamma^2 H_1^2$ is larger than $(T_1 T_2)^{-1}$, coherences are introduced and there are departures from the predictions of the Bloch equations for $\gamma^2 H_1^2 T_1 T_2 \gg 1$, especially in the behavior of χ'. Redfield[11] has examined such effects in nuclear magnetic resonance.

2-5 Experimental Detection of the Resonance

So far we have been content to justify our interest in the susceptibility χ by showing that the rate of energy absorption A by unit volume of sample is proportional to χ''. However, it is yet to be shown that specific experimental arrangements actually measure χ'' as a meter response.

Perhaps the simplest experiment conceptually is illustrated in Fig. 2-10, which represents a transmission spectrometer. A klystron generates microwaves that are transmitted down a rectangular waveguide in a TE_{10} mode. The microwave energy falls upon a crystal rectifier, which we suppose to be operating in the square-law region. Thus the crystal current is directly proportional to the microwave power falling on it. A paramagnetic crystal glued to the end of a stick is placed just inside the waveguide through a hole in the narrow face,

[10] J. P. Lloyd and G. E. Pake, *Phys. Rev.*, **94,** 579 (1954).
[11] A. G. Redfield, *Phys. Rev.*, **98,** 1787 (1955); *Phys. Rev.*, **101,** 67 (1956).

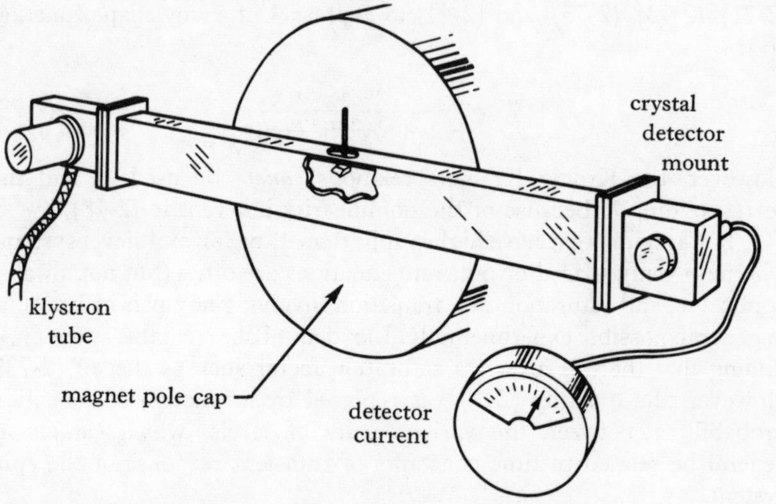

Fig. 2-10 Sketch of an extremely simple transmission spectrometer for detection of paramagnetic resonance, with a cutaway view showing a paramagnetic crystal inserted into the waveguide.

and the external magnetic field is varied through the resonance condition $\omega_0 = \omega$.

An interesting facet of this simple spectrometer (which definitely is not a sensitive one) is that the microwave magnetic field experienced by the crystal is a rotating field, apart from effects of reflections at the sample and at the detector. (Isolators or attenuators may be inserted after the klystron and before the detector to minimize these effects.) To see that the microwave field *is* a rotating one, we note in Fig. 2-11 the magnetic field pattern for a TE_{10} mode, viewed perpendicular to

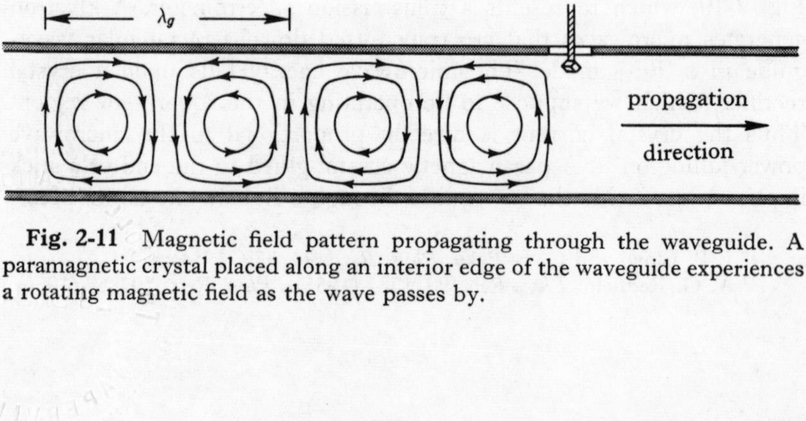

Fig. 2-11 Magnetic field pattern propagating through the waveguide. A paramagnetic crystal placed along an interior edge of the waveguide experiences a rotating magnetic field as the wave passes by.

the broad face of the waveguide. This magnetic field pattern propagates down the waveguide at the guide phase velocity. It is evident that, as the field pattern flows down the waveguide, the field vector at the position of the crystal will rotate in a counterclockwise direction.

If the crystal is placed along the upper edge of the guide in Fig. 2-11, the magnetic field it sees will rotate counterclockwise. Such a simple spectrometer is useful in the teaching laboratory to demonstrate, for a given direction of the external $\mathbf{H}_0$ field, the sign of the electronic magnetic moment, as considerably greater absorption occurs in the crystal position for which the $\mathbf{H}_1$ field rotates in the same sense as the Larmor precession to $\mathbf{H}_0$. (There is a small absorption in the other position because reflections build up small-intensity standing waves charactized by an oscillating $\mathbf{H}_1$ with both rotating components present.)

A plot of crystal current as a function of external field will now result in a curve such as Fig. 2-12, because the detector current is proportional to the power falling on the detector crystal, and in resonance an amount of power $A = 2H_1^2\omega\chi''$, per unit sample volume, is absorbed from the train of microwaves. Because of this absorption from the power that otherwise would fall on the detector, Fig. 2-12 is in effect an inversion of Fig. 2-6.

The effects of noise inherent in the crystal detector and in the klystron can be reduced by the technique of field modulation. If a small magnetic field sinusoidally varying at an audio or radio frequency is superimposed upon $\mathbf{H}_0$, we see from Fig. 2-12 that a component of detector current at that frequency will in general exist in the neighborhood of the resonance. In fact, if the modulation amplitude is smaller

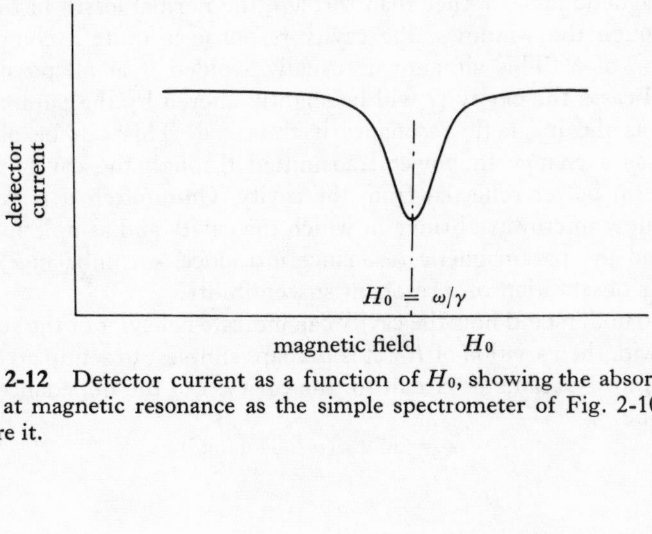

Fig. 2-12 Detector current as a function of H_0, showing the absorption of power at magnetic resonance as the simple spectrometer of Fig. 2-10 would measure it.

than the magnetic resonance width, a simple Taylor expansion shows that this component will be proportional to the derivative of χ'' with respect to H_0 or ω_0. By beating this signal with a reference signal at the modulation frequency, a d-c signal will thus be obtained proportional to $d\chi''(\omega_0)/d\omega_0$. Although the derivative response is sometimes inconvenient to interpret and although occasionally one finds it necessary to integrate it to obtain χ'', the technique has an advantage—it accepts only the noise within a narrow bandwidth near the modulation frequency. By adjusting to very long times of observation, this bandwidth can be made as small as one desires, but in practical cases it is seldom less than 0.1 sec^{-1}. Workers in paramagnetic resonance, as in nuclear resonance, quickly learn to work directly with the derivative, which is actually more sensitive to slight tendencies toward structure in the curve of χ'' versus frequency than is the χ'' curve itself.

Greater sensitivity for small to modest numbers of unpaired electrons is obtained by using a resonant cavity. The advantage of any such resonant structure is that the standing-wave pattern set up within it leads to very large H_1 field values. In general the signal ultimately observed is increased by a factor Q, where Q is the quality factor of the cavity:

$$Q = \frac{2\pi(\text{stored energy})}{\text{cavity energy losses per cycle}} \tag{2-79}$$

In typical paramagnetic resonance spectrometers the cavity Q may be anywhere from about 1000 upward. However, it is clear that a larger sample will also increase the energy absorption. If it should happen that the sample is so large as to determine the cavity Q through the paramagnetic losses rather than through the normal losses in the walls or through the windows, the cavity response is quite a complicated function of χ. This situation is usually avoided if at all possible. In normal cases the cavity Q will be slightly altered by the paramagnetic losses as the magnetic resonance is traversed. This can be observed either as a change in power transmitted through the cavity or as a change in power reflected from the cavity. Quite often it is desirable to set up a microwave bridge in which the cavity and sample form one arm and the paramagnetic resonance introduces an unbalance, which permits observation of a resonant susceptibility.

To understand how the cavity can indicate behavior of the susceptibility with the variation of H_0, it is perhaps simplest to set up an equivalent lumped-parameter circuit for the cavity. Let the impedance of the cavity be

$$Z = R + i(\omega L - 1/\omega C) \tag{2-80}$$

where R, L, and C are the equivalent resistance, inductance, and capacitance of the cavity. Since not all the volume occupied by the cavity magnetic energy is filled with the sample, we use a filling factor η to write

$$L = L_0[(1 - \eta) + \eta(1 + 4\pi X)] = L_0(1 + 4\pi\eta X) \qquad (2\text{-}81)$$

where $1 + 4\pi X$ is the permeability of the sample and $0 < \eta < 1$.

Let $\omega_r = 1/(L_0C)^{1/2}$ be the cavity resonant frequency when the sample is off magnetic resonance. Then

$$Z = R + iL_0(\omega^2 - \omega_r^2)/\omega + iL_0\omega 4\pi\eta X \qquad (2\text{-}82)$$

and, putting in the complex form for X, we have the cavity impedance:

$$Z = R + 4\pi\eta\omega L_0 X'' + i[4\pi L_0\omega\eta X' + (L_0/\omega)(\omega^2 - \omega_r^2)] \qquad (2\text{-}83)$$

The Q of such a simple RLC circuit is $\omega L/R$. At circuit resonance $\omega = \omega_r$, we find

$$Z_r = R(1 + 4\pi\eta Q X'') + i4\pi L_0\omega\eta X' \qquad (2\text{-}84)$$

Since the resistive term fixes the energy dissipation, (2-84) shows directly the way in which the resonant structure augments by a factor Q the effect of X''.

But (2-84) also makes clear another problem, because the reactive term shifts the cavity resonance from ω_r; if X' varies to large-enough values near magnetic resonance, the cavity will be appreciably detuned. There are at least two common ways of avoiding this effect. One is to use the cavity as an element in a microwave bridge so tuned as to be sensitive to resistive unbalance but not to reactive unbalance. Another is to stabilize the klystron frequency on the cavity. Then the klystron frequency shifts as X' varies so that the reactive term in Z is always zero. Again, two common experimental procedures are in use for stabilizing on the cavity. The Pound stabilizer[12] is quite effective. Another system, used in some commercial spectrometers, simply introduces a small modulation of the klystron reflector voltage at about 10 kc sec^{-1}. As the klystron drifts off the cavity resonance, there is a reflected signal at the modulation frequency. Precisely on cavity resonance, the reflected signal is zero at that frequency. If the reflected signal is phase-sensitive detected, an error signal is obtained which can be used to retune the klystron to the cavity resonance. This is automatic frequency control, or afc.

It should perhaps be emphasized explicitly that any of the experimental arrangements of the cavity, microwave bridge, etc., can achieve

[12] R. V. Pound, *Rev. Sci. Instr.*, **17,** 490 (1946); *Proc. Inst. Radio Engrs.* **35,** 1405 (1947).

the reduction in detector and/or klystron noise by magnetic field modulation and coherent detection, as discussed earlier in this section. To reproduce faithfully the derivative of χ'', it is clear that the field modulation should be a small fraction of the magnetic resonance width $\Delta H_{1/2}$, and, if a stabilization system employing klystron frequency modulation is used, the modulation amplitude and frequency must be less than the magnetic resonance width expressed as a frequency, $\Delta\nu_{1/2} = \gamma\,\Delta H_{1/2}/2\pi$. When such conditions are not met, the spectrometer response may still be interpretable in terms of χ, but not without careful analysis.

2-6 Types of Spectrometers and Sensitivity Considerations

It is not our purpose to discuss in detail even a fraction of the wide variety of spectrometers that have been designed and built or the infinite number of variations that could be made upon them. A large number of spectrometer designs have been discussed in the literature, and the most realistic goal we can set for this section is to provide a useful guide to these published designs, as well as to an analysis of sensitivity and signal-to-noise performance.

The most comprehensive treatment of sensitivity and considerations of noise reduction is that by Feher,[13] who analyzes the effect of paramagnetic resonance on the cavity impedance and treats a number of possible spectrometer arrangements. Cavity coupling is discussed for both the transmission and reflection systems. After an examination of sources of noise, Feher then treats a number of possible detection schemes: the barretter (or bolometer) used in straight detection with a magic tee and a reflection cavity; balanced mixer detection with barretters; a crystal used in straight detection; straight crystal detection with optimum microwave bucking; and the superheterodyne. Since the Feher article appeared, higher field-modulation frequencies have come into more extensive use in order to take advantage of the (frequency)$^{-1}$ noise characteristics of crystals, and some of Feher's sensitivity curves can be replotted accordingly. Evidence has appeared[14] that

[13] G. Feher, *Bell System Tech. J.*, **36,** 449 (1957).

[14] R. H. Sands, in "Symposium on Spectroscopy," Am. Soc. Testing Materials Spec. Tech. Publ. 269, Philadelphia, 1959, pp. 165–171. D. T. Teaney, M. P. Klein, and A. M. Portis, *Rev. Sci. Instr.*, **32,** 721 (1961) also observe this effect for the superheterodyne bridge spectrometer, and they present a design of a superheterodyne induction spectrometer which uses a bimodal cavity and is free of the effects of klystron noise up to power levels of about 500 mw.

the superheterodyne is less effective than Feher anticipated at higher klystron powers because klystron frequency noise, not detector noise, becomes dominant. Since this noise spectrum also seems to go as $(\text{frequency})^{-1}$, higher modulation frequency is helpful whether source or detector noise is dominant. An important spectrometer analysis which one should use in conjunction with the Feher article is that of Goldsborough and Mandel.[15]

Of course, much of the foregoing has presumed some familiarity with microwave components and circuitry. Standard texts on these topics are available to the student. In addition there are a number of brief treatments especially directed toward the reader interested in microwave spectroscopy. Several of these are listed in the bibliography that follows.

Microwave techniques reviewed for magnetic resonance and spectroscopy:

W. Gordy, W. V. Smith, and R. F. Trambarulo, "Microwave Spectroscopy," Wiley, New York, 1953, Chap. 1.

D. J. E. Ingram, "Spectroscopy at Radio and Microwave Frequencies," Butterworth's, London, 1955, Chaps. 2, 3, and 4.

C. H. Townes and A. L. Schawlow, "Microwave Spectroscopy," McGraw-Hill, New York, 1955, Chaps. 14–17.

D. J. E. Ingram, "Free Radicals as Studied by Electron Spin Resonance," Academic Press, New York, 1958, Chap. 3.

Roy H. Anderson, "Molecular Physics," Vol. 3 of Methods of Experimental Physics, Academic Press, New York, 1962.

Specific paramagnetic resonance spectrometers:

J. M. Hershon and G. K. Fraenkel, *Rev. Sci. Instr.*, **26,** 34 (1955). The spectrometer described operates at X-band and employs superheterodyne detection and Pound stabilization.

M. W. P. Strandberg, M. Tinkham, I. H. Solt, Jr., and C. E. Davis, Jr., *Rev. Sci. Instr.*, **27,** 596 (1956). This spectrometer locks the klystron frequency to the sample cavity. There is also a description of a radiofrequency circuit for paramagnetic resonance observation at frequencies of ≈ 100 Mc sec^{-1}.

H. A. Buckmaster and H. E. D. Scovil, *Can. J. Phys.*, **34,** 711 (1956). This spectrometer operates at K-band (1.25-cm microwaves) and techniques of operating at temperatures of liquid helium are described.

K. D. Bowers, R. A. Kamper, and R. B. D. Knight, *J. Sci. Instr.*, **34,** 49 (1957). Operating at X-band, this instrument uses 115 kc sec^{-1} for the modulation frequency.

J. B. Mock, *Rev. Sci. Instr.*, **31,** 551 (1960). This spectrometer employs a backward wave oscillator and a broad-band transmission-type microwave

[15] J. P. Goldsborough and M. Mandel, *Rev. Sci. Instr.*, **31,** 1044 (1960).

structure operating at frequencies in the 100 kMc sec^{-1} range. It is used at liquid helium temperatures.

D. T. Teaney, M. P. Klein, and A. M. Portis, *Rev. Sci. Instr.*, **32,** 721 (1961); A. M. Portis and D. Teaney, *J. Appl. Phys.*, **29,** 1692 (1958). The earlier article describes a bimodal cavity which achieves the balance normally obtained with a microwave bridge by means of a symmetrical geometry. The device is a microwave analog of the nuclear induction apparatus used by F. Bloch, W. W. Hansen, and M. Packard [*Phys. Rev.*, **70,** 474 (1946)], and is used for paramagnetic resonance in a microwave superheterodyne induction spectrometer, described in the later paper. The advantage of such geometrical balance is its relative insensitivity to frequency changes with the result that frequency noise, which is shown to limit the signal-to-noise ratio for the superheterodyne bridge spectrometer at higher power levels, does not cause the sensitivity of the superheterodyne induction spectrometer to depart from that theoretically expected.

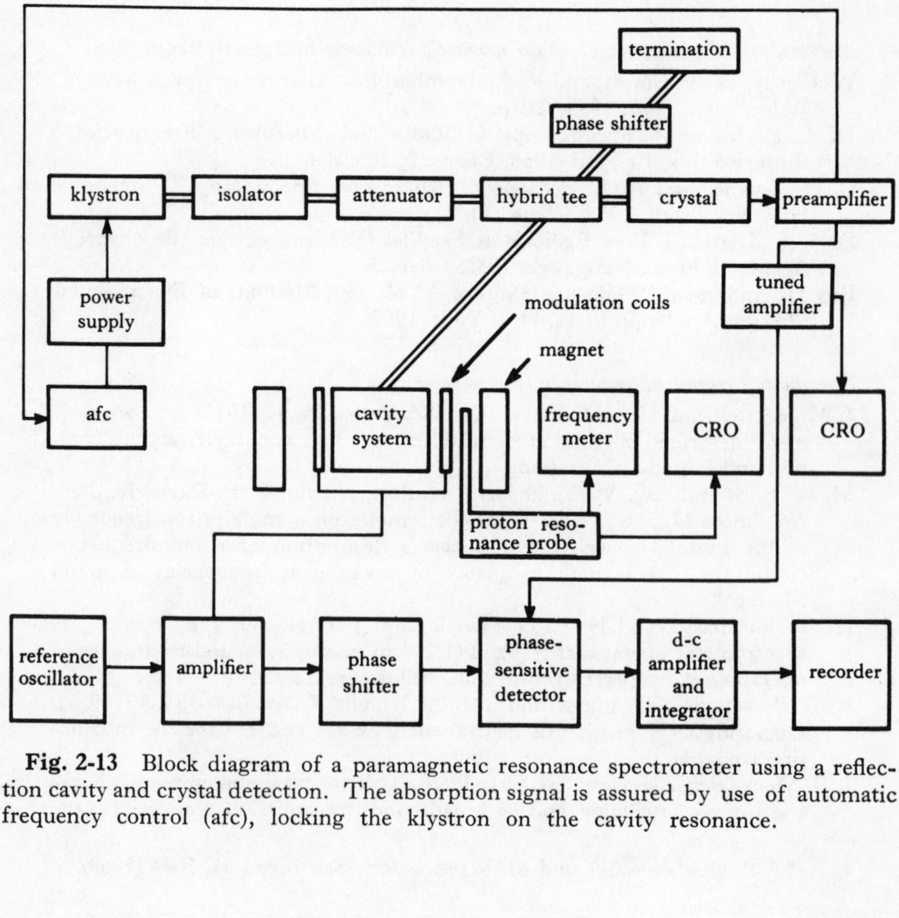

Fig. 2-13 Block diagram of a paramagnetic resonance spectrometer using a reflection cavity and crystal detection. The absorption signal is assured by use of automatic frequency control (afc), locking the klystron on the cavity resonance.

Finally, Fig. 2-13 presents a block diagram of a simple spectrometer using a reflection cavity and straight crystal detection. The diagram includes a proton nuclear resonance detector for magnetic field measurement. From such a diagram the reader can obtain some feeling for the chain of electronic gear that even a simple and quite orthodox spectrometer requires.

[3]

Crystal Fields and the Effective Spin Hamiltonian

3-1 The Nature of the Crystal Field Problem

When observing the emission spectrum of an element in one of its possible ionization states, we are accustomed to dealing with the ions in a hot vapor or perhaps in a rarefied gaseous conductor. Thus the properties of emission spectra are logically thought to be associated with what is in very good approximation a free ion, and when the (small) perturbing effects of collisions are taken in account, we are able to interpret quite accurately the spectrum emitted from a discharge tube. Our interpretation of such spectra leans heavily on the conservation laws applicable to the free ion, and it is the constants of electron motion—for example, angular momentum—of the various ionic energy states in terms of which we explain or "predict" the experimental observations.

In Sec. 1-3 we previewed the problem posed for us by the binding of paramagnetic ions into the structure of a paramagnetic crystal. When one pictures how close to the paramagnetic ion are the neighboring atoms, ions, or molecules and recognizes the intimate association of all of them into the large ordered structure, it may indeed seem quite startling that the free-ion ground state explains magnetic susceptibilities in rare earth crystals (Table 1-1) and quite natural that the free-ion ground state does not explain the iron-group properties (Table 1-2). Our implication in Sec. 1-3 that the iron group is anomalous seems naive from this point of view. Why should we have expected in the first place that the bound ion is at all like the free ion?

Actually, neither extreme view applies. We have ample experimental evidence that certain molecules retain their essential identity even though bound into a crystal, e.g., H_2O molecules in crystalline hydrates. The same is true of many ions, but we must be prepared for complications presented by neighboring ions and the binding to them. Electronic wave functions in the ion will be somewhat altered, and wave functions from neighboring electrons may overlap the ion (with due regard for such cardinal precepts of electron behavior as the Pauli principle).

Ideally we should like to solve the Schroedinger equation for the electrons of the entire crystal. This, of course, is not yet possible, and a second approach would perhaps be to treat a cluster of atoms, molecules, or ions with the paramagnetic ion at the center. For example, certain crystals are characterized by an octahedral disposition of water molecules about the positive ion, with the negatively charged "tail" of each water molecule dipole oriented toward the positive ion. Figure 3-1 is a schematic illustration of the plane of four water molecules and the positive ion of such a complex. Of course, even this complex is relatively

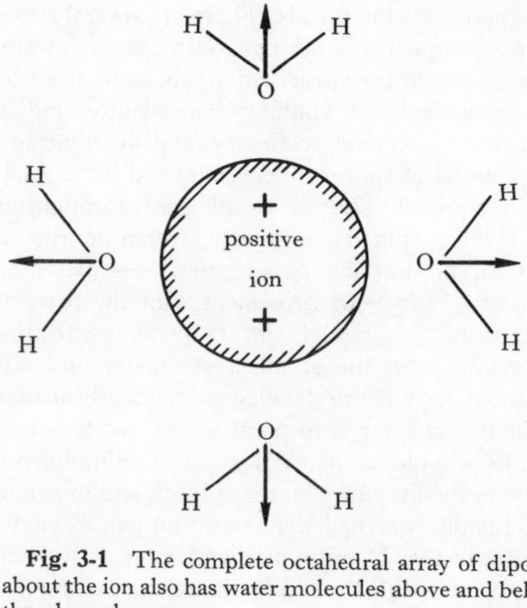

Fig. 3-1 The complete octahedral array of dipoles about the ion also has water molecules above and below the plane shown.

difficult to treat quantum mechanically. Some efforts in this direction have been made, but considerable approximation is involved in obtaining answers.

A third approach, in which the conceptual approximations are gross but the calculations can usually be carried through, is that of the so-called *crystal field theory*. As so often is true in physics, this kind of approach is heavily used on the purely practical grounds that answers can be obtained. The crystal field theory assumes that the paramagnetic ion resides in a crystalline electric potential whose sources are point charges (ions) or point dipoles (e.g., H_2O molecules) lying wholly outside the paramagnetic ion. Interaction with this additional potential is thus added to the Hamiltonian of the free ion in order to ascertain the new energy states. The crystalline potential or field must clearly have the symmetry of the array of its sources, and indeed this symmetry manifests itself heavily in fixing the properties of the ionic energy states. For this reason group theoretical methods provide the most compact techniques for analyzing the problem, and there is an extensive literature on the subject.

We shall not go into the details of the group theory, secular determinants, etc., which are required to calculate, within the crystal field approximation, the anticipated energy states and ground-state properties of paramagnetic ions in crystals. There are several reasons for this:

1. Most readers probably are not well versed in group theoretical methods, without which the presentation would be most lengthy.

2. Often each electronic configuration requires individual treatment for each possible crystal symmetry, and different alternatives as to relative magnitudes of spin-orbit coupling and the crystal field interaction must be examined. Thus no simple generalizations are possible.

3. The effective spin Hamiltonian, which is the approximate Hamiltonian used to describe paramagnetic resonance experiments, often is quantitatively in poor agreement with the predictions of the oversimplified crystal field model, and its qualitative features are often predictable directly from the simplest symmetry and physical considerations without recourse to detailed crystal field calculations. Thus the program of this chapter is to point to but not to solve the crystal field problem, to provide an instructional if oversimplified example, to serve as a guide to the literature on the subject, and to summarize some of the results. Finally, we shall write down for paramagnetic resonance experiments an effective Hamiltonian containing only spin operators, justifying wherever possible by simple physical or symmetry arguments the inclusion of certain kinds of interaction terms. Magnitudes of these

interactions will be determinable by experiment, and we shall try to indicate in passing how such interactions might arise in carrying through a crystal field calculation.

We begin by listing the kinds of terms we expect in the Hamiltonian for the electrons of a paramagnetic ion in a crystal in the absence of an external magnetic field:

$$\mathcal{H} = \sum(\mathbf{p}_i^2/2m) - (Ze^2/r_i) + (e^2/r_{ij}) + \lambda_{ij}\mathbf{l}_i\cdot\mathbf{s}_j + a_i\mathbf{j}_i\cdot\mathbf{I} - e_i\Phi_c(\mathbf{r}_i) \tag{3-1}$$

Here we take as an origin the nucleus of the paramagnetic ion. The summation indices vary from term to term. The first term is the total electron kinetic energy of the paramagnetic ion, and the sum is over the index i designating each electron of the ion. The second term is the coulomb attraction between the nucleus and these electrons. The third term is the coulomb repulsion between electrons and is summed only over pairs of electrons. The fourth term is the spin-orbit coupling, and each i and j ranges over all electrons. The fifth term is the magnetic interaction (or hyperfine interaction) between each electron and the nucleus. Up to this point we have included terms that would be expected for a free ion (although we have not included every possible form that the hyperfine interaction could take, and a simplified form, $\mathbf{L}\cdot\mathbf{S}$, of the spin-orbit term is often employed). The last term is the crystal field interaction, in which it is supposed that crystal sources external to the ion give rise to the electrostatic potential Φ_c at the ion with which each electron $-e_i$ interacts. Thus, for $\mathbf{r}_i$ of interest to us,

$$\nabla^2\Phi_c(\mathbf{r}) = 0 \tag{3-2}$$

Of course, we know a reasonable amount about free-ion energy states and even their wave functions through such treatments as the self-consistent field, and one might suppose that all one needs to do is treat the crystal field interaction as a perturbation. In some instances this is correct, but in others the crystal field interaction exceeds the spin-orbit coupling. One should then solve a different zero-order problem, treating the spin-orbit term as a perturbation. In fact it becomes necessary to distinguish several cases.

Weak crystal field. The interaction $-\sum_i e_i\Phi_c(\mathbf{r}_i)$ is weaker than the spin-orbit interaction. This situation typifies ionic compounds of the rare earths and certain actinide compounds. The electrons of the paramagnetic shell lie fairly deep within the ion and are well shielded from the crystalline field.

Medium crystal field. The magnetic electrons range over the outer regions of the ion and experience stronger crystal field interactions than their own spin-orbit coupling. This leads to a reduction or even essentially to an elimination of the orbital magnetic moment—the "quenching" of orbital angular momentum found for hydrated ions of the iron group.

Strong crystal field. There is covalent bonding, which means that the orbits of the paramagnetic electrons and those for electrons of neighboring diamagnetic ions or atoms overlap appreciably. A basic assumption of the crystal field approximation is clearly not valid, as sources for the crystal field are not wholly external to the paramagnetic ion. This leads to a reduction in the free-ion spin magnetic moment as well as in the orbital moment. The situation is found for complexes of the $4d$ and $5d$ groups, and for cyanides of the $3d$ group.

Before we turn to our instructional example, some features of the techniques used may be indicated. The two review articles (References 6 and 7 of Chapter 1) by the Oxford group review the methods, and the recent book by Low[1] gives a somewhat more extensive treatment, using group theoretical methods.

We are accustomed to writing our electron orbitals in terms of spherical harmonics, and it becomes especially useful therefore to expand the potential function Φ_c in Legendre polynomials. Specifically, to find the electron energy states we require matrix elements of the potential function Φ_c, and we can readily see that terms beyond a certain point in the expansion have, to first order, zero matrix elements for electron orbitals of a given L value. If

$$\Phi_c = \sum_{L'} \sum_{M'} A_{L'}^{M'} P_{L'}^{M'}(\cos\theta) \exp(iM'\phi) = \sum_{L'} \sum_{M'} \Phi_{L'}^{M'} \qquad (3\text{-}3)$$

one can see that for D and F states only terms up to $L' = 4$ and 6 need be considered. To understand this, note that electron orbitals involve spherical harmonics of order 2 for D states and order 3 for F states. The matrix elements of the potential terms are of the form

$$\int \psi_L^M \Phi_{L'}^{M'} \psi_L^M \, d\tau$$

which integrals vanish for $L' > 2L$, because the expansion of $(\psi_L^M)^2$ involves spherical harmonics of order up to but not exceeding $2L$. The orthogonality of spherical harmonics then assures zero for the matrix

[1] W. Low, "Paramagnetic Resonance in Solids," Academic Press, New York, 1960, supplementary Vol. 2 of the series Solid State Physics, edited by F. Seitz and D. Turnbull.

element if $L' > 2L$. The highest value of L' required in (3-3) is therefore 4 for D-state matrix elements and 6 for F-state matrix elements.

A further simplification is that all terms in (3-3) with L' odd have vanishing matrix elements. This can be seen because the product $\psi_L^M \psi_L^M$ is unchanged upon inversion in the origin of a cartesian coordinate system, whereas odd L terms of (3-3) change sign. And the term $L' = 0$ in (3-3) is merely a constant shifting all levels equally without changing relative separations.

We can therefore represent the crystal field potential for D states by just two terms in (3-3), those with $L' = 2$ and $L' = 4$. For F electrons a term in $L' = 6$ must also appear. The next step is to form such sums of polynomials for arrays of crystal field sources having various anticipated symmetries. Table II in the book by Low[1] lists the relative combinations of spherical harmonics in potentials having commonly encountered symmetries, such as sixfold cubic or our eightfold cubic. The expansions may also be cast into cartesian forms, as in Low's Table IV. The cubic potential for D states, for example, becomes

$$\Phi_c(\text{cubic, } D \text{ state}) = c(x^4 + y^4 + z^4 - \tfrac{3}{5}r^4) \qquad (3\text{-}4)$$

In order to treat this as a perturbation upon the ionic potential, we need matrix elements of (3-4). The determination of these matrix elements is aided by the operator-equivalent method of Stevens,[2] which makes use of the fact that x, y, and z in operators such as (3-4) have matrix elements within a given L manifold which are proportional to those of L_x, L_y, and L_z, or, if it is appropriate to take into account the spin angular momenta as well, proportional to those of J_x, J_y, and J_z. Thus, apart from a multiplicative constant, the matrix elements of (3-4) are proportional to those of a fourth-degree "polynomial" of angular momentum operators. However, because the various angular momentum components do not commute as do x, y, and z, the construction of the equivalent angular momentum operator requires considerable care. Tables giving such operator equivalents for the various potentials appear in the article by Stevens[2] and a collection of required tables for the whole procedure is reproduced by Low.[1]

The proportionality of the matrix elements of one operator to those of another follows from the transformation properties of the operators and is most elegantly discussed from the point of view of group theory. However, a discussion of the relationship between the matrix elements of space coordinates and of corresponding angular momentum operators,

[2] K. W. H. Stevens, *Proc. Phys. Soc.* (*London*), **A65,** 209 (1952).

based only upon commutation rules and not using group theory, is given by Feenberg and Pake.[3]

Now the question arises as to whether the spin-orbit coupling is smaller than, or comparable to, the crystal field interaction. Under suitable conditions, one may need at first only the secular determinant for the degenerate orbital states of the free ion as determined by the crystal field matrix elements. Because of the oversimplifying assumptions of the crystal field model, we know these matrix elements at best to a multiplicative constant, which however we may later be able to fix from experiment. After solution of the secular equation, one next applies the spin-orbit interaction as a perturbation. Whether perturbation theory can be applied depends upon whether λ in $\lambda\mathbf{L}\cdot\mathbf{S}$ is small enough; for an indication of its magnitude we use the free-ion value from optical spectroscopy. If λ is not smaller than the crystal field interaction, electron spin must be introduced for the free-ion degenerate ground state, and both the spin-orbit coupling and the crystal field have to be treated in the same secular determinant, which unfortunately is now likely to be a rather large one.

Even if one uses group theoretical methods to decide quickly how a crystal field of given symmetry lifts orbital degeneracies, it is a common occurrence in the treatment of paramagnetic crystals that a sizable secular determinant is involved.

Although there are a number of very well known books on group theory and quantum mechanics, the student who wishes to learn to apply these elegant methods to paramagnetic ions in crystals has, until recently, had a difficult time sifting through a great deal of material to find what he wants. There have now appeared discussions which more directly get to the heart of the problem. One is the book by Heine,[4] which within its first 200 pages develops the formalism and carries through *g*-value calculations for two examples, $Ce(C_2H_5SO_4)_3 \cdot 9H_2O$ and $CrSO_4 \cdot 5H_2O$.

Perhaps the most up-to-date discussion is that of Herzfeld and Meijer[5] in a chapter dealing specifically with group theory and the

[3] E. Feenberg and G. E. Pake, "Notes on the Quantum Theory of Angular Momentum," Stanford University Press, Stanford, Calif., 1959 (a paperback reprinting of the 1953 Addison-Wesley edition).

[4] V. Heine, "Group Theory in Quantum Mechanics," Pergamon Press, New York, 1960.

[5] C. M. Herzfeld and P. H. E. Meijer, Group Theory and Crystal Field Theory, a chapter to be published in Vol. 12 of the series Solid State Physics edited by F. Seitz and D. Turnbull, Academic Press, New York. The writer wishes to thank Dr. Herzfeld for the opportunity to study the chapter before the appearance of the volume.

crystal field. The references in this article constitute an extensive and complete bibliography to the subject. In fact, an excellent program of study to accompany the introduction to paramagnetic resonance provided by this book is the study of the Herzfeld and Meijer chapter, supplemented by recourse to the two Clarendon Laboratory reviews (References 6 and 7 of Chapter 1) and to Low[1] for the extent to which experiment and theory have elucidated the properties and important parameters of specific ions and crystals.

Finally, we mention two important theorems which follow from group theoretical analysis. One is the Jahn-Teller theorem, which states that a nonlinear molecule of a given symmetry having a degenerate ground state is in fact unstable and distorts itself so as to lift the degeneracy. This means for crystal field theory that an ion-water molecule cluster, appearing, for example, to have a given symmetry and degeneracy, may in fact be distorted so that lower symmetry is present and degeneracy is lifted. For reasons such as the Jahn-Teller effect or more-distant atomic-neighbor interactions, it is frequently necessary to add a small component of some kind of axial field, say tetragonal or trigonal, to the cubic fields indicated by the apparent symmetry of a cluster such as octahedral $X \cdot 6H_2O$. A good introductory treatment of the Jahn-Teller theorem, with references, appears in the Herzfeld-Meijer chapter.[5]

The second theorem is that of Kramers, which states that a purely electrostatic field acting upon a system of an odd number of electrons can never reduce its degeneracy below two. A magnetic field (an axial vector) is necessary to lift the Kramers degeneracy, and indeed paramagnetic resonance may be observed between the two levels of such a doublet when a magnetic field is present. Again, see Herzfeld and Meijer, Sec. 16, for a discussion and references.[5] If Kramers' theorem did not exist, the electron splittings within the ion would be very great indeed, and we should not be able to excite the transitions corresponding to paramagnetic resonance with such low frequencies as those provided by microwave generators.

3-2 An Instructional Example

We treat as a physical example the simple case of a $3d^1$ configuration and ^2D term for an ion which resides in a lattice site of tetragonal symmetry obtained through a distortion of cubic symmetry. Before the distortion, we begin with an array of six negative charges at distance $\pm a$ on each of the positive and negative coordinate axes.

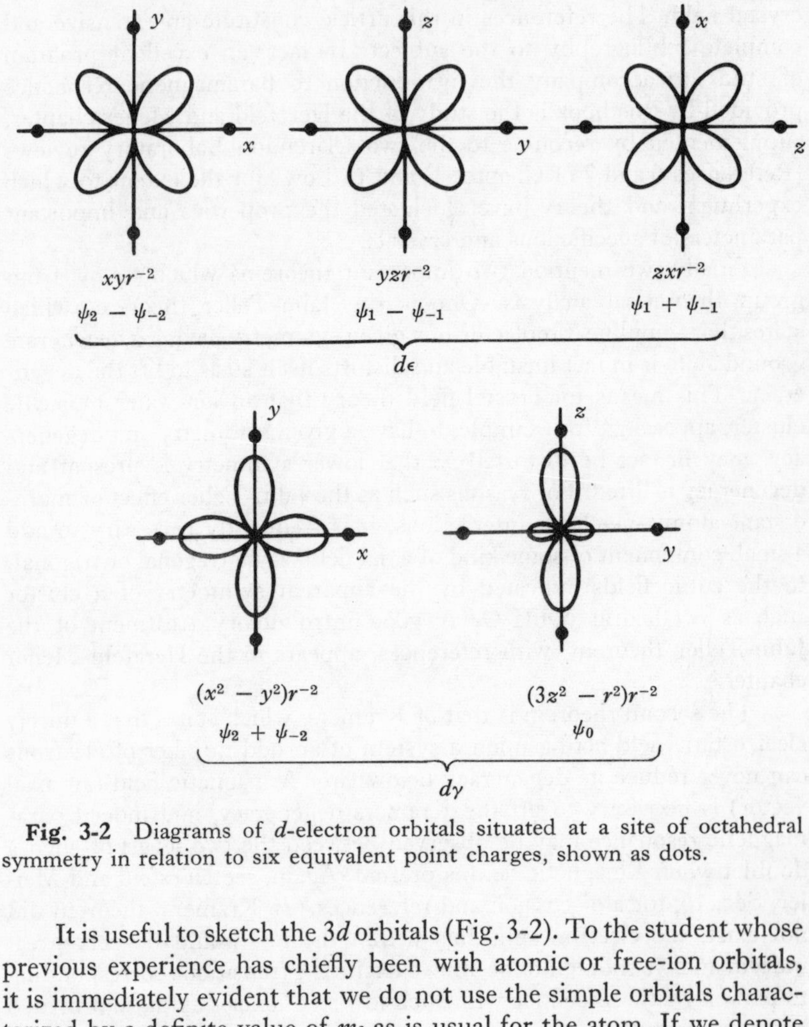

Fig. 3-2 Diagrams of *d*-electron orbitals situated at a site of octahedral symmetry in relation to six equivalent point charges, shown as dots.

It is useful to sketch the 3*d* orbitals (Fig. 3-2). To the student whose previous experience has chiefly been with atomic or free-ion orbitals, it is immediately evident that we do not use the simple orbitals characterized by a definite value of m_l as is usual for the atom. If we denote these orbitals by $\psi_l^{m_l}$, each such orbital contains all its ϕ dependence in a factor $\exp(im_l\phi)$, and the wave function is evidently an eigenfunction of the operator $L_z = (\hbar/i)\partial/\partial\phi$ with eigenvalue $m_l\hbar$. Now the operator L_z generates coordinate rotations about the z axis. For a spherically symmetric potential, as in a free atom, the Hamiltonian will be invariant under such rotations and will therefore commute with the L_z operator.[6]

[6] For a brief discussion of angular momentum operators and the generation of rotations, see Chap. 2 of Ref. 3.

Clearly the rotational symmetry appropriate to the atom does not exist in the presence of the cubic potential. By group theoretical methods one can select proper linear combinations of the orbitals appropriate to the lower symmetry. The classic work dealing with the problem is the definitive 1929 paper of Bethe, now available in a paperbound translation.[7] Without appealing to group theory, we handle the $3d^1$ example simply by forming the real and imaginary parts of the $\psi_l^{m_l}$. From the nature of the $\exp(im_l\phi)$ factor, this corresponds to forming $\psi_l^{m_l} \pm \psi_l^{-m_l}$. Clearly these combinations conform to inversion symmetry, in that they no longer single out a particular direction in space as a sense of rotation does; they in effect replace running or rotating waves with standing waves. Figure 3-2 pictures the resulting functions.

From the diagrams it is not surprising that the *xy*, *yz*, and *zx* orbitals (called $d\epsilon$ orbitals) all have the same electrostatic interaction with the octahedral array of negative charges. The two remaining orbitals are called $d\gamma$ orbitals. It is not obvious from the diagrams that the two $d\gamma$ orbitals have the same interaction energy but, granting this for the present, it is apparent that their interaction energy is higher than that for $d\epsilon$ in consequence of the extension of regions of high charge density directly toward the negative charges of the octahedral array. Thus we conclude that a cubic field partially lifts the fivefold orbital degeneracy of the $3d^1$ atomic configuration, giving two energy levels with a splitting conventionally denoted by Δ. The lower level, for our example of an octahedral array of negative charges, is triply degenerate and the upper level is doubly degenerate. This leaves spin-orbit coupling yet to be accounted for, and is thus in the spirit of the medium field case, for which the next step is to take the spin-orbit coupling into account as a perturbation upon the levels of Fig. 3-3. The group theoretical treatment[7] very quickly tells that a cubic field splits the ^2D term of $3d^1$ into a twofold level and a threefold level. However, it does not indicate which is lower on the basis of symmetry alone; we could in our example invert the order of energy levels by placing *positive* charges on the axes and the symmetry would of course still be octahedral cubic.

From these simple considerations, the student can readily anticipate how the ^2D levels would further split if a tetragonality were introduced by, for example, small symmetrical displacements of the charges at $\pm a$ on the z axis. The *xz* and *yz* orbitals of $d\epsilon$ will be equally affected in their energy of repulsive interaction, and the *xy* orbital will apparently experience an effect of different magnitude. The two $d\gamma$ orbitals

[7] H. A. Bethe, *Ann. Physik*, **3**, 133 (1929). A paperbound English translation is available from Consultants Bureau, Inc., New York.

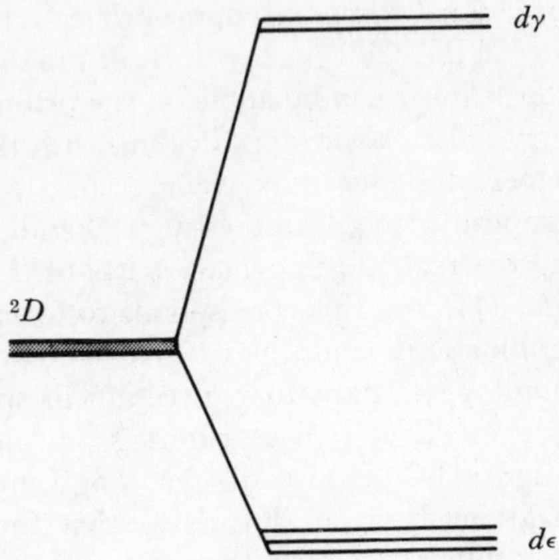

Fig. 3-3 Splitting of the ^2D levels by a cubic field.

bear quite different relationships to the z axis and thus they will be split in energy. We see that a tetragonal field leads to one doubly degenerate level and three singlets. We sketch in Fig. 3-4 the level arrangement for a tetragonal distortion in which the $d\epsilon$ singlet is lowest-lying. The nature of the distortion giving this level arrangement; i.e., whether the charges on the $\pm z$ axes are moved closer to or farther from the ion, may be determined, if the student is careful, from simple electrostatic considerations, using the orbit pictures in Fig. 3-2. Otherwise, the result can be taken from Fig. 6 of the Bethe article.[7] (We observe, now that the tetragonal field component has been added, that

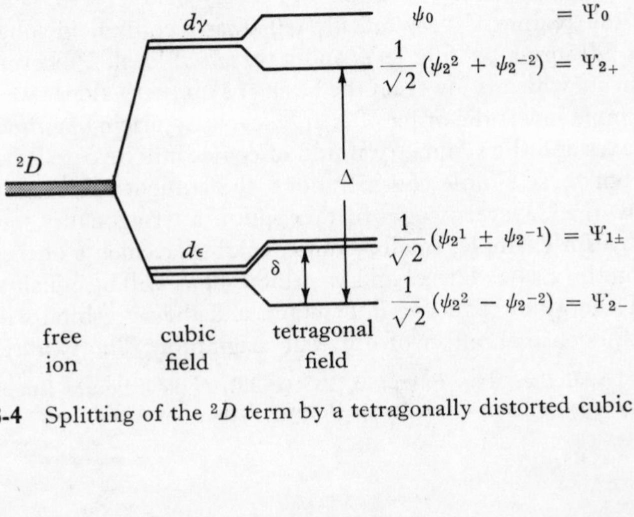

Fig. 3-4 Splitting of the ^2D term by a tetragonally distorted cubic field.

the existence of an energy difference between the two $d\gamma$ orbitals is evident from examination of Fig. 3-2 with the tetragonal distortion along the z direction. Thus it is no longer essential to have understood earlier that the $d\gamma$ orbitals were degenerate in a cubic field, only that they were both of higher energy than the $d\epsilon$ orbitals.)

Figure 3-4 is still an oversimplification, for the spin of the electron doubles the degeneracy of each orbital level. Direct products of the orbitals with the α and β spin functions (having $\langle S_z \rangle = +\frac{1}{2}$ and $\langle S_z \rangle = -\frac{1}{2}$, respectively) must now be formed in order to treat the spin-orbit coupling. This is the first occurrence of spin operators in the problem, and the spin functions can no longer remain suppressed. The following defines our notation:

$$\begin{aligned}
\Psi_{\alpha 2\pm} &= \alpha(1/\sqrt{2})(\psi_2{}^2 \pm \psi_2{}^{-2}) \\
\Psi_{\beta 2\pm} &= \beta(1/\sqrt{2})(\psi_2{}^2 \pm \psi_2{}^{-2}) \\
\Psi_{\alpha 1\pm} &= \alpha(1/\sqrt{2})(\psi_2{}^1 \pm \psi_2{}^{-1}) \\
\Psi_{\beta 1\pm} &= \beta(1/\sqrt{2})(\psi_2{}^1 \pm \psi_2{}^{-1}) \\
\Psi_{\alpha 0} &= \alpha\psi_2{}^0 \\
\Psi_{\beta 0} &= \beta\psi_2{}^0
\end{aligned} \tag{3-5}$$

From Fig. 3-4, the ground states after introduction of the tetragonal field component are $\Psi_{\alpha 2-}$ and $\Psi_{\beta 2-}$. Although these two states are degenerate in this approximation, we shall be interested in them ultimately in a magnetic field, which will remove the degeneracy. Thus we may apply first-order perturbation theory to determine the effect of spin-orbit coupling, which we shall see is to mix various of the other states of (3-5) into the ground state. For the form of the spin-orbit interaction we use[8]

$$\lambda\mathbf{L}\cdot\mathbf{S} = \lambda[L_zS_z + (1/2)(L_+S_- + L_-S_+)] \tag{3-6}$$

where $L_\pm = L_x \pm iL_y$. From the familiar result of first-order perturba-

[8] It is perhaps worthwhile to recall how an interaction of the form $\mathbf{L}\cdot\mathbf{S}$ arises. As the electron carrying spin moves about the atomic core, the spin magnetic moment may be visualized as moving through an electrostatic field $\mathbf{E}$ arising from the shielded nucleus. If the electron has velocity $\mathbf{v}$, then the moving spin moment sees an effective magnetic field $\mathbf{B}' = (\mathbf{v}/c) \times \mathbf{E}$ and has the ordinary magnetic interaction $-\boldsymbol{\mu}_{\text{spin}}\cdot\mathbf{B}'$. For a spherically symmetric potential, $E = -\nabla\phi(r) = -(\partial\phi/\partial r)(\mathbf{r}/r)$, and $\mathbf{B}'$ is readily shown to be proportional to $\mathbf{r} \times m\mathbf{v} = \mathbf{L}$, giving finally the interaction we conventionally denote by $\lambda\mathbf{L}\cdot\mathbf{S}$.

tion theory, the new wave functions Ψ'_m after first-order correction are

$$\Psi'_m = \Psi_m - \sum_k{}' \Psi_k \frac{(k|\lambda\mathbf{L}\cdot\mathbf{S}|m)}{E_k - E_m} \tag{3-7}$$

Referring to Fig. 3-4 to define the energy separations, we note that we must require $\lambda < \delta,\Delta$ in order to apply first-order perturbation theory. Although the diagram in Fig. 3-4 suggests $\Delta > \delta$, this is not in fact necessary. Bethe's Fig. 6 shows that for higher tetragonality the separations of our Fig. 3-4 within $d\epsilon$ and $d\gamma$ can exceed the separation Δ, causing the degenerate pair of $d\epsilon$ levels to cross over the lower $d\gamma$ level.

From the wave functions of (3-5) using (3-7) and (3-6) in conjunction with the well-known matrix elements of **L** and **S**, the perturbed wave functions are found by a very straightforward, if slightly tedious, calculation to be

$$\begin{aligned} \Psi'_{\alpha 2-} &= \alpha[(1/\sqrt{2})(\psi^2 - \psi^{-2}) - (\lambda/\Delta\sqrt{2})(\psi^2 + \psi^{-2})] + (\lambda/\delta\sqrt{2})\beta\psi^{-1} \\ \Psi'_{\beta 2-} &= \beta[(1/\sqrt{2})(\psi^2 - \psi^{-2}) + (\lambda/\Delta\sqrt{2})(\psi^2 + \psi^{-2})] - (\lambda/\delta\sqrt{2})\alpha\psi^{1} \end{aligned} \tag{3-8}$$

If we denote $\epsilon = \lambda/\Delta$ and $\eta = \lambda/\delta$, it now becomes a simple matter to show that the expectation values or diagonal inner products of L_z are

$$\begin{aligned} (\Psi'_{\alpha 2-}, L_z\Psi'_{\alpha 2-}) &= -4\epsilon - \tfrac{1}{2}\eta^2 \\ (\Psi'_{\beta 2-}, L_z\Psi'_{\beta 2-}) &= 4\epsilon + \tfrac{1}{2}\eta^2 \end{aligned} \tag{3-9}$$

whereas we would clearly have found for the ground-state orbital of Fig. 3-4, before spin-orbit coupling, that $\langle L_z \rangle = 0$. The vanishing of $\langle L_z \rangle$ after the crystal field splitting of Fig. 3-4 is an illustration of what is called in the literature the "quenching" of orbital angular momentum. We have seen in Chapter 1 that, experimentally, quenching is indicated by the susceptibilities of crystals of the iron-group ions.

However, our result (3-9) shows that, if the effect of the lower symmetry of the crystal field is to "quench out" orbital angular momentum, then spin-orbit coupling reinstates a small amount of angular momentum, of order $\epsilon = \lambda/\Delta$, where Δ is the crystal field splitting. (We shall hereafter suppose for simplicity that η and ϵ are small quantities, so that we may drop either ϵ^2 or η^2 against ϵ or η.) Because of this small amount of admixed orbital angular momentum, we do not expect the iron-group ions to show precisely "spin-only" properties.

Indeed, we can now examine the effect of an external magnetic field along the z axis (note that z is now the axis of crystal tetragonal symmetry and will not in general be the magnetic field direction). For this special case we need the expectation values of

$$\mathscr{H}'_z = (L_z + g_e S_z)\beta H_z \tag{3-10}$$

for each of the two states (3-8). Here β is the Bohr magneton and the electron magnetic moment operator, allowing for both spin and orbital contributions, is

$$\boldsymbol{\mu} = -\beta(\mathbf{L} + g_e\mathbf{S}) \tag{3-11}$$

with $g_e = 2.0023$, the "free electron" g. We find, to first order in small quantities, that

$$\begin{aligned}(\Psi'_{\alpha 2-}, \mathscr{H}'_z\Psi'_{\alpha 2-}) &= (\tfrac{1}{2}g_e - 4\epsilon)\beta H_z \\ (\Psi'_{\beta 2-}, \mathscr{H}'_z\Psi'_{\beta 2-}) &= (-\tfrac{1}{2}g_e + 4\epsilon)\beta H_z\end{aligned} \tag{3-12}$$

from which the magnetic splitting at which magnetic resonance could be expected is

$$h\nu = (g_e - 8\epsilon)\beta H_z \tag{3-13}$$

Comparison with (1-1) and (2-4) indicates that spin-orbit coupling thus modifies the spectroscopic splitting factor or g value from the free electron value to $g_z = g_e - 8(\lambda/\Delta)$ for H_z.

Consider next the effect of a magnetic field in the x direction. (By symmetry this is equivalent to the y direction, since the tetragonal distortion was only along z.) The perturbing operator for a constant H_x is

$$\mathscr{H}'_x = (L_x + g_e S_x)\beta H_x \tag{3-14}$$

Our choice of basis spin functions, α and β, have as eigenvalues the z components of $\mathbf{S}$, in which representation S_x has no diagonal elements. We must therefore use a secular determinant, and the student can readily determine from (3-8) that

$$(\Psi'_{\alpha 2-}, (L_x + g_e S_x)\beta H_x \Psi'_{\beta 2-}) = (\tfrac{1}{2}g_e - \eta)\beta H_x \tag{3-15}$$

The resulting secular equation

$$\begin{vmatrix} -E & (\tfrac{1}{2}g_e - \eta)\beta H_x \\ (\tfrac{1}{2}g_e - \eta)\beta H_x & -E \end{vmatrix} = 0 \tag{3-16}$$

is easily solved to give

$$E = \pm(\tfrac{1}{2}g_e - \eta)\beta H_x \tag{3-17}$$

The resonance condition is

$$h\nu = \Delta E = (g_e - 2\eta)\beta H_x \tag{3-18}$$

Thus our simple example has

$$g_x = g_y = g_e - 2(\lambda/\delta) \text{ with } g_z = g_e - 8(\lambda/\Delta)$$

A few words are now appropriate as to whether the foregoing example is realistic. The $3d^1$ configuration leads to a free-ion ^2D term by Hund's rules. Typical values of Δ are $\approx 10^4$ cm^{-1}, as observed experimentally by optical absorption. Octahedral complexes do occur for Ti^{3+}, but the lower symmetry distortions are not great and they lead to δ values of 10^2 to 10^3 cm^{-1}. Since the spin-orbit coupling is $\lambda = 154$ cm^{-1}, the assumption $\lambda < \delta$ for our example is violated. This means that $CsTi(SO_4)_2{\cdot}12H_2O$, for instance, does not have widely separated levels of the low-lying $d\epsilon$ orbital triplet, and an orbital singlet will be the completely populated ground state only at lower temperatures. For $KTi(C_2O_4)_2{\cdot}2H_2O$ the g values are (see Appendix, p. 178) $g_x = g_y = 1.96$ and $g_z = 1.86$. The complex is not octadedral, however. If there were grounds for expecting high tetragonality, we could fit these results with $\lambda = 154$ cm^{-1}, $\delta = 7{,}700$ cm^{-1}, and $\Delta = 8{,}800$ cm^{-1}.

A simple example of the kind we have presented in this section is also given by Pryce,[9] who treats a ^2D term arising from the $3d^9$ configuration of Cu^{++}. This corresponds to a hole in the $3d^{10}$ complete shell, and as such it can be treated as if it were a single positively charged electron in a $3d^1$ configuration. Of course, this inverts the $d\gamma$ and $d\epsilon$ orbital levels in Fig. 3-3. With a tetragonal field component of proper sign, the Ψ_{2+} orbital will lie lowest. Spin-orbit coupling mixes in some of the upper Ψ_{2-} and Ψ_{1+} orbitals, resulting approximately in $g_z = g_e - 4(\lambda/\Delta)$ and $g_x = g_y = g_e - \lambda/\Delta$. Because the shell is more than half full,[10] λ is negative, and the typical experimental g values of about 2.4 and 2.1 are in very good agreement with the theory.

The student may find it useful, as a check upon his understanding of the sequence of steps, to solve the $3d^9$ problem as an exercise and to compare it afterward with the results given by Pryce.[9]

3-3 Crystal Field Effects on $3d^n$ Configurations

D-**State Ions.** Hund's rules (Sec. 1-3 and Table 2-2) indicate that free ions with $3d^1$, $3d^4$, $3d^6$, and $3d^9$ are all in D states. Consider $3d^4$ and $3d^9$. The Hund requirement of maximum S means for $3d^4$ that

[9] M. H. L. Pryce, *Nuovo cimento*, **6** (*Suppl.*), 817 (1957).

[10] E. U. Condon and G. H. Shortley, "Theory of Atomic Spectra," Cambridge University Press, New York, 1951, Chap. XIII.

each electron spin "points" the same way, so that all but one of the $2L + 1 = 5$ orbitals must be occupied to obey the Pauli principle. If all $2L + 1$ were occupied, the resultant component of orbital angular momentum in any direction would be zero as in $3d^5$ (S-state ions will be treated later) and the charge distribution would be spherically symmetric. Now $3d^9$ simply adds such a $3d^5$ spherically symmetric distribution of zero orbital angular momentum to the $3d^4$ distribution, and the orbital angular momentum properties of $3d^4$ and $3d^9$ are the same. Thus the two configurations $3d^4(Cr^{++}, Mn^{3+})$ and $3d^9(Cu^{++})$ split the same way in the crystal field. In a similar way, $3d^1(Ti^{3+}, VO^{++})$ and $3d^6(Fe^{++}, Co^{3+})$ split the same in the crystal field, for they may be regarded as one electron added to the spherical distributions $3d^0$ and $3d^5$ (the $3d^9$ and $3d^4$ are single holes in spherical distributions $3d^{10}$ and $3d^5$). From our examples of Sec. 3-2, we can then sketch (Fig. 3-5) splittings of these configurations in octahedral cubic fields. The relation of one scheme to the other (i.e., inverting the level structure) follows because a hole behaves as if it has a charge opposite to that of an electron.

Of course, $3d^1$ and $3d^6$ have different total spin S and thus will differ somewhat in the effects of spin-orbit coupling. In many examples, the distortions from octahedral splitting are small and the low-lying orbital triplet is not widely split. As a result, the approximations of our example in Sec. 3-2 often are not valid, and there is poor quenching of angular momentum.

For $3d^4$ and $3d^9$, one must again take into account the difference in spin. However, lower symmetry fields usually give a reasonably separated orbital ground state, and angular momentum is nearly completely quenched.

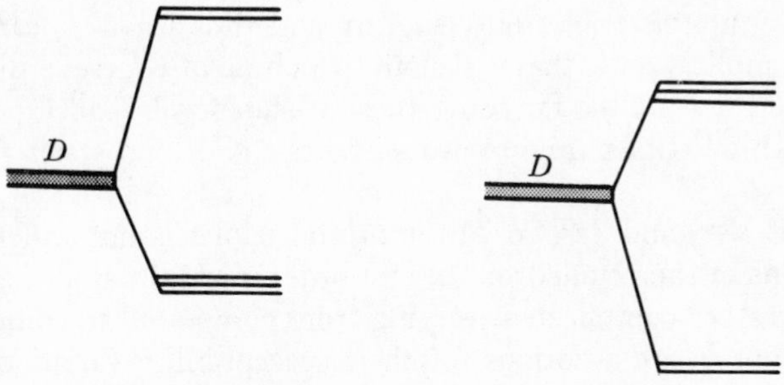

$3d^1$ and $3d^6$ $3d^4$ and $3d^9$

Fig. 3-5 D-term splittings in a cubic octahedral field arising from negatively charged sources.

***F*-State Ions.** The over-all angular momentum properties of several electrons coupled into an F state require the multiparticle wave function to transform under rotations like spherical harmonics of order 3. As we know from a single electron having $l = 3$, these harmonic polynomials may be written

$$xyz$$

$$x(y^2 - z^2); \quad y(z^2 - x^2); \quad z(x^2 - y^2) \tag{3-19}$$

$$x(2x^2 - 3y^2 - 3z^2); \quad y(2y^2 - 3z^2 - 3x^2); \quad z(2z^2 - 3x^2 - 3y^2)$$

The listing is in a particular order, for it is clear that permuting x, y, and z for any function of a given horizontal line gives another function of that line. But permuting x, y, and z axes for an octahedral cubic array of field sources returns us always to a configuration identical to the original (i.e., the x, y, and z axes are indistinguishable from one another). Thus we see that an F term splits into $1 + 3 + 3$.

Again using considerations of the $L = 0$ character of $3d^0$, $3d^5$, and $3d^{10}$, we expect qualitative similarity between $3d^3$(V^{++} and Cr^{3+}) and $3d^8$(Ni^{++}). It turns out that the orbital singlet lies lowest for these configurations, so that even in pure octahedral cubic symmetry, the orbital degeneracy of the ground level is lifted. This lowest level is thus a simple spin multiplet, $S = \frac{3}{2}$ for $3d^3$ and $S = 1$ for $3d^8$. The g value is isotropic in the cubic field with

$$g = g_e - 8\lambda/\Delta \tag{3-20}$$

where Δ is the energy distance to the states characterized by the angular dependence given in the second line of (3-19). Typical distortions of the octahedron split this triplet only slightly and thus leave g nearly isotropic. A complication is that a P state (which is, of course, a different LS multiplet) lies not too far above these F-state levels, and it perturbs the other orbital triplet. Figure 3-6 sketches the orbital states for this case.

For $3d^2$(V^{3+}) and $3d^7$(Co^{++}) the orbital triplet is not widely split by distortions of the octahedron (to first order, not split at all), and the situation is rather complicated, varying from compound to compound. Co^{++} compounds are notorious for their susceptibility variations, and we thus understand somewhat more clearly why compounds providing the data in the last column of Table 1-2 gave agreement with neither "free ion" nor "spin only." Sometimes one can study paramagnetic resonance in these difficult cases by working at very low temperatures,

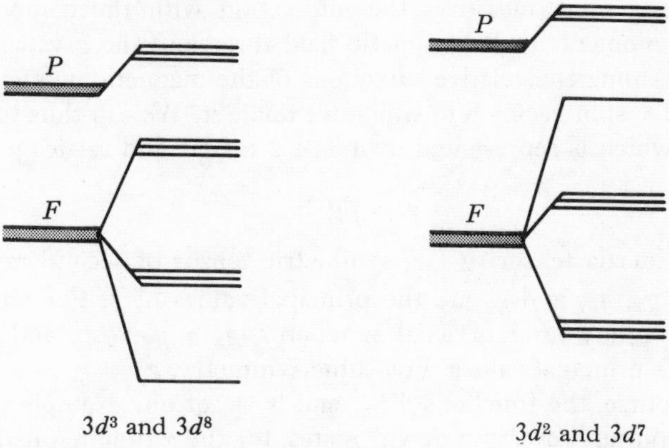

Fig. 3-6 Splitting of F states in a cubic octahedral field.

where only a lowest-lying Kramers doublet is appreciably populated. However, g-value variations are large.

***S*-State Ions.** When we have a $3d^5$ configuration (Mn^{++} and Fe^{3+} we should expect spin-only effects ($S = \frac{5}{2}$). Since $L = 0$, there are no first-order effects of spin-orbit coupling, and there are no first-order effects of the crystal field on the $2S + 1 =$ sixfold spin degeneracy. More will be said about these ions in the latter part of Sec. 3-4.

It is clear from the foregoing brief résumé of the iron group that much detail is needed to describe each ion in each crystalline environment. (Note that we discussed in our examples only octahedral cubic symmetry, with possible tetragonal distortions.) Different symmetries and relative magnitudes of the various interactions lead to a great many details. The Clarendon review articles (Refs. 6 and 7 of Chap. 1) and the book by Low[1] have collected many of these particulars, as well as references to the original papers, for all the transition group ions.

3-4 The Effective Spin Hamiltonian

In both the $3d^1$ and $3d^9$ examples we found $g_x = g_y \neq g_z$, since the tetragonal symmetry leaves x and y indistinguishable from each other but distinguishable from z. We saw that this has to do with the fact that spin-orbit coupling mixes a small amount of orbital angular momentum into a system from which the crystal field had removed or "quenched" it, and it is not surprising that the effect of this admixture depends upon the direction of $\mathbf{H}$ relative to the crystal field symmetry axis.

Since the g value measures the interaction with the component of magnetic moment in the magnetic field direction, the g values essentially determine the relative directions of the magnetic moment $\boldsymbol{\mu}$ and the effective spin vector **S** to which we relate it. We can thus think of a tensor $\underline{\mathbf{g}}$ which is represented by a 3×3 matrix and relates $\boldsymbol{\mu}$ to **S**:

$$\boldsymbol{\mu} = \beta\underline{\mathbf{g}}\cdot\mathbf{S} \tag{3-21}$$

Like the inertia tensor, $\underline{\mathbf{g}}$ is a symmetric tensor of second rank. The values of g_x, g_y, and g_z are the principal values of g. For tetragonal, trigonal, or any kind of axial symmetry, $g_x = g_y \equiv g_\perp$ and $g_z \equiv g_\parallel$ denote the principal values. For cubic symmetry, $g_\perp = g_\parallel$.

Of course, the functions $\Psi'_{\alpha 2-}$ and $\Psi'_{\beta 2-}$ of our example were not purely "spin up" or "spin down" states, for the α function had some β mixed into it and vice versa. Nonetheless, because these become two distinct states in a magnetic field, it is convenient to assign a spin S (here $\frac{1}{2}$) to the system, where $2S + 1$ is the number of levels into which a magnetic field splits the ground state arising under crystal field and spin-orbit effects. Such a spin is in effect a fictitious spin to which we try to relate all the magnetic properties of the material. Our examples could thus be described by an *effective spin Hamiltonian*, as it is called, in which the Zeeman interaction with an external field can be written

$$\mathscr{H} = \beta[g_\perp(S_xH_x + S_yH_y) + g_\parallel S_zH_z] \tag{3-22}$$

The student can quickly verify that (3-22) yields the results of our illustrative calculation (Sec. 3-2) for energy differences in a magnetic field.

Pryce[11] and Abragam and Pryce[12] have pursued the notion of an effective spin Hamiltonian further by indicating, in a more general way than our examples afforded, the kinds of terms to be obtained upon carrying out a full second-order calculation to terms of order λ^2 as well as the λH terms. Neglecting nuclear moment interactions for the present, the result may be written

$$\mathscr{H} = \sum_{i,j=1}^{3} [\beta g_e(\delta_{ij} - 2\lambda\Lambda_{ij})S_iH_j - \lambda^2\Lambda_{ij}S_iS_j]$$
$$+ \text{ diamagnetic terms in } H_iH_j \tag{3-23}$$

[11] M. H. L. Pryce, *Proc. Phys. Soc.* (*London*), **A63**, 25 (1950).

[12] A. Abragam and M. H. L. Pryce, *Proc. Roy. Soc.* (*London*), **A205**, 135 (1951).

where Λ_{ij} is defined in relation to the ground state (0) and excited states ($n > 0$) as

$$\Lambda_{ij} = \sum_{n \neq 0} \frac{(0|L_i|n)(n|L_j|0)}{E_n - E_0} \tag{3-24}$$

The tensor $\underline{\Lambda}$ is real, symmetric, and positive definite. We readily recall calculating Λ's in our examples of Sec. 3-2.

In the principal axis system of a crystal with axial symmetry, the $\underline{\Lambda}$ tensor is diagonal with $\Lambda_{zz} = \Lambda_{\parallel}$ and $\Lambda_{xx} = \Lambda_{yy} = \Lambda_{\perp}$. Under these conditions, $\mathscr{H}$ of (3-23) can be simplified, since

$$S_x^2 + S_y^2 = S(S + 1) - S_z^2$$

to give

$$\mathscr{H} = g_{\parallel}\beta H_z S_z + g_{\perp}\beta(H_x S_x + H_y S_y) + D[S_z^2 - \tfrac{1}{3}S(S + 1)] \tag{3-25}$$

where

$$\begin{aligned} g_{\parallel} &= g_e(1 - \lambda\Lambda_{\parallel}) \\ g_{\perp} &= g_e(1 - \lambda\Lambda_{\perp}) \\ D &= \lambda^2(\Lambda_{\perp} - \Lambda_{\parallel}) \end{aligned} \tag{3-26}$$

One constant term (in spin variables, that is) has not been dropped from (3-25); the $-\frac{1}{3}S(S + 1)$ is conventionally retained in order to give the D term a traceless form.

We note that the term in S_z^2, which we did not consider in our simple examples, is of no consequence for spin $\frac{1}{2}$, as $\langle S_z^2 \rangle$ will have the same value for both spin functions (whether the axis of spin quantization is taken along z or not).

At this stage, let us recognize the difficulties inherent in attempting to predict quantitatively all the parameters in a Hamiltonian such as (3-25) for a general crystal and ion. Even if a dominant symmetry such as octahedral or tetrahedral cubic is apparent from the crystal structure, the nature of distortions arising from a possible Jahn-Teller effect is unknown and must be guessed. When the ionic crystal field approximation seems likely to be quite good, small tendencies toward covalency can have profound effects on parameter magnitudes, and the extended nature of the charge distribution of neighboring ions or molecular dipoles may make point representation quantitatively poor. Whether the perturbation methods will work at all depends upon relative magnitudes of a number of these unknowns. If crystal field plus spin-orbit splittings are not large, we may have more than one populated orbital and a temperature-dependent superposition of magnetic resonance spectra arising from several occupied orbital states.

Physically, however, we know in a general way the kind of interactions to expect and the kind of terms that would arise on pursuing a prescribed crystalline field to a given order, if a spin Hamiltonian is applicable at all. If spin-orbit and magnetic field perturbations were pursued to order λ^2 and λH, we would get terms no higher than quadratic in effective spin operators, which means symmetric tensors of second rank as coefficients. These tensors have three principal values which completely specify them. Thus we could, without benefit of a theory that calculated parameters from earlier principles, attempt to fit paramagnetic resonances with terms such as

$$\beta(g_x S_x H_x + g_y S_y H_y + g_z S_z H_z) + D' S_z^2 + E' S_x^2 + F' S_y^2 \qquad (3\text{-}27)$$

Next let us recall the existence of hyperfine interactions, which are chiefly magnetic dipole interactions between the electronic magnetic moment and the nuclear magnetic moment of the paramagnetic ion (for the present we neglect nuclear moments of neighboring ions). In our effective spin Hamiltonian we attempt to relate the electronic moment to the spin vector **S**. Thus we anticipate hyperfine-structure terms arising from the Fermi contact term[13]

$$(8\pi/3) g_e g_N \beta \beta_N \delta(\mathbf{r}_e - \mathbf{r}_N) \mathbf{I} \cdot \mathbf{S} \qquad (3\text{-}28)$$

and from the ordinary dipole-dipole coupling,

$$-g_N g_e \beta_N \beta \langle r^{-3} \rangle [\mathbf{I} \cdot \mathbf{S} - 3(\mathbf{I} \cdot \hat{\mathbf{r}})(\mathbf{S} \cdot \hat{\mathbf{r}})] \qquad (3\text{-}29)$$

Here g_N and β_N are the nuclear g value and nuclear magneton, respectively. Again we expect bilinear terms in components $I_i S_j$, the coefficients of which will be elements of a symmetric second-rank tensor. In a principal-axis system, we could then write

$$\mathscr{H}_{\text{hyperfine}} = A_z I_z S_z + A_x I_x S_x + A_y I_y S_y \qquad (3\text{-}30)$$

For the present we suppose this principal-axis system to be the same as that for (3-27), but there are conceivable situations where this would not be true. Combining (3-30) and (3-27), we obtain the spin Hamiltonian in the principal-axis system,

$$\mathscr{H} = \beta(g_x S_x H_x + g_y S_y H_y + g_z S_z H_z) + D' S_z^2 + E' S_x^2 + F' S_y^2 + A_z I_z S_z + A_x I_x S_x + A_y I_y S_y \qquad (3\text{-}31)$$

[13] See F. J. Milford, *Am. J. Phys.*, **28,** 521 (1960), for a simple derivation of this interaction and for references to other discussions.

A simplification is possible, if we write the term $E'S_x^2 + F'S_y^2$ as

$$\tfrac{1}{2}(E' + F')(S_x^2 + S_y^2) + \tfrac{1}{2}(E' - F')(S_x^2 - S_y^2)$$

and use

$$S_x^2 + S_y^2 = S(S + 1) - S_z^2 \tag{3-32}$$

Then letting $\frac{1}{2}(E' - F') = E$ and $D' - \frac{1}{2}(E' + F') = D$, while subtracting the constant term $[\frac{1}{3}D + \frac{1}{2}(E' + F')]S(S + 1)$, gives us a conventional form of the effective spin Hamiltonian:

$$\begin{aligned}\mathscr{H} = {} & \beta(g_x S_x H_x + g_y S_y H_y + g_z S_z H_z) \\ & + D[S_z^2 - \tfrac{1}{3}S(S + 1)] + E(S_x^2 - S_y^2) \\ & + A_z I_z S_z + A_x I_x S_x + A_y I_y S_y\end{aligned} \tag{3-33}$$

The first line of (3-33) is the Zeeman interaction, the second line gives to the resonance what we call the fine structure, and the third line is the hyperfine structure interaction. We have omitted here nuclear terms that do not involve electron operators; they can be readily included for those applications which require them. One should realize that, in high order, such energies as nuclear quadrupole couplings may affect the electronic energy states via the hyperfine term.

An important special case occurs for (3-32) when there is axial symmetry (tetragonal, trigonal, or hexagonal). Then we may take the z axis to be the symmetry axis and write

$$\begin{aligned} g_z = g_\parallel; \quad & g_x = g_y = g_\perp \\ A_z = A_\parallel; \quad & A_x = A_y = A_\perp \end{aligned} \tag{3-34}$$

Furthermore, $\langle S_x^2 \rangle = \langle S_y^2 \rangle$ and we have

$$\begin{aligned}\mathscr{H}_{\text{axial}} = {} & \beta[g_\parallel S_z H_z + g_\perp(S_x H_x + S_y H_y)] + D[S_z^2 - \tfrac{1}{3}S(S + 1)] \\ & + A_\parallel I_z S_z + A_\perp(I_x S_x + I_y S_y)\end{aligned} \tag{3-35}$$

It was mentioned at the end of Sec. 3-3 that the S-state ions have no first-order effects of spin-orbit coupling or the crystal field. This means that any theoretical determination of the spin Hamiltonian must go to high orders with accompanying increases in uncertainties. When there is axial symmetry, experimental results can be fitted rather well by

$$\mathscr{H}_S = g\beta\mathbf{H}\cdot\mathbf{S} + C(S_x^4 + S_y^4 + S_z^4) + DS_z^2 \tag{3-36}$$

Van Vleck and Penney[14] obtain such quartic terms in a fifth-order

[14] J. H. Van Vleck and W. G. Penney, *Phil. Mag.*, **17**, 961 (1934).

perturbation calculation involving the octahedral field to one power and λ^4. The S_z^2 term arises, of course, from an axial symmetry component, and such a term can be obtained in fourth order, as well as from configuration interactions within the ion which cause small departures of the electron cloud from spherical symmetry. Note that, although a term in S_z^2 is included, g is very often effectively isotropic.

Inclusion of hyperfine coupling terms in (3-36) appears to be unnecessary, at least for the contact term (3-28). For example, the $3d^5$ configuration leading to ^6S is a superposition of d orbitals which vanish at the nucleus. The δ function therefore is expected to pick out a vanishingly small coefficient for $\mathbf{I} \cdot \mathbf{S}$. However, there was experimentally discovered early in the investigation of manganese salts an isotropic hyperfine coupling for Mn^{++} corresponding to an A of about 0.009 cm^{-1}, or 270 Mc sec^{-1}. Abragam[15] proposed that this anomalous hyperfine coupling arises from a configuration interaction which admixes to $3s^2 3d^5$ some $3s3d^5 4s$. The unpaired s electrons give contributions to the expectation value of the δ function. However, it has been difficult to prove theoretically that this so-called "promotion hypothesis" gives large-enough hyperfine couplings to explain experiment. Low[16] gives references to the theoretical papers on the subject.

One may ask why we include electron-nucleus magnetic dipole-dipole coupling but do not include electron-electron magnetic dipolar interactions. These interactions will in fact be discussed later on (Chapter 4). Meanwhile, it should be emphasized that paramagnetic resonance is often observed in a magnetically dilute crystal by substituting a very small fraction of paramagnetic ions for diamagnetic metal ions. For example, a few Cu^{++} ions may replace Zn^{++} in $K_2Zn(SO_4)_2 \cdot 6H_2O$. As a result, there will be considerable distance between a Cu^{++} and its nearest Cu^{++} neighbor. The reason for such dilution is to eliminate the magnetic interactions, and thus to deal with an otherwise isolated ion for which the chief complexities over the free-ion case are provided by the crystal field.

3-5 Use of the Spin Hamiltonian to Interpret Paramagnetic Resonances

When a crystal is placed in a magnetic field, we are concerned with the crystal axes as well as the magnetic field direction. As we have seen in the foregoing sections, the axis of crystal symmetry is conventionally

[15] A. Abragam, *Phys. Rev.*, **79**, 534 (1950).
[16] Ref. 1, p. 122.

denoted z, whereas in other connections we are also used to calling the direction of an external magnetic field the z direction. In general the crystal axis and $\mathbf{H}_0$ will have different directions. Henceforth, we shall use x, y, and z as coordinates fixed in the laboratory with $\mathbf{H}_0$ along z. The crystal axes will be called p, q, and r; an axis of symmetry, if any, will be in the r direction. We shall not work out examples having orthorhombic symmetry ($g_p \neq g_q \neq g_r \neq g_p$). When dealing with axial symmetry, we shall make axis transformations so that S_p, for example, is expressed in terms of S_x, S_y, S_z, for which we can refer to any convenient reference to find the well-known matrix elements. Figure 3-7 indicates the definitions of the angles that are to be used in the transformation.

Effect of Crystal Orientation on the Zeeman Splitting. Consider $\mathscr{H}_{\text{Zeeman}}$ of (3-22), which can be written as

$$\mathscr{H}_Z = \beta\,\Delta g H_r S_r + \beta g_\perp \mathbf{H}_0 \cdot \mathbf{S} \tag{3-37}$$

where $\Delta g = g_\parallel - g_\perp$. Since our convention is to take $\mathbf{H}_0$ along z, $\mathbf{H}_0 \cdot \mathbf{S} = H_0 S_z$. Reference to Fig. 3-7 verifies that

$$H_r = H_0 \cos\theta \tag{3-38}$$

and that

$$\begin{aligned} S_r &= S_z \cos\theta + S_x \sin\theta\cos\phi + S_y \sin\theta \sin\phi \\ &= S_z\cos\theta + \tfrac{1}{2}(S_+ e^{-i\phi} + S_- e^{+i\phi})\sin\theta \end{aligned} \tag{3-39}$$

Making use of these transformation equations, we find

$$\mathscr{H}_Z = \beta H_0[(\Delta g \cos^2\theta + g_\perp)S_z + \Delta g \cos\theta \sin\theta\,\tfrac{1}{2}(S_+e^{-i\phi} + S_-e^{+i\phi})] \tag{3-40}$$

For the special case, often encountered, that $S = \frac{1}{2}$, the well-known matrix elements of $\mathbf{S}$ give the secular equation

$$\begin{vmatrix} \frac{1}{2}(\Delta g \cos^2\theta + g_\perp) - E/\beta H_0 & \frac{1}{2}\Delta g \sin\theta\cos\theta \\ \frac{1}{2}\,\Delta g \sin\theta\cos\theta & -\frac{1}{2}(\Delta g\cos^2\theta + g_\perp) - E/\beta H_0 \end{vmatrix} = 0$$

Keeping in mind that $\Delta g = g_\parallel - g_\perp$ one finds

$$(E/\beta H_0)^2 = \tfrac{1}{4}(g_\parallel{}^2\cos^2\theta + g_\perp{}^2\sin^2\theta) \tag{3-41}$$

from which

$$E/\beta H_0 = \pm\tfrac{1}{2}\,(g_\parallel{}^2\cos^2\theta + g_\perp{}^2\sin^2\theta)^{1/2} \tag{3-42}$$

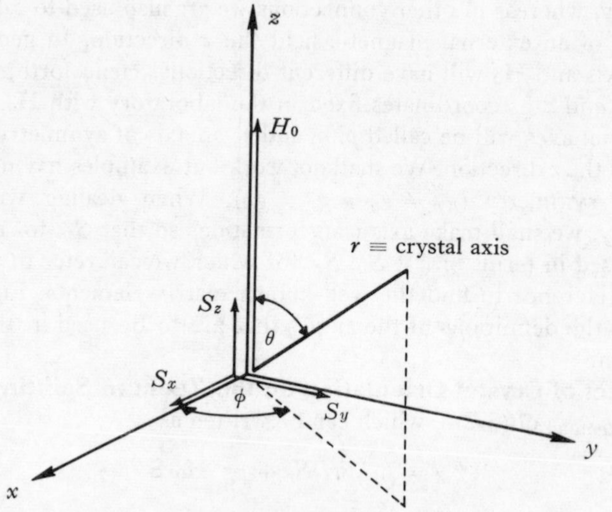

Fig. 3-7 Definition of angles for description of the orientation of a crystal with symmetry axis r in a laboratory frame x, y, z with $\mathbf{H}_0$ along z.

The resonance condition is thus

$$\hbar\omega = g(\theta)\beta H_0$$
$$g(\theta) = (g_{\parallel}{}^2 \cos^2\theta + g_{\perp}{}^2 \sin^2\theta)^{1/2} \qquad (3\text{-}43)$$

Evidently $g(0) = g_{\parallel}$ and $g(\pi/2) = g_{\perp}$ as they must.

The result (3-43) is consistent with an extensive amount of experimental data for axial crystals.

We have used the somewhat laborious procedure of the secular determinant to obtain (3-42) because in Chapter 5 we shall need to use (3-39) and similar expressions to discuss hyperfine structure for a tumbling molecular complex. If our only aim were to obtain (3-42), a shorter procedure would be to write $\mathscr{H}_Z$ as

$$\mathscr{H}_Z = \beta(g_{\parallel} H \cos\theta\, S_r + g_{\perp} H \sin\theta\, S_{\perp}) \qquad (3\text{-}44)$$

where $S_{\perp}$ is the component of $\mathbf{S}$ perpendicular to r in the rH plane. Upon transforming to a new coordinate system with the z' axis along a direction in the rH plane having components $g_{\parallel} \cos\theta$ and $g_{\perp} \sin\theta$, respectively, along the r and $\perp$ axes, (3-42) follows immediately from $\langle S_{z'} \rangle = \pm\frac{1}{2}$.

Fine Structure. Effects of the term DS_r^2 upon the paramagnetic resonance spectrum are called the fine structure. From (3-26), we recall that $D \approx \lambda^2/\Delta$. Typically, $\lambda \approx 10^2$ cm^{-1} and $\Delta \approx 10^4$ cm^{-1}, so that $D \approx 1$ cm^{-1}. Of course, it can vary an order of magnitude in either direction from this estimate. Thus, depending upon the external magnetic field, D may very well be comparable to the Zeeman interaction. When such is the case, it is necessary to include the D interaction in the secular determinant.

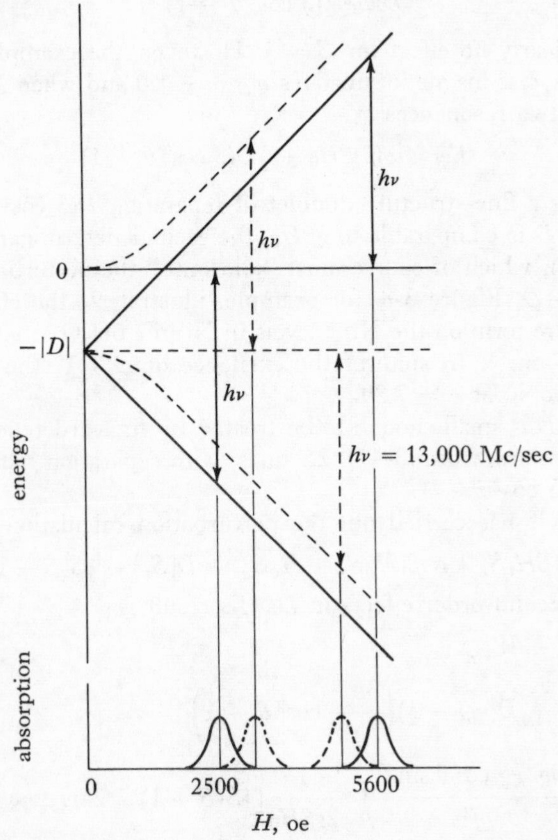

Fig. 3-8 Energy levels and fine-structure doublets in $NiSiF_6 \cdot 6H_2O$ for Ni^{++}. The solid lines are for the orientation $\theta = 0$ and the dashed lines show the position to which the levels and resonances move for $\theta = \pi/2$. The figure assumes $D = -0.17$ cm^{-1}, which occurs at 90°K. The resonances are sketched for 13,000 Mc sec^{-1}. No attempt has been made to show the proper relative intensities of the resonances.

When D is small, its effect is readily ascertained by a simple perturbation calculation. Substituting (3-39) for S_r in DS_r^2 gives

$$S_r^2 = S_z^2 \cos^2\theta + \tfrac{1}{4}\sin^2\theta(S_+S_- + S_-S_+) + \text{off-diag. terms} \qquad (3\text{-}45)$$

But $\frac{1}{2}(S_+S_- + S_-S_+) = S_x^2 + S_y^2 = S(S+1) - S_z^2$ and

$$DS_r^2 = DS_z^2(\cos^2\theta - \tfrac{1}{2}\sin^2\theta) + \text{constant or off-diag. terms} \qquad (3\text{-}46)$$

The diagonal elements of (3-46) are

$$Dm_S^2\,\tfrac{1}{2}(3\cos^2\theta - 1) \qquad (3\text{-}47)$$

There is clearly no effect for $S = \frac{1}{2}$. However, the example of Ni^{++}, with $S = 1$, has magnetic substates $m_S = \pm 1,0$ and when $D \ll g\beta H_0$, we expect two resonances at

$$\hbar\omega = g(\theta)\beta H_0 \pm \tfrac{1}{2}D(3\cos^2\theta - 1) \qquad (3\text{-}48)$$

which gives a fine-structure doublet of separation $D(3\cos^2\theta - 1)$.

When D is comparable to $g\beta H_0$, the secular determinant provides the solution, which of course must "join onto" the perturbation result for $g\beta H_0 \gg D$. Figure 3-8, for example, illustrates[17] the effect of the fine-structure term on the Ni^{++} levels in $NiSiF_6 \cdot 6H_2O$ at 90°K, where $D = -0.17\ \text{cm}^{-1}$. In spite of the existence of $D \neq 0$, the g value is nearly isotropic at $g = 2.29$.

When D is small enough to be treated by first-order perturbation theory, there are, from (3-47), $2S$ lines, with separation between lines varying as $3\cos^2\theta - 1$.

Bleaney[18] has carried out the perturbation calculation for

$$\mathscr{H} = g_\parallel\beta H_r S_r + g_\perp\beta(H_p S_p + H_q S_q) + D[S_r^2 - \tfrac{1}{3}S(S+1)] \qquad (3\text{-}49)$$

including second-order effects in D. His result is

$$\begin{aligned} h\nu &= W_{m_S} - W_{m_S-1} \\ &= g\beta H_0 + D(m_S - \tfrac{1}{2})\left(\frac{3g_\parallel^2}{g^2}\cos^2\theta - 1\right) \\ &\quad - \left(\frac{Dg_\parallel g_\perp \cos\theta\sin\theta}{g^2}\right)^2 \frac{1}{2g\beta H_0}[4S(S+1) - 24m_S(m_S-1) - 9] \\ &\quad + \left(\frac{Dg_\perp^2\sin^2\theta}{g^2}\right)^2 \frac{1}{8g\beta H_0}[2S(S+1) - 6m_S(m_S-1) - 3] \end{aligned} \qquad (3\text{-}50)$$

[17] R. P. Penrose and K. W. H. Stevens, *Proc. Phys. Soc. (London)*, **A63,** 29 (1950).

[18] B. Bleaney, *Phil. Mag.*, **42,** 441 (1951).

Wherever g appears in (3-50), the form (3-43) is meant.

Weger and Low[19] have solved the same problem for rhombic symmetry of the fine structure.

Hyperfine Structure. There are a substantial number of examples for which the magnetic interaction (3-30) between electron and nucleus is effectively isotropic, i.e., $A_x = A_y = A_z = A$. To illustrate hyperfine structure, we shall assume such isotropy. It is clear that similar methods will handle the more general case.

When a Fermi interaction $A\mathbf{I}\cdot\mathbf{S}$ is present, there will be a zero field splitting or splittings arising from the different F values corresponding to $\mathbf{F} = \mathbf{I} + \mathbf{S}$. The simple vector model gives

$$A\langle\mathbf{I}\cdot\mathbf{S}\rangle = A\frac{F(F+1) - I(I+1) - S(S+1)}{2} \tag{3-51}$$

In a magnetic field (assuming isotropic g for illustrative simplicity), each F level is further split. It is necessary to diagonalize

$$\mathscr{H} = g\beta H_0 S_z - g_N\beta_N H_0 I_z + A\mathbf{I}\cdot\mathbf{S} \tag{3-52}$$

in which g_N is the nuclear g value, defined as in (1-1) except that nuclei are positively charged and the negative sign of (1-1) is not used. The nuclear magneton is $\beta_N = e\hbar/2Mc$. Because the magnitude of nuclear moments is about 10^{-3} Bohr magneton, corresponding to the greater mass of the proton, the second term of (3-52) is always much smaller than the first. The hyperfine term, however, may vary from smaller than the nuclear Zeeman interaction to larger than the electronic Zeeman term.

The diagonalization of (3-52) first arose in connection with atomic spectra, and the resulting energy levels are often called the Breit-Rabi levels.[20] Atomic beam experiments enabled more quantitative study of these level schemes, and a good general discussion of the problem is presented by Ramsey.[21]

Figure 3-9 sketches the levels for two different nuclear spins, $I = \frac{1}{2}$ and $I = 1$, with $S + \frac{1}{2}$.

In high magnetic fields or for small enough A, a first-order perturbation calculation suffices. Indeed, this is quite frequently true for hyperfine structure and much less frequently so for the fine structure of Sec. 3-5. The energy levels arising from (3-52) are quickly seen to be

$$E(m_S,m_I) = g\beta H_0 m_S - g_N\beta_N H_0 m_I + Am_I m_S \tag{3-53}$$

[19] Ref. 1, p. 57.

[20] G. Breit and I. I. Rabi, *Phys. Rev.*, **38,** 2082 (1931).

[21] N. F. Ramsey, "Molecular Beams," Oxford University Press, New York, 1956.

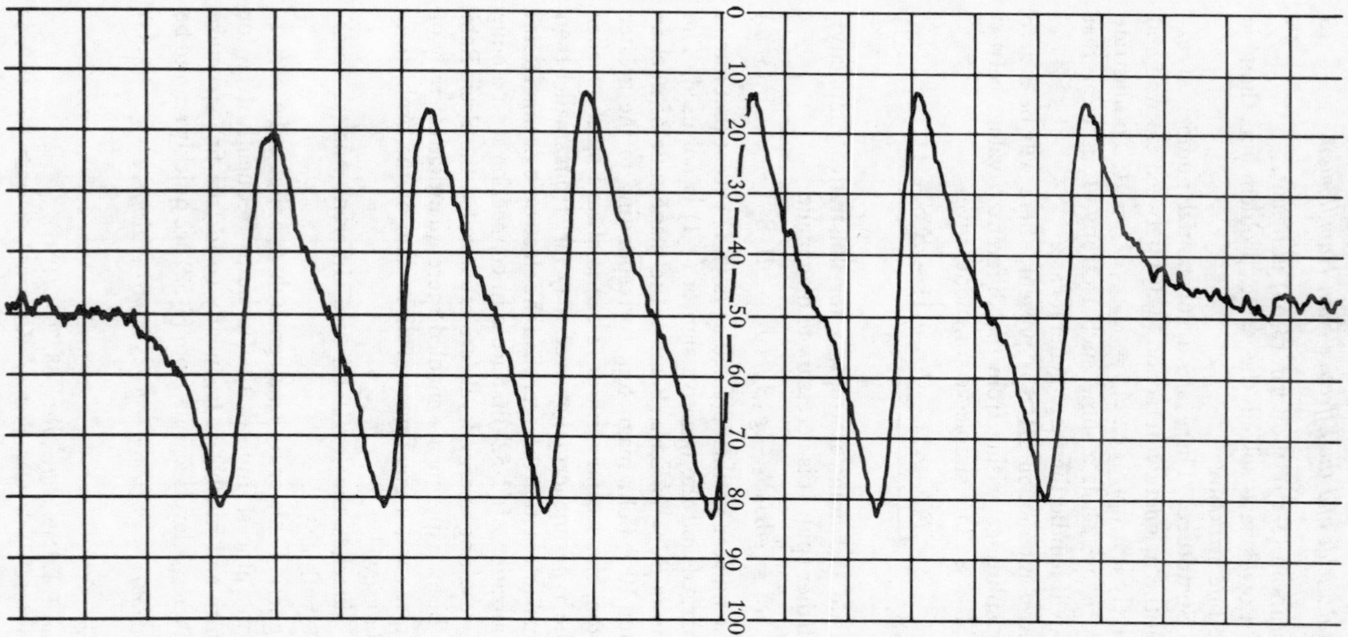

Fig. 3-10 Absorption-curve derivative for the hyperfine sextet arising from the $I = \frac{5}{2}$ nuclear spin of Mn^{55} in Mn^{++} ions in aqueous solution. The magnetic field sweep is not quite linear. There is a separation of about 95 oe between adjacent lines, corresponding to $A = 266$ Mc sec^{-1}. The spectrum was observed at 10,000 Mc sec^{+1}. (*Courtesy of W. O. Hamilton.*)

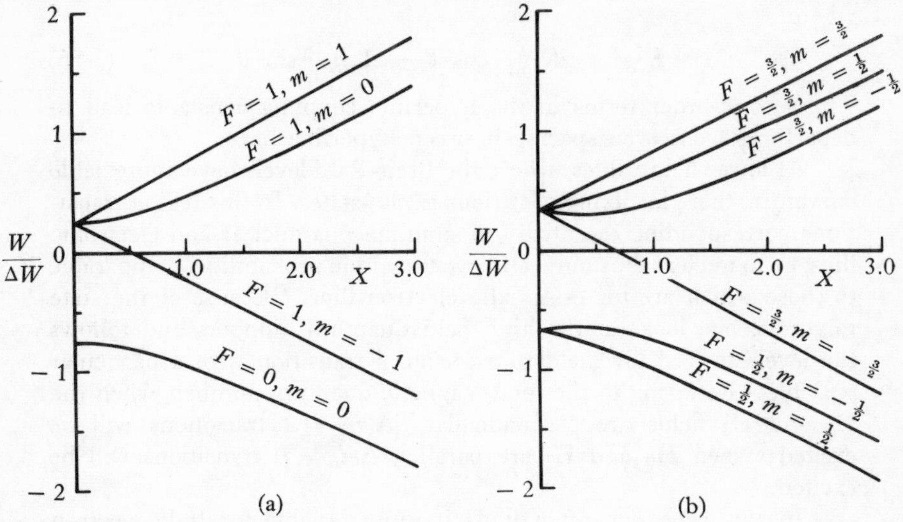

Fig. 3-9 Breit-Rabi levels for $S = \frac{1}{2}$ for (a) $I = \frac{1}{2}$ and (b) $I = 1$. The separation ΔW is related to A of (3–52) by $\Delta W = (2I+1)A/2$. The quantity X is defined as $X = (g\beta - g_N\beta_N)H_0/\Delta W$.

resulting in electron magnetic dipole transitions ($|\Delta m_S| = 1$) at the following frequencies:

$$\hbar\omega = g\beta H_0 + Am_I \tag{3-54}$$

where of course $m_I = -I, \ -I + 1, \ ..., \ +I$. This leads to $2I + 1$ hyperfine lines with spacing between adjacent lines of A/h cps or $A/g\beta$ oersteds. Figure 3-10 presents an experimentally observed hyperfine splitting of the Mn^{++} resonance by the Mn^{55} nucleus, which has $I = \frac{5}{2}$ and $A = 0.0089 \text{ cm}^{-1}$ corresponding to 266 Mc sec^{-1}. This is the S-state anomalous hyperfine coupling discussed in Sec. 3-4.

Bleaney[18] has carried the perturbation calculation to second order, including axial hyperfine coupling. The total Hamiltonian has $A_\parallel I_r S_r + A_\perp(I_p S_p + I_q S_q)$ added to (3-49), and the complete frequency expression is obtained by adding the following to (3-50):

$$Km_I + \frac{A_\perp^2}{4g\beta H_0}\left(\frac{A_\parallel^2 + K^2}{K^2}\right)[I(I+1) - m_I^2] + \frac{A_\perp^2}{2g\beta H_0}\left(\frac{A_\parallel}{K}\right)(2m_S - 1)m_I$$

$$+ \frac{1}{2g\beta H_0}\left(\frac{A_\parallel^2 - A_\perp^2}{K}\right)^2 \frac{g_\parallel g_\perp}{g^2} \sin^2\theta \cos^2\theta \, m_I^2 \tag{3-55}$$

where

$$K^2g^2 = A_{\parallel}^2 g_{\parallel}^2 \cos^2 \theta + A_{\perp}^2 g_{\perp}^2 \sin^2 \theta \tag{3-56}$$

The second-order terms in the hyperfine coupling constants lead to departures from even spacing between hyperfine lines.

At lower field values, where the Breit-Rabi levels have appreciable curvature, there is mixing of various m_S,m_I states. In this region transitions corresponding essentially to simultaneous nuclear and electronic flips, or to nuclear flips only, all have transition probabilities comparable to those which are for essentially electron flips. (Because of the state mixtures, one looks at the high field quantum numbers and follows the levels toward low field to associate a transition with a particular spin flip.) Referring to the total magnetic quantum number, when the $\mathbf{H}_0$ and $\mathbf{H}_1$ fields are perpendicular, $|\Delta m_F| = 1$ transitions will be excited; when $\mathbf{H}_0$ and $\mathbf{H}_1$ are parallel, $\Delta m_F = 0$ transitions will be excited.

In this way, one often finds it quite feasible to study electron resonance using radiofrequencies rather than microwave frequencies. One of the earliest examples of radiofrequency investigation of hyperfine structure was the study by Townsend et al.[22] of the paramagnetic ion $ON(SO_3)_2^{=}$ in aqueous solutions.

[22] J. Townsend, S. I. Weissman, and G. E. Pake, *Phys. Rev.*, **89,** 606 (1953).

[4]

Interactions between Neighboring Paramagnetic Ions

4-1 The Many-Spin Problem, Including Dipolar and Exchange Interactions

All our work in Chapter 3 dealt with ions isolated from one another but located within a lattice where they were subject to crystalline electric fields. Observations have also been made for nondilute systems, in which the magnetic dipole-dipole interaction between paramagnetic neighbors should surely broaden the line. Depending upon the spatial location of near-neighbors and the orientation of their magnetic moments, the magnetic dipole local field at a particular site should take on values from near zero to several times a typical measure of the nearest-neighbor dipole field, which is βr_0^{-3} where r_0 is the nearest-neighbor distance. Thus one expects a line profile to reflect the distribution of these dipolar fields and to have a width comparable to, or greater than, βr_0^{-3}.

Very early in the history of paramagnetic resonance it was noted that magnetic resonance lines were usually sharper than one would suppose on this basis.[1] For example, the width between half-maximum points on the resonance of $MnSO_4 \cdot 4H_2O$ is about 400 oersteds (Fig. 1-2), whereas one might estimate it to be perhaps 1000 oersteds. This discrepancy may not seem too serious, in the absence of a precise theory. But it is disturbing to note that $MnSO_4$, which has a closer

[1] C. J. Gorter and J. H. Van Vleck, *Phys. Rev.*, **72,** 1128 (1947).

spacing of Mn^{++} ions because the diluting water molecules are no longer present in the lattice, has a *narrower* line,[2] 300 oersteds, in spite of moving the ions closer to one another, which reduces r_0.

To develop a real theory of the dipolar width requires more than a simple vector summation of the magnetic fields of the dipoles at neighboring lattices sites. Each of the ions is equivalent (or, in more complicated lattices, there are a few species of equivalent ions), and we are required to treat an assembly of a large number of interacting ions. This is a many-body problem which was essentially solved in 1948 by Van Vleck.[2] In this calculation, Van Vleck not only provided a quantitative measure of dipolar broadening but he also solved the mystery of the anomalously narrow lines, which he showed to be caused by the exchange interactions between neighboring paramagnetic ions. We shall want to understand something of this calculation, and we therefore write the Hamiltonian for dipolar interactions between paramagnetic ions which we suppose, for the present, to be identical and in identical sites which give an isotropic g value. (We specifically neglect at this stage hyperfine interactions or possible fine structure.)

$$\mathscr{H} = \mathscr{H}_Z + \mathscr{H}_d$$

$$\mathscr{H}_Z = \sum_{j=1}^{N} g\beta H_0 S_{zj} \tag{4-1}$$

$$\mathscr{H}_d = \sum_{k>j} g^2\beta^2 r_{jk}^{-3}[\mathbf{S}_j\cdot\mathbf{S}_k - 3(\mathbf{S}_j\cdot\hat{\mathbf{r}}_{jk})(\mathbf{S}_k\cdot\hat{\mathbf{r}}_{jk})]$$

The caret over $\hat{\mathbf{r}}_{jk}$ denotes a unit vector along $\mathbf{r}_{jk}$. It will be necessary later on to add the exchange interaction, but for the moment we examine the complexities of the problem using (4-1). In fact, we begin by examining the Zeeman Hamiltonian $\mathscr{H}_Z$. Figure 4-1 is a sketch of the ladder of $2(NS) + 1$ levels, nearly all of which are highly degenerate, which are readily seen to arise because $\mathscr{H}_Z$ is in diagonal form. For illustrative purposes S is taken to be one-half and the number of spins is $N \sim 10^{22}$. The two nondegenerate states at the ends of the ladder are, respectively, $\alpha(1)\alpha(2)\cdots\alpha(N)$ and $\beta(1)\beta(2)\cdots\beta(N)$, each of which is an eigenfunction of $\mathbf{S}^2$ with $S = N/2$. Each successive state toward $E = 0$ is obtained by turning over one more spin, but there is of course a large choice as to which spin is turned over, accounting for the huge degeneracies toward the center of the ladder of levels.

Next we imagine that, somehow, we have got all the proper orthogonal linear combinations within each degenerate manifold, which will

[2] J. H. Van Vleck, *Phys. Rev.*, **74,** 1168 (1948).

Energy	*Degeneracy*
$g\beta H_0 \frac{N}{2}$	1
$g\beta H_0\left(\frac{N}{2} - 1\right)$	N
$g\beta H_0\left(\frac{N}{2} - 2\right)$	$N(N-1)/2!$
⋮	
0	$N!/[(N/2)!]^2$
⋮	
$-g\beta H_0\left(\frac{N}{2} - 2\right)$	$N(N-1)/2!$
$-g\beta H_0\left(\frac{N}{2} - 1\right)$	N
$-g\beta H_0 \frac{N}{2}$	1

Fig. 4-1 Ladder of energy levels in a magnetic field for N noninteracting particles of spin $\frac{1}{2}$. The degeneracy of a level with t spins having $m_S = +\frac{1}{2}$ and $N-t$ spins having $m_S = -\frac{1}{2}$ is $N!/(N-t)!t!$

give diagonal secular determinants of the perturbing interaction $\mathscr{H}_d$. Let these functions be denoted $\varphi(\xi_m,m)$ where ξ_m is a degeneracy index for each of the zero-order states within the manifold having level $E_m = g\beta H_0 m$. What, we now ask, will be the effect of $\mathscr{H}_d$ on the wave functions $\varphi(\xi_m,m)$?

Although the answer cannot be determined in numerical detail for our large number N, a qualitative answer is readily seen from the properties of the matrix elements of angular momentum and from the form of the perturbation. For this purpose we write $\mathscr{H}_d$ in terms of operators with very sharp selection rules, according to the identity

$$\begin{aligned}\mathbf{S}_j\cdot\mathbf{S}_k - 3(\mathbf{S}_j\cdot\hat{\mathbf{r}}_{jk})(\mathbf{S}_k\cdot\hat{\mathbf{r}}_{jk}) &= -S_{zj}S_{zk}(3\cos^2\theta_{jk} - 1)\\ &+ \tfrac{1}{4}(S_{+j}S_{-k} + S_{-j}S_{+k})(3\cos^2\theta_{jk} - 1)\\ &- \tfrac{3}{2}(S_{zj}S_{+k} + S_{+j}S_{zk})\sin\theta_{jk}\cos\theta_{jk}\, e^{-i\phi_{jk}}\\ &- \tfrac{3}{2}(S_{zj}S_{-k} + S_{-j}S_{zk})\sin\theta_{jk}\cos\theta_{jk}\, e^{i\phi_{jk}}\\ &- \tfrac{3}{4}(S_{+j}S_{+k}\, e^{-2i\phi_{jk}} + S_{-j}S_{-k}\, e^{2i\phi_{jk}})\sin^2\theta_{jk} \qquad (4\text{-}2)\end{aligned}$$

Recall now that m in $\varphi(\xi_m,m)$ is the eigenvalue of total

$$S_z = \sum_{j=1}^{N} S_{zj}$$

and that matrix elements of $\mathbf{S}_j$ are proportional (Ref. 3 of Chapter 3) to those of $\mathbf{S}$. Then the matrix elements of $\mathscr{H}_d$ can be seen from (4-2) to connect states with $\Delta m = 0, \pm 1$, and ± 2. The most important perturbing terms mixed by $\mathscr{H}_d$ into $\varphi(\xi_m,m)$ will be those from nearest neighbors at distance r_0, and the mixing coefficients will be of order $\beta^2 r_0^{-3}/\beta H_0$, since perturbation theory gives these coefficients as $(m'|\mathscr{H}_d|m)/(E_m - E_{m'})$. The perturbed wave functions are thus

$$\begin{aligned}\varphi'(\xi_m,m) = K[&\varphi(\xi_m,m) + a_1\varphi(\xi_{m+1}, m + 1)\\ &+ a_2\varphi(\xi_{m+2}, m + 2) + a_{-1}\varphi(\xi_{m-1}, m - 1)\\ &+ a_{-2}\varphi(\xi_{m-2}, m - 2)]\end{aligned} \tag{4-3}$$

where the a's are the mixing coefficients and K is a normalizing factor. Strictly speaking a summation over each degeneracy index within the admixed levels m' should be included, but the essential point of the present argument is the amount of admixture of different m values, and we do not need such refinements.

Now we consider the application of a microwave frequency magnetic field at right angles to $\mathbf{H}_0$, and recall that the transition probability is proportional to the square of the matrix element of S_x. It is, of course, a property of our unperturbed states $\varphi(\xi_m,m)$ that S_x connects states with $|\Delta m| = 1$ by means of matrix elements of order unity. The effect of the perturbed states (4-3) is clearly that there are matrix elements of S_x connecting other states:

$$\left.\begin{array}{l}(\varphi'(m),\ S_x\varphi'(m))\\ (\varphi'(m),\ S_x\varphi'(m \pm 2))\\ (\varphi'(m),\ S_x\varphi'(m \pm 3))\end{array}\right\} \approx a \approx \beta r_0^{-3}/H_0 \tag{4-4}$$

There will thus be transitions of intensity $a^2 \approx (\beta r_0^{-3}/H_0)^2$ relative to the main resonance having $|\Delta m| = 1$, and to conserve energy these weaker transitions must have $\hbar\omega \cong 0, 2g\beta H_0$, and $3g\beta H_0$. At fixed H_0, we thus expect an absorption spectrum qualitatively, as shown in Fig. 4-2. The student can, as a simple exercise, convince himself that there are also lines at $4\omega_0$, $5\omega_0$, etc., of intensity a^4.

In order to proceed with his calculation of the broadening of the line at ω_0 and to study the influence of the exchange interaction upon

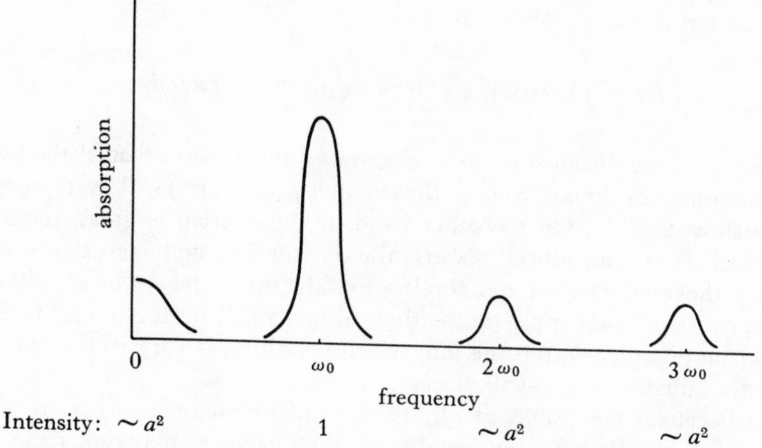

Fig. 4-2 Schematic illustration of subsidiary weaker resonances, in addition to the Larmor line, introduced by the dipolar coupling between spins.

it, Van Vleck necessarily had to add to (4-1) the exchange interaction. The most familiar feature of the exchange interaction is that we hold it to be the influence that aligns the elementary magnets within a ferromagnetic or antiferromagnetic domain. Such an interaction is in general present in all paramagnetic substances, but it does not manifest itself in a cooperative alignment until the temperature is reduced to the point at which thermal energies kT are comparable to the exchange interaction between a pair of spins.

We shall not present here a derivation of the form of the exchange interaction. For a simple two-particle model introducing the basic ideas, the discussion by Van Vleck is recommended.[3] A more general extension to any pair of electrons in a many-electron system is given by Dirac.[4] The result is that coulomb interactions between the electrons of two neighboring ions lead, through the Pauli principle, to an effective interaction between the spins of the two electrons having the form

$$\mathscr{H}_e^{ij} = -\,2J_{ij}\mathbf{S}_i\cdot\mathbf{S}_j$$

[3] J. H. Van Vleck, "Electric and Magnetic Susceptibilities," Oxford University Press, New York, 1932, p. 316.

[4] P. A. M. Dirac, "Principles of Quantum Mechanics," 4th ed., Oxford University Press, New York, 1958, Sec. 58.

where J_{ij} is the exchange integral, defined in terms of the wave functions ψ_A on ion A and ψ_B on ion B as

$$J_{ij} = \iint \psi_A(\mathbf{r}_i)\psi_B(\mathbf{r}_j)(e^2/\mathbf{r}_{ij})\psi_A(\mathbf{r}_j)\psi_B(\mathbf{r}_i)\, d\tau_i\, d\tau_j \tag{4-5}$$

Here r_{ij} is the distance between electrons i and j. Note that, if the two wave functions do not overlap, the product $\psi_A(\mathbf{r}_i)\psi_B(\mathbf{r}_i)$ will everywhere vanish as will J_{ij}. On the other hand, if the overlap is great, serious difficulties are introduced because the ψ_A and ψ_B functions usually are not orthogonal when A and B relate to different centers. The condition that overlap is not great means that J_{ij} is a small perturbation on the electron energies within the ion, which condition is very well satisfied for the substances we shall discuss.

Because the value of J_{ij} is dependent upon overlap of ψ_A and ψ_B, it falls off very rapidly as the distance between ions is increased. For this reason it is customary to consider exchange interaction only between ions which are nearest-neighbors. Consequently the total Hamiltonian with which Van Vleck begins his calculations is (4-1) plus

$$\mathscr{H}_e = -\sum_{\substack{\text{nearest-}\\\text{neighbor}\\\text{pairs}}} 2J_{ij}\mathbf{S}_i\cdot\mathbf{S}_j \tag{4-6}$$

Commonly one supposes all nearest-neighbor pairs to be identically situated within the pair, and thus $J_{ij} = J$ can be slipped outside the summation sign in (4-6). When combined with a tensor-interaction term having a form like the magnetic dipole-dipole coupling, (4-6) plus the tensor term has the most general form a coupling between two spin-$\frac{1}{2}$ particles can have.[5] The tensor exchange term is called the anisotropic exchange coupling, which will typically be of smaller magnitude than J.[6] We shall not include it explicitly in our work, as it is always included in principle by a simple redefinition of the coupling factor in the expression (4-2) for $\mathscr{H}_d{}^{ij}$.

One might further suppose that, because a term in $\mathbf{S}_i\cdot\mathbf{S}_j$ is part of the dipolar interaction, the effect of isotropic exchange is simply that of adding more dipolar coupling. There are numerous situations in which it has precisely the opposite effect, as we shall see upon following through the Van Vleck calculation in Sec. 4-2.

[5] J. Van Kranendonk and J. H. Van Vleck, *Rev. Mod. Phys.*, **30,** 1 (1958).
[6] J. H. Van Vleck, *Phys. Rev.*, **52,** 1178 (1937).

4-2 The Van Vleck Calculation of the Second Moment

Think of the Hamiltonian for a crystal of N-interacting spins

$$\mathscr{H} = \mathscr{H}_Z + \mathscr{H}_d + \mathscr{H}_e \tag{4-7}$$

as having been diagonalized. Let n stand for the set of quantum numbers of the various eigenstates. The magnetic resonance near ω_0 is then regarded as an envelope of sharp lines, each of which corresponds to the excess of absorption over emission, owing to the Boltzmann population excess in the lower state, for a transition between a state n and a state n' (Fig. 4-3). For a given H_1, the intensity of each of these lines is proportional to $|(n|S_x|n')|^2$. The mean-square resonance frequency, or second moment of the resonance, is found by weighing $\omega_{nn'}{}^2$ for each line with its intensity:

$$\langle\omega^2\rangle_{\text{av}} = \frac{\sum_n \sum_{n'} \omega_{nn'}{}^2 |(n|S_x|n')|^2}{\sum_n \sum_{n'} |(n|S_x|n')|^2} \tag{4-8}$$

Here the temperature-dependent terms arising from the Boltzmann factors do not appear because of the high-temperature approximation $\hbar\omega_0 \ll kT$ (cf. Chapter 7 for more details of the high-temperature approximation). We are in effect using for the transition probability a form such as (2-56) with $g(\nu) = 2\pi f(\omega) = 2\pi\delta(\omega - \omega_{nn'})$,

$$w_{nn'} = 2\pi\gamma^2 H_1{}^2 |(n|S_x|n')|^2 \delta(\omega - \omega_{nn'})$$

although $f(\omega)$ may actually have a narrow finite width, corresponding to

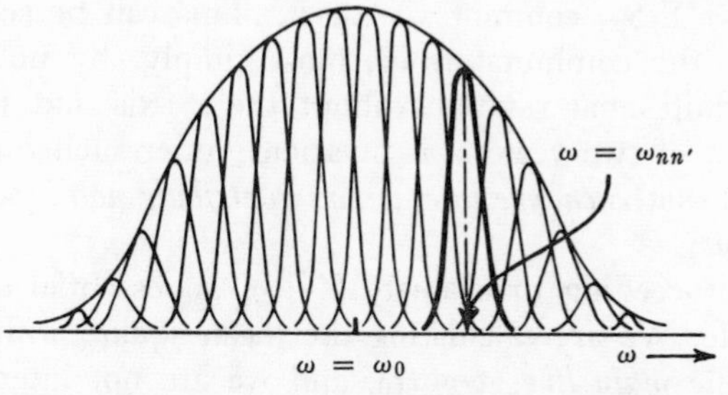

Fig. 4-3 Sketch illustrating the way in which individual sharper transitions between states of the complete Hamiltonian, with dipolar interactions, make up the total absorption line.

the long T_1 which we suppose to exist. We have then integrated over all ω to obtain the average in (4-8). Van Vleck's success in the calculation is possible because he can express (4-8) as the trace or diagonal sum of a matrix, which sum can be calculated in any convenient representation because of the well-known property that the trace of a matrix is independent of representation. The denominator of (4-8) is clearly the diagonal sum of a matrix product. The numerator is

$$\hbar^{-2} \sum_n \sum_{n'} [(n|\mathscr{H}|n) - (n'|\mathscr{H}|n')]^2 (n|S_x|n')(n'|S_x|n)$$
$$= -\hbar^2 \operatorname{tr}[\mathscr{H}S_x - S_x\mathscr{H}]^2 \tag{4-9}$$

as can perhaps most readily be seen by identifying each term in the expression

$$\operatorname{tr}[\mathscr{H}S_x\mathscr{H}S_x - S_x\mathscr{H}^2S_x - \mathscr{H}S_x{}^2\mathscr{H} + S_x\mathscr{H}S_x\mathscr{H}]$$

with one in the left member of (4-9). The resulting expression is

$$\langle\omega^2\rangle_{\text{av}} = -\frac{\operatorname{tr}[\mathscr{H}S_x - S_x\mathscr{H}]^2}{\hbar^2 \operatorname{tr} S_x{}^2} \tag{4-10}$$

Equation (4-10) is in fact only a special case of the general expression,[7,8]

$$\hbar^{2k}\langle\omega^{2k}\rangle_{\text{av}} = (-1)^k \operatorname{tr}[\mathscr{H},[\mathscr{H},\ldots[\mathscr{H},S_x]\ldots]]^2/\operatorname{tr} S_x{}^2$$
$$\langle\omega^{2k}\rangle_{\text{av}} = \operatorname{tr}[(d/dt)^k S_x]^2/\operatorname{tr} S_x{}^2 \tag{4-11}$$

where k is an integer $\geqslant 1$ and there are k commutator brackets. The time derivative is of course the Heisenberg time derivative of the operator.

Returning to (4-10) we note before we proceed with the calculation that the exchange interaction (4-6) contributes nothing to $\langle\omega^2\rangle_{\text{av}}$ because $S_x = \Sigma_j S_{xj}$ commutes with it. This can be seen by direct evaluation of the commutators or, most simply, by noting that S_x generates infinitesimal rotations about the x axis and that $\mathbf{S}_i \cdot \mathbf{S}_j$, a scalar product of two vectors, is invariant under such rotations. It is thus apparent that *exchange interactions contribute nothing to the mean-square frequency*.

Before proceeding to evaluate (4-10), an essential simplification must be made. We are calculating the mean-square width or second moment of the *main line* at $g\beta H_0$, and we are not interested in the subsidiary lines of Fig. 4-2. These lines, although weaker, are weighted

[7] I. Waller, *Z. Physik*, **79**, 381 (1932).
[8] L. J. F. Broer, *Physica*, **10**, 801 (1943).

heavily by large frequency displacements from the center of the main line and they would contribute appreciably to the second moment measured from the center of the main line. We define $\Omega = \omega - \omega_0$. Then the second moment about the line center will be denoted as μ_Ω^2:

$$\mu_\Omega^2 = \langle \Omega^2 \rangle_{av} = \langle (\omega - \omega_0)^2 \rangle_{av} \tag{4-12}$$

To eliminate the subsidiary lines, Van Vleck therefore proceeds to *truncation* of the Hamiltonian, i.e., removal of the off-diagonal parts of $\mathscr{H}_d$ which produce the mixing that leads to the lines at 0, $2g\beta H_0$, and $3g\beta H_0$.

$$\mathscr{H}_{\text{trunc}} = \sum g\beta H_0 S_{zj} + g^2\beta^2 \sum_{j>k} r_{jk}^{-3} \tfrac{1}{2}(3\cos^2\theta_{jk} - 1)$$

$$\times [\mathbf{S}_j \cdot \mathbf{S}_k - 3S_{zj}S_{zk}] - 2J \sum_{j>k} \mathbf{S}_j \cdot \mathbf{S}_k \tag{4-13}$$

The last term is summed only over nearest-neighbor pairs. It should be noted that $\mathbf{S}_j \cdot \mathbf{S}_k = S_{jz}S_{kz} + \frac{1}{2}(S_{+j}S_{-k} + S_{-j}S_{+k})$, but we have retained the scalar products explicitly in (4-13) because they commute with S_x and thus may be dropped in calculating the mean-square frequency.

Evaluating the required commutators and taking the necessary traces is straightforward if one uses the familiar representation in which each S_{zi} is diagonal. We illustrate the nature of the calculation by treating only $\mathscr{H}_Z$, which we anticipate should certainly correspond to a δ-function line at $\omega_0 = g\beta H_0/\hbar$, inasmuch as no interactions are present to broaden the resonance. We thus must evaluate the commutator and its square,

$$[\sum_j S_{zj}, \sum_i S_{xi}] = \sum_j [S_{zj}, S_{xj}] = i \sum_j S_{yj}$$

$$(i \sum_j S_{yj})^2 = - \sum_j \sum_k S_{yj}S_{yk} \tag{4-14}$$

then take the trace. Now it is readily seen that, within its own manifold, $(\text{tr})_j\, S_{yj} = (\text{tr})_j\, S_{zj} = (\text{tr})_j\, S_{xj} = 0$. The only important terms in (4-14) are thus those with $j = k$.

$$\text{tr}[\mathscr{H}_Z S_x - S_x \mathscr{H}_Z]^2 = - g^2\beta^2 H_0^2\, \text{tr}(\sum_{j=1}^{N} S_{yj}^2) \tag{4-15}$$

Now S_{yj} is diagonal in the magnetic quantum numbers of the $N - 1$

spins other than spin j. Thus the matrix element of S_{yj} is

$$(m_1 m_2 \cdots m_j \cdots m_N | S_{yj} | m_1' m_2' \cdots m_j' \cdots m_N')$$
$$= \delta_{m_1 m'_1} \delta_{m_2 m'_2} \cdots (m_j | S_{yj} | m_j') \cdots \delta_{m_N m'_N} \qquad (4\text{-}16)$$

Within the m_j manifold alone,

$$(\mathrm{tr})_j\, S_{yj}^2 = \tfrac{1}{3} S(S+1)(2S+1) \qquad (4\text{-}17)$$

If one now observes that

$$\mathrm{tr}\, 1 = \sum_{m_1=-S}^{S} \sum_{m_2=-S}^{S} \cdots \sum_{m_N=-S}^{S} 1 = (2S+1)^N \qquad (4\text{-}18)$$

it readily follows from (4-16) and (4-17) that

$$\mathrm{tr}\, S_{yj}^2 = \tfrac{1}{3} S(S+1)(2S+1)^N$$

and the result for (4-15) is

$$\mathrm{tr}[\mathscr{H}_Z S_x - S_x \mathscr{H}_Z]^2 = -\, g^2\beta^2 H_0^2 \left(\frac{N}{3}\right) S(S+1)(2S+1)^N \qquad (4\text{-}19)$$

The denominator in (4-10) is similarly $\frac{1}{3} NS(S+1)(2S+1)^N$, so that we obtain

$$\langle \omega^2 \rangle_{\mathrm{av}} = g^2\beta^2 H_0^2/\hbar^2 = \gamma^2 H_0^2 = \omega_0^2 \qquad (4\text{-}20)$$

as expected.

Van Vleck[2] carries through the calculation of dipolar broadening as included in (4-13) and finds

$$\hbar \langle \omega^2 \rangle_{\mathrm{av}} = g^2\beta^2 H_0^2 + \tfrac{3}{4} S(S+1) \sum_j g^4\beta^4 r_{jk}^{-6} (3\cos^2\theta_{jk} - 1)^2 \qquad (4\text{-}21)$$

Here the site k upon which the sum is based is a typical interior ion site of the crystal. As we noted earlier, exchange does not influence the second moment.

We can give (4-21) more meaning in situations where the resonance is narrow compared to ω_0 by noting that the symmetry of possible m_j values in essence assures a symmetrical line at ω_0. Then recalling our definition (4-12) and generalizing the notation $\mu_\Omega{}^n$ as the nth moment we conclude from the symmetry of the line that $\mu_\Omega{}^1 = 0$. Then

$$\begin{aligned} \langle \omega^2 \rangle_{\mathrm{av}} &= \langle (\omega_0 + \Omega)^2 \rangle_{\mathrm{av}} = \omega_0^2 + \mu_\Omega{}^2 \\ \mu_\Omega{}^2 &= \langle \omega^2 \rangle_{\mathrm{av}} - \omega_0^2 \end{aligned} \qquad (4\text{-}22)$$

The second moment of the line centered at ω_0 and having shape function $F(\Omega)$, where $\Omega = \omega - \omega_0$, is obtainable from the definition (4-12) of the second moment and from (4-21) as

$$\mu_\Omega{}^2 = \int_{-\infty}^{\infty} F(\Omega)\Omega^2\, d\Omega \qquad \left[\int_{-\infty}^{\infty} F(\Omega)\, d\Omega = 1\right]$$

$$= \tfrac{3}{4}S(S+1)\hbar^{-2} \sum_j g^4\beta^4 r_{jk}^{-6}(3\cos^2\theta_{jk} - 1)^2 \qquad \text{(4-23)}$$

When the line is sharp, we saw in such special solutions as those of Sec. 1-3 that varying the magnetic field for fixed ω changes ω_0 in a way quite equivalent to varying ω near resonance in fixed external field H_0. Thus there is an equivalent magnetic field second moment,

$$\mu_{\Delta H}{}^2 \equiv \langle(\Delta H)^2\rangle_{av}$$

$$g^2\beta^2\langle(\Delta H)^2\rangle_{av} = \hbar^2\langle\Omega^2\rangle_{av} \qquad \text{(4-24)}$$

$$\gamma^2\mu_{\Delta H}{}^2 = \mu_\Omega{}^2$$

and

$$\mu_{\Delta H}{}^2 = \tfrac{3}{4}S(S+1) \sum_j g^2\beta^2 r_{jk}{}^{-6}(3\cos^2\theta_{jk} - 1)^2 \qquad \text{(4-25)}$$

Finally, if all orientations of microcrystals are present in a polycrystalline sample, (4-25) gives

$$\mu_{\Delta H}{}^2 = \tfrac{3}{5}S(S+1)g^2\beta^2 \sum_j r_{jk}{}^{-6} \qquad \text{(4-26)}$$

Equation (4-26) is a precise statement of the ideas expressed early in Sec. 4-1 regarding the distribution of local dipolar fields. The failure of exchange to influence (4-26) at all, however, appears as something of a surprise, since exchange is expected to influence line width. This mystery will be cleared up in Sec. 4-3. Experimental studies[9,10] of nuclear magnetic resonance line widths for the simple cubic array of F^{19} nuclei in a CaF_2 single crystal (Ca^{40} has no nuclear magnetic moment) have fully verified (4-26).

4-3 The Fourth Moment and the Effect of Exchange

On reexamination of Sec. 4-2 we observe that

$$\hbar^2\langle\Omega^2\rangle = -\operatorname{tr}[\mathscr{H}_d, S_x]^2/\operatorname{tr} S_x{}^2 \qquad \text{(4-27)}$$

[9] G. E. Pake and E. M. Purcell, *Phys. Rev.*, **74**, 1184 (1948).
[10] C. R. Bruce, *Phys. Rev.*, **107**, 43 (1957).

where we suppose that the relevant part of $\mathscr{H}_d$ after truncation is used. Although it was permissible to drop $\mathscr{H}_e$ from (4-27) because $[\mathscr{H}_e, S_x] = 0$, $\mathscr{H}_e$ cannot be dropped from the fourth-moment calculation because it does not commute with $[\mathscr{H}_d, S_x]$. To an order-of-magnitude approximation, one can write (4-11), for $k = 2$, in a form similar to (4-27):

$$\hbar^4 \langle \Omega^4 \rangle \approx \mathrm{tr}[\mathscr{H}_e + \mathscr{H}_d, [\mathscr{H}_d, S_x]]^2 / \mathrm{tr}\, S_x^2 \tag{4-28}$$

Equation (4-28) is not precisely an equality because, recalling that odd moments vanish for a symmetrical line,

$$\begin{aligned} \langle (\omega_0 + \Omega)^4 \rangle_{\mathrm{av}} &= \omega_0^4 + 6\omega_0^2 \langle \Omega^2 \rangle_{\mathrm{av}} + \langle \Omega^4 \rangle_{\mathrm{av}} \\ &= \omega_0^4 + 6\omega_0^2 \mu_\Omega^2 + \mu_\Omega^4 \end{aligned} \tag{4-29}$$

and the cross term is not included in (4-28).

The fourth-moment calculation is too long to include here. Examination of Van Vleck's result[2] quickly reveals how $\hbar^4 \mu_\Omega^4$ depends upon the magnitude of exchange couplings. If J is the exchange integral and $E_d \approx g^4 \beta^4 r_0^{-6}$, where r_0 is the nearest-neighbor distance, then

$$\hbar^4 \mu_\Omega^4 \approx J^2 E_d^2 + E_d^4 \tag{4-30}$$

follows from Van Vleck's result or even from inspection of (4-28). In the same approximation (4-23) states

$$\hbar^2 \mu_\Omega^2 \approx E_d^2 \tag{4-31}$$

First consider (4-30) and (4-31) when no exchange interaction is present. Then it follows that

$$(\hbar^2 \mu_\Omega^2)^2 \approx \hbar^4 \mu_\Omega^4 \tag{4-32}$$

and this coupled with (4-31) is characteristic of a simple absorption curve confined to a frequency interval of order $E_d/\hbar$ at ω_0. For example, a Gaussian curve of width $E_d/\hbar$ would have this property. In fact, it is readily shown that the ratio $(\mu_\Omega^4)^{1/4}/(\mu_\Omega^2)^{1/2}$ is 1.32 for a Gaussian and 1.16 for a rectangular-shaped curve.

It is evident, however, that the presence of a J larger than E_d has the effect of greatly increasing μ_Ω^4 while leaving μ_Ω^2 totally unaffected. Here is the indication of the exchange-narrowing phenomenon. Figure 4-4 sketches first a Gaussian curve which might not differ greatly from the line shape under influence of dipolar broadening alone.

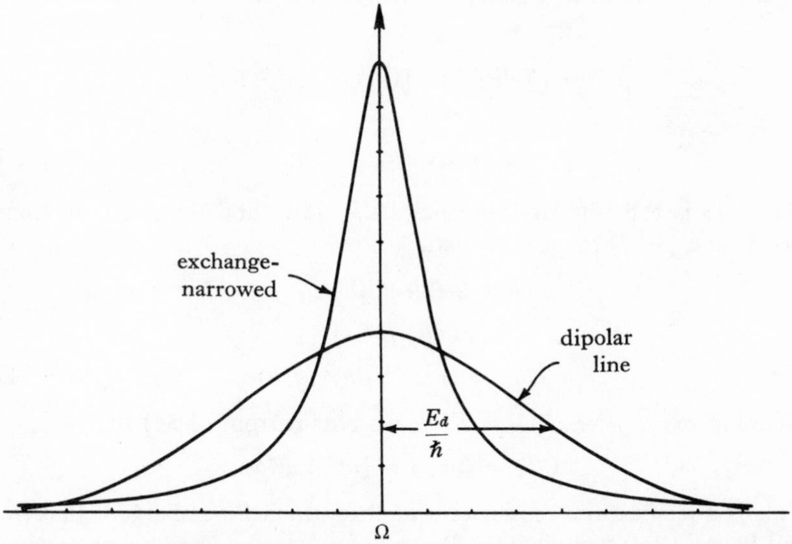

Fig. 4-4 Comparison of resonance line shapes for two identical lattices, except that one lattice has exchange and the other does not.

If exchange were added to the same lattice of ions, the line must alter in such a way as to increase $\mu_\Omega{}^4$ while preserving $\mu_\Omega{}^2$ and its intensity, $\mu_\Omega{}^0$. The key to the requisite change in shape lies in the great influence of the wings of the line on $\mu_\Omega{}^n = \int_{-\infty}^{\infty} \Omega^n F(\Omega)\, d\Omega$. If one takes intensity out of the line at points near $\Omega \approx E_d/\hbar$, then he can put some of it in the wings, increasing $\mu_\Omega{}^4$ until the second moment is nearly restored, and throw whatever remains into a sharp peak near $\Omega = 0$, which will contribute very little to $\mu_\Omega{}^2$ or to $\mu_\Omega{}^4$. Of course, the resulting line will have an enhanced $\mu_\Omega{}^4$ because $(\Omega)^4$ weighs the wings more heavily than does $(\Omega)^2$. Figure 4-4 sketches the qualitative change in line shape, which will be regarded experimentally as a narrowing of the line.

More recent theoretical studies, to be mentioned in Sec. 7-2, have verified an early theoretical model of Anderson,[11] who suggested than when $J \gg E_d$, the resonance is essentially a Lorentz curve (2-57) with a cutoff at $\pm\hbar\Omega \sim J$. The effect of the center of the line on any

[11] P. W. Anderson, unpublished lecture notes used at the Bell Telephone Laboratories, 1952.

of the moments is negligible, so that from (2-57) and (2-58)

$$\mu_\Omega{}^n = (T_2/\pi) \int_{-J/\hbar}^{J/\hbar} [\Omega^n/(1 + T_2{}^2\Omega^2)]\, d\Omega$$

$$\cong (2/\pi)(J/\hbar)^{n-1}/(n-1)T_2 \qquad (4\text{-}33)$$

But $1/T_2$ is the angular-frequency half-width, and we conclude from (4-31) and (4-33) for $n = 2$ that

$$\mu_\Omega{}^2 \approx (2/\pi)(J/\hbar)/T_2$$
$$\approx (E_d/\hbar)^2$$
$$1/T_2 \approx (\pi/2)(E_d/\hbar)^2/(J/\hbar) \qquad (4\text{-}34)$$

Defining $\omega_d \equiv \hbar^{-1}E_d$, $\omega_e \equiv \hbar^{-1}J$, we obtain from (4-34) that

$$1/T_2 = \Delta\omega_{1/2} = (\pi/2)\omega_d{}^2/\omega_e \qquad (4\text{-}35)$$

This is a result quite reminiscent of that which Bloembergen, Purcell, and Pound (Ref. 6 of Chapter 2) obtain for extreme motional narrowing of a nuclear resonance line for a liquid, with $1/\omega_e$ here replacing τ_c, the correlation time for molecular motion in the liquid. Anderson and Weiss[12] have indeed viewed exchange narrowing as a physically similar phenomenon, wherein the portion $J[S_{+i}S_{-j} + S_{-i}S_{+j}]$ of $2J\mathbf{S}_i\cdot\mathbf{S}_j$ is thought of as flipping neighboring oppositely oriented spins at a rate J/h, thereby leading to an effective migration of spin orientation through the lattice. With this model they obtain (4-35). Motional narrowing will be discussed in Sec. 5-3 for paramagnetic resonance in liquids. The general theoretical treatment of line narrowing occurs in Chapter 7.

We should note in passing that (4-34) can be subjected to an order-of-magnitude experimental check by use of the Curie temperature's close relationship to J. For example, the Weiss molecular field gives a relation

$$3kT_c = 2zJS(S+1) \qquad (4\text{-}36)$$

where z is the number of nearest-neighbors. Such comparisons are made by Anderson and Weiss,[12] who find good agreement (to within about a factor 3 or so, which is partially associated with a somewhat esoteric phenomenon called the "10/3 effect," discussed in Sec. 7-2). For example, $MnSO_4$ is calculated by Anderson, using (4-35) and (4-36), to have a width of about 100 oersteds, whereas 330 oersteds is observed.

[12] P. W. Anderson and P. R. Weiss, *Rev. Mod. Phys.*, **25**, 269 (1953).

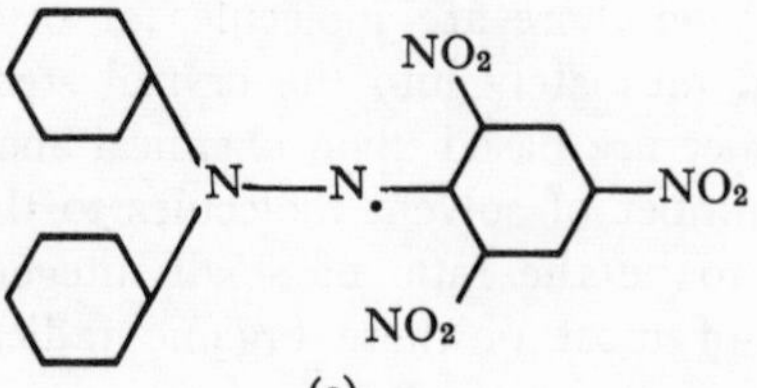

(a)

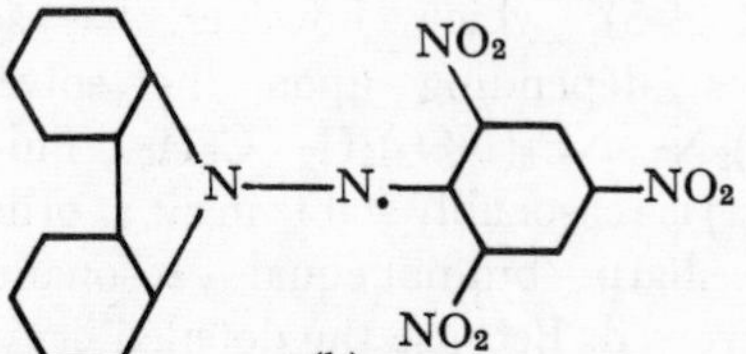

(b)

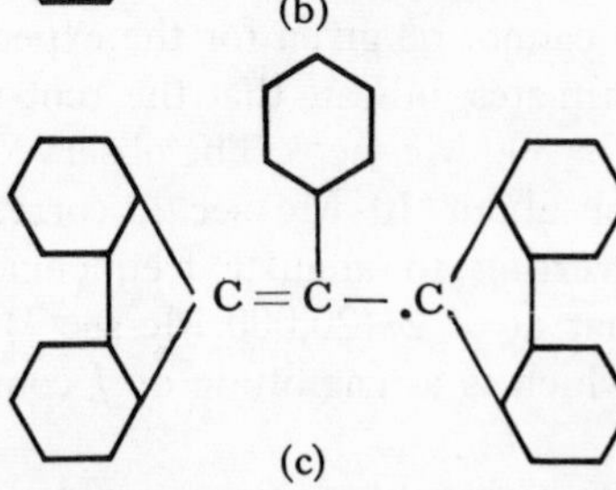

(c)

Fig. 4-5 Schematic structures of some organic radical molecules that form relatively stable molecular crystals under ordinary conditions of temperature and pressure: (a) diphenyl picryl hydrazyl (DPPH), (b) picryl amino carbazyl, (c) bisdiphenylene phenyl allyl.

In addition to the ionic crystals such as $MnSO_4$ mentioned above, another class of crystalline materials has been discovered[13] which exhibits more extreme examples of exchange narrowing. These are the crystalline organic radicals, examples of the chemical formulas of which are given in Fig. 4-5.

The crystals are molecular or Van der Waals crystals, with a typical molecular weight being near perhaps 400. The molecule is paramagnetic

[13] A. N. Holden, C. Kittel, F. R. Merritt, and W. A. Yager, *Phys. Rev.*, **75,** 1614 (1949); **77,** 147 (1950). C. H. Townes and J. Turkevich, *Phys. Rev.*, **77,** 148 (1950).

by virtue of an unused valence in the molecule, leaving it with an unpaired electron. Often there are molecules of organic solvent, such as benzene, bound intimately into the crystal structure in a regular way. This is a conjecture based upon chemical analysis, which shows the ratio of the number of solvent molecules to the number of free-radical molecules to be the ratio of small integers.[14] However, the crystal structures of most of these organic radicals have not been determined.

The most common of these materials is DPPH, diphenyl picryl hydrazyl (see Fig. 4-5), which, however, has somewhat different magnetic properties, depending upon the solvent. The benzene complex is $(C_6H_5)_2N—NC_6(NO_2)_3H_2 \cdot C_6H_6$. This material (also the chloroform complex) is reasonably stable in air at ordinary temperatures. Both materials have sharp—but not equal— resonance widths which are quite exchange-narrowed. Because the detailed crystal structure is unknown, precise values cannot be given for the expected dipolar second moment. However, estimates indicate that the root-mean-square width is about 100 oersteds, or 300 Mc sec^{-1}. The observed resonance width[15] is near 3 oersteds, or about 10 Mc sec^{-1}, corresponding to $T_2 = 2.4 \times 10^{-8}$ sec. Converting to angular frequencies as required by (4-35) we estimate that $\omega_e = 2\pi(20{,}000 \text{ Mc sec}^{-1}) = J/\hbar$. From this we find $J/k \cong 1°$K, which is a magnitude of J confirmed by specific-heat measurements.[16]

There are two interesting conclusions one draws from the results on DPPH and similar materials. First, exchange narrowing is pronounced, giving in fact as little as 1 per cent of the dipolar width that would be present without exchange. Second, the model seems to check quantitatively with $\omega_e \approx J/\hbar$. Indeed, the line shape in these materials is to a very good approximation the Lorentz shape of the Anderson-Weiss model, for which some theoretical justification will be given in Sec. 7-2.

It may be asked how there can be exchange interaction between DPPH molecules when it is simply an unpaired electron of a central nitrogen atom that provides the magnetic properties. The answer is that the unpaired electron's wave function is highly "delocalized,"

[14] J. A. Lyons and W. F. Watson, *J. Polymer Sci.*, **18,** 141 (1955).

[15] J. P. Goldsborough, M. Mandel, and G. E. Pake, *Phys. Rev. Letters*, **4,** 13 (1960).

[16] J. P. Goldsborough, M. Mandel, and G. E. Pake, Proceedings of the VII International Conference on Low Temperature Physics, Univ. of Toronto Press, 1960, p. 235. Also W. O. Hamilton, unpublished.

that is, spread out widely over the molecular skeleton and even beyond its limits, making overlap possible. This is known from the measurable isotropic hyperfine couplings to nuclei throughout the entire molecular structure.[17] These hyperfine splittings can be rendered measurable if the free-radical molecules are dissolved in dilute liquid solution so that exchange effects are removed and rapid tumbling averages away anisotropic hyperfine effects (see Sec. 5-3 for a discussion of this averaging process).

Before concluding this chapter it is worthwhile to mention the effects of dilution and temperature upon the moments of the line shape. The Van Vleck calculation treats infinite temperature in the sense that Boltzmann factors affecting line shape are all taken to be unity. The first theoretical discussion to include consideration of finite temperatures was that of Pryce and Stevens,[18] who set forth a general framework for calculating moments of the line under a variety of conditions. A recent extension of the work of Van Vleck, Pryce, and Stevens to finite temperatures was carried forth by McMillan and Opechowski,[19] who find a nonvanishing first moment (line shift) at lower temperatures as well as a temperature dependence of the second moment. They consider a specific example, nickel fluorosilicate, and show that appreciable temperature dependence of μ_Ω^1 and μ_Ω^2 is to be expected below 10°K.

The effect of dilution upon the high-temperature moments and line shape has been discussed by Kittel and Abrahams.[20] Using the usual arguments based upon relative magnitudes of μ_Ω^4 and $(\mu_\Omega^2)^2$, they conclude that a rigid lattice with 10 per cent or more of its lattice sites occupied by elementary paramagnets has a dipolar width varying approximately as $\sqrt{f}$, where f is the fraction of sites occupied. For $f < 0.01$, the line is Lorentzian in its measurable central region and has a width proportional to f.

If exchange interactions are present, the effect of dilution depends upon specific structural features of the sample, such as whether the sample is a solid with randomly occupied lattice sites, as supposed above, or whether it has the character of a more or less regular lattice with an expanded lattice parameter. (For example, Coulomb repul-

[17] G. E. Pake, S. I. Weissman, and J. Townsend, *Disc. Faraday Soc.*, **19,** 147 (1955).

[18] M. H. L. Pryce and K. W. H. Stevens, *Proc. Phys. Soc.* (*London*), **A63,** 36 (1950).

[19] M. McMillan and W. Opechowski, *Can. J. Phys.*, **38,** 1168 (1960).

[20] C. Kittel and E. Abrahams, *Phys. Rev.*, **90,** 238 (1953).

sions between positive paramagnetic ions in a viscous liquid solution might lead to a diluted sample somewhat approximated by this model; with low viscosity, complicating effects of liquid motion must be considered also.) Generally, one expects the exchange interaction, which requires overlap of wave functions, to fall off more rapidly with increasing distance than does the dipolar interaction varying as r^{-3}. Thus, the first effect of dilution upon an exchange-narrowed resonance can be a broadening.

[5]

Paramagnetic Resonance in Liquids

5-1 The Spin Hamiltonian for a Tumbling Paramagnetic Complex

It is well known that many ions in liquid solution, especially those of the transition groups, exhibit relatively stable short-range order between the ion and the nearest surrounding solvent neighbors.[1] Complexes form that are similar to the clusters found in solid crystals, and the symmetry of the immediate environment of the ion may be as high as cubic, with a strong possibility of an axial component. There is, however, a fundamental difference, in that the complex within the liquid tumbles in a random way as it is jostled by the molecular motions of the solvent liquid.

To determine the effect of the motion upon the paramagnetic resonance spectrum, we write the spin Hamiltonian in two parts, one which is invariant under rotations and the other which is orientation-dependent and therefore is a random function of time as the complex tumbles.

We begin with the axial spin Hamiltonian

$$\mathscr{H} = \beta[g_{\parallel}H_rS_r + g_{\perp}(H_pS_p + H_qS_q)] + DS_r^2 + A_{\parallel}I_rS_r + A_{\perp}(I_pS_p + I_qS_q) \qquad (5\text{-}1)$$

[1] B. A. Robinson and R. H. Stokes, "Electrolyte Solutions," 2nd ed, Academic Press, New York, 1959.

which can be written in terms of the laboratory coordinates using transformations (3-38) and (3-39). It is desirable to collect the angular terms into the form of spherical harmonics, since they have the property of averaging to zero for rapid random motions, i.e., motions in which the symmetry axis r is equally likely to intersect any element $d\Omega$ of the unit sphere wherever $d\Omega$ may be located on the sphere. We illustrate the procedure with the Zeeman part of (5-1), which was found to be [Eq. (3-40)] expressible as

$$\mathscr{H}_Z = \beta H_0[(\Delta g \cos^2\theta + g_\perp)S_z + \Delta g \cos\theta \sin\theta \times \tfrac{1}{2}(S_+e^{-i\phi} + S_-e^{i\phi})] \tag{5-2}$$

where $\Delta g = g_\parallel - g_\perp$. Now $\cos^2\theta$ averages to $\frac{1}{3}$ over a sphere, and the combination $\cos^2\theta - \frac{1}{3}$ may be achieved by adding in and subtracting out $\frac{1}{3}\Delta g\beta H_0 S_z$:

$$\mathscr{H}_Z^{\text{diag}} = \beta H_0 S_z[\Delta g(\cos^2\theta - \tfrac{1}{3}) + (g_\perp + \tfrac{1}{3}\Delta g)] \tag{5-3}$$

We shall denote $g = g_\perp + \frac{1}{3}\Delta g = \frac{2}{3}g_\perp + \frac{1}{3}g_\parallel$.

In a similar way, the hyperfine terms of (5-1) can be put into the desired form. Fine structure has been treated in (3-46), but now we also write the off-diagonal terms:

$$\begin{aligned}\mathscr{H} = {} & g\beta H_0 S_z + a\mathbf{I}\cdot\mathbf{S} + (D/2)(3\cos^2\theta - 1)S_z^2 \\ & + (D/2)\sin\theta\cos\theta[(S_zS_+ + S_+S_z)e^{-i\phi} + (S_zS_- + S_-S_z)e^{i\phi}] \\ & + \tfrac{1}{3}(\Delta g\beta H_0 + bI_z)(3\cos^2\theta - 1)S_z \\ & + (b/2)\sin\theta\cos\theta(I_+e^{-i\phi} + I_-e^{i\phi})S_z \\ & + \tfrac{1}{2}(\Delta g\beta H_0 + bI_z)\sin\theta\cos\theta(S_+e^{-i\phi} + S_-e^{i\phi}) \\ & + (b/4)\sin^2\theta(I_+S_+e^{-2i\phi} + I_-S_-e^{2i\phi}) \\ & - (b/12)(3\cos^2\theta - 1)(I_+S_- + I_-S_+)\end{aligned} \tag{5-4}$$

McConnell[2] was the first to write the Hamiltonian in this way, but he did not include the terms in D, as he visualized the case $S = \frac{1}{2}$. A term in $D\mathbf{S}^2$ has been omitted, as it shifts all levels equally. The following definitions are employed in (5-4):

$$\begin{aligned} g &= \tfrac{1}{3}g_\parallel + \tfrac{2}{3}g_\perp \\ \Delta g &= g_\parallel - g_\perp \\ a &= \tfrac{1}{3}A_\parallel + \tfrac{2}{3}A_\perp \\ b &= A_\parallel - A_\perp \end{aligned} \tag{5-5}$$

[2] H. M. McConnell, *J. Chem. Phys.*, **25**, 709 (1956).

The first two terms, in the first line of $\mathscr{H}$, are independent of orientation and thus are not functions of time as the complex tumbles.

All the remaining terms in (5-4) acquire through their angle factors a random time dependence. If the random motions are extremely rapid, which means if the motional frequencies, times $\hbar$, exceed the interaction energy in question, the time-dependent terms average to zero and have little effect. This is a limiting case of situations which can occur experimentally. In general, however, the time-dependent terms lead to important effects. If we wish to understand them, it will be necessary to make a brief excursion into the properties of random functions. Those readers familiar with nuclear magnetic resonance will recognize that we have a problem similar to that treated by Bloembergen, Purcell, and Pound (Ref. 6 of Chapter 2) for nuclear resonances in liquids.

5-2 Random Functions and Correlations[3]

To illustrate the problem now before us, consider as an example the function $3\cos^2\theta - 1$, which appears as a coefficient in the Hamiltonian (5-4). If θ is the angle between a fixed direction in space and an axis within a randomly tumbling molecule, over long-enough times the axis will point with equal likelihood through all equal surface elements of the unit sphere, and the mean value of $3\cos^2\theta - 1$ will be

$$\overline{3\cos^2\theta - 1} = \frac{\int_0^\pi (3\cos^2\theta - 1)2\pi\sin\theta\, d\theta}{\int_0^\pi 2\pi\sin\theta\, d\theta} = 0 \qquad (5\text{-}6)$$

The question arises as to how long a time one must wait to have the tumbling axis sample all orientations, or at least enough of them for the average to tend closely to zero. For concreteness, suppose that Fig. 5-1

[3] In this section the author parallels to some extent a discussion by A. Abragam, "Principles of Nuclear Magnetism," Oxford University Press, New York, 1961. For a more systematic and detailed development, the student is referred to "Selected Papers on Noise and Stochastic Processes," N. Wax (ed.), Dover, New York, 1954. The papers by S. Chandrasekhar [*Rev. Mod. Phys.*, **15,** 1 (1943)] and M. C. Wang and G. E. Uhlenbeck [*Rev. Mod. Phys.*, **17,** 323 (1945)] in the Wax selection are especially recommended.

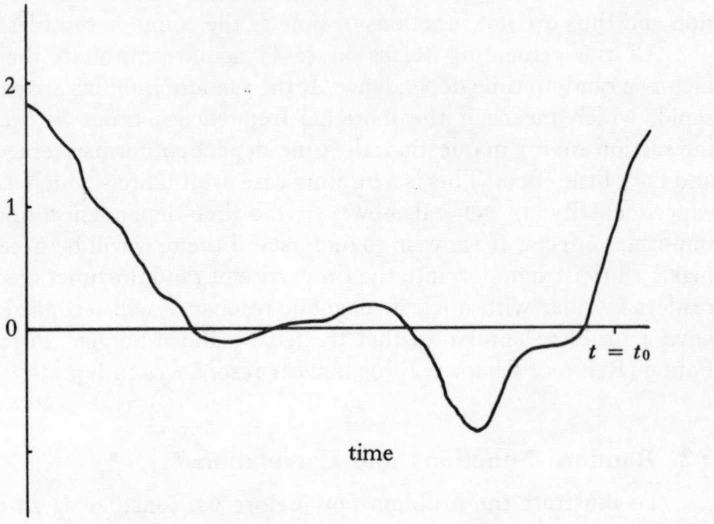

Fig. 5-1 An imagined random variation with time of $3\cos^2\theta(t) - 1$, with proper spherical weighting $\sin\theta(t)$, as a molecular complex tumbles in a liquid.

represents the variation of $[3\cos^2\theta(t) - 1]\sin\theta(t)$ with time, as θ in turn varies with time. Over the time interval t_0 shown, $[3\cos^2\theta(t) - 1] \times \sin\theta(t)$ surely does not appear to average very close to zero, and it seems likely that one would have to observe the motion for perhaps several t_0 before the average would be zero, within 5 per cent of the amplitude from -1 to $+2$. It is also apparent that there is a length of interval—choose, for example, $t_0/10$ or smaller—such that the value of the function at the end of the interval is quite likely of the same sign, and perhaps even of similar magnitude, as at the beginning of the interval. This latter statement is true in a statistical sense for any choice of starting point for the small interval. We say that over such an interval the values of the function are *correlated*. Clearly the correlation is better the shorter the interval.

One can try to be more quantitative by defining a correlation function $K(t_1,t_2)$ for a random function $f(x(t))$. We now have in mind that f is a prescribed function of x, which, however, varies randomly with t, where $f(x(t))$ has an average value, $(1/T)\int_{t_1}^{t_1+T} f(x(t))\,dt$, of zero over a long time interval T. The correlation function is defined as

$$K(t_1,t_2) = \overline{f(x(t_1))f^*(x(t_2))} \tag{5-7}$$

where the asterisk indicates a complex conjugate, since $f(x(t))$ may in general be complex, and the bar denotes an ensemble average; i.e., we suppose that there are many identical systems (here our molecular complex) and we average the product for the two instants t_1 and t_2 over all the molecules.

In terms of the conditional probability $p(x_1t_1; x_2t_2)\,dx_1\,dx_2$ that a molecule has x_1 in dx_1 at t_1 and x_2 in dx_2 at time t_2,

$$K(t_1,t_2) = \iint p(x_1t_1; x_2t_2)f(x_1)f^*(x_2)\,dx_1\,dx_2 \qquad (5\text{-}8)$$

We shall suppose that we deal with a stationary random process, one which depends not at all upon the origin in time but only upon $\tau = |t_2 - t_1|$. Then

$$p(x_1,x_2,\tau) = p(x_1,x_2,-\tau) = p(x_2,x_1,\tau) \qquad (5\text{-}9)$$

and from

$$K(\tau) = \iint p(x_1,x_2,\tau)f(x_1)f^*(x_2)\,dx_1\,dx_2$$

it follows that

$$K(-\tau) = K^*(\tau) = K(\tau) \qquad (5\text{-}10)$$

Then (5-7) becomes for stationary random processes

$$K(\tau) = \overline{f(x(t))f^*(x(t+\tau))} \qquad (5\text{-}11)$$

We define now $k(\tau)$ such that $k(0) = 1$ as follows:

$$K(\tau) = K(0)k(\tau) = \overline{|f(x(t))|^2}k(\tau) \qquad (5\text{-}12)$$

Since the process is stationary, the ensemble average of $|f(x(t))|^2$ can be performed for any instant of time. In our ensemble all orientations of the molecular axis are equally likely, and the ensemble average of $|3\cos^2\theta(t) - 1|^2$ is simply the average of $(3\cos^2\theta - 1)^2$ over a sphere.

Abragam[3] illustrates the calculation of the correlation function for a model in which the complex is considered to be a sphere of radius a immersed in a fluid of viscosity η, with the viscous resisting torque on the sphere given by Stokes' law.[4] The r axis is taken to be a particular direction fixed in the tumbling sphere. If $f(\cos\theta(t))$ is any second-

[4] A. Sommerfeld, "Mechanics of Deformable Bodies," Academic Press, New York, 1950, p. 251.

order spherical harmonic, Abragam finds, by using the diffusion equations to examine the flow of $p(x_1,x_2,\tau)$ with time, that

$$K(\tau) = \overline{|f(\cos\theta(t))|^2} \exp(-|\tau|/\tau_c) \tag{5-13}$$

where

$$\tau_c = 4\pi\eta a^3/3kT \tag{5-14}$$

For our example of $3\cos^2\theta - 1 = f(\cos\theta(t))$ we suppose that there is an isotropic distribution of the axis directions within the ensemble of molecular systems, giving $\overline{(3\cos^2\theta - 1)^2} = \frac{4}{5}$.

The function $k(\tau)$ certainly need not have the simple exponential form of (5-13). Sometimes a Gaussian is used, and in more general cases it oscillates. In any case, it depends in detail upon the model that is used, and it is common practice to assume a form for $k(\tau)$ that is mathematically convenient and has the properties $k(0) = 1$, $k(\tau \to \infty) \to 0$, and $k(\tau_c) \approx k(0)/2$. The mathematical definition of τ_c is thus not precise, but it is clear that τ_c is a measure of the length of time over which some correlation persists. It is called the *correlation time* and it is evidently much longer for a sugar molecule in molasses in January than it is for the same molecule dissolved in water at room temperature. The value for a typical molecule in water is $\sim 10^{-11}$ sec.

The correlation function lends mathematical precision to some of our qualitative ideas about the loss of correlation within an assembly of tumbling molecules. Moreover, it is directly useful in a quantitative description of relaxation processes within the liquid. We wish next to demonstrate this fact by calculating the transition probability for electron spins under the influence of a random perturbation.

Let us consider $\mathscr{H} = \mathscr{H}_0 + \mathscr{H}_1(t)$, where $\mathscr{H}_1(t)$ arises from a perturbing interaction between the spins, which also depends upon lattice coordinates. The spins are, in effect, a subsystem of the entire system, which includes in addition the many degrees of freedom of atomic and molecular motions. The interaction $\mathscr{H}_1$ in our problem will consist of the angle-dependent terms of (5-4) and becomes a time-dependent operator in the Heisenberg sense, with the time dependence introduced by the Hamiltonian for the lattice motions. Because the liquid "lattice" has very many degrees of freedom, we suppose that $\mathscr{H}_1(t)$, incorporating this time dependence, can be treated as a random function of time instead of performing the more rigorous but extremely difficult quantum mechanical calculation for the entire system consisting of spin subsystem and lattice.

To see how we handle $\mathscr{H}_1(t)$ as a random function, we expand the perturbed spin functions in terms of the eigenfunctions of $\mathscr{H}_0$:

$$\psi = \sum_{m''} a_{m''}(t) u_{m''} e^{-iE_{m''}t/\hbar} \tag{5-15}$$

The coefficients obey the Schroedinger equation (2-48):

$$i\hbar\, da_{m'}/dt = \sum_{m''} (m'|\mathscr{H}_1(t)|m'') a_{m''}(t) e^{i\omega_{m'm''}t} \tag{5-16}$$

Supposing that $a_{m''} = \delta_{m''m}$ at $t = 0$, the $a_{m'}(m' \neq m)$ initially unfold in time as

$$a_{m'}(t) = (i\hbar)^{-1} \int_0^t (m'|\mathscr{H}_1(t')|m) e^{i\omega_{m'm}t'}\, dt' \tag{5-17}$$

The probability that, after t seconds, a system initially in state m will be found in m' is

$$P_{m'm} = a_{m'}a_{m'}^* \tag{5-18}$$

and we seek a transition rate $w_{m'm} = dP_{m'm}/dt$:

$$w_{m'm} = a_{m'} \frac{da_{m'}^*}{dt} + \text{c.c.} \tag{5-19}$$

Placing (5-17) into (5-19) gives

$$w_{m'm} = \hbar^{-2}(m|\mathscr{H}_1(t)|m') e^{-i\omega_{m'm}t} \int_0^t (m'|\mathscr{H}_1(t')|m) e^{i\omega_{m'm}t'}\, dt' + \text{c.c.}$$

$$= \hbar^{-2} \int_0^t (m'|\mathscr{H}_1(t')|m)(m|\mathscr{H}_1(t)|m') e^{-i\omega_{m'm}(t-t')}\, dt' + \text{c.c.} \tag{5-20}$$

Up to this point we have simply reproduced a very familiar calculation of wave-mechanical perturbation theory. Now we want to consider that the $\mathscr{H}_1(t)$ in (5-20) is a random function, and so therefore is its matrix element. The measurable quantity in our assembly of molecular complexes is the ensemble average $\overline{w_{m'm}}$. Taking such an average of

(5-20), while at the same time transforming to the variable $\tau = t - t'$, yields from (5-20),

$$\overline{w_{m'm}} = \hbar^{-2} \int_{\tau=0}^{\tau=t} \overline{f^*(t-\tau)f(t)}e^{-i\omega_{m'm}\tau}\, d\tau + \text{c.c.} \tag{5-21}$$

In (5-20) we have written $f(t)$ for $(m|\mathscr{H}_1(t)|m')$ in order to emphasize that the integrand contains in fact the correlation function $K(-\tau) = K(\tau)$ as defined in (5-10) and (5-11). Making use of $K(\tau) = K(-\tau)$, one can cast (5-21) into the form

$$\overline{w_{m'm}} = \hbar^{-2} \int_{-t}^{t} K(\tau)e^{-i\omega_{m'm}\tau}\, d\tau \tag{5-22}$$

If we suppose that the correlation time τ_c is short compared to times t of interest (which means for this calculation $\tau_c \ll t$), loss of correlation will have carried the integrand to zero before τ reaches t, and the limits can be called $\pm\infty$. Recalling (2-70) as the definition of T_1 in terms of $\overline{w_{m'm}}$, we have for high temperatures

$$\left(\frac{1}{2T_1}\right)_{m'm} = \overline{w_{m'm}} = \hbar^{-2} \int_{-\infty}^{\infty} K(\tau)e^{-i\omega_{m'm}\tau}\, d\tau \tag{5-23}$$

The contribution of $m \to m'$ transitions to the relaxation rate $1/T_1$ is thus proportional to the Fourier transform of the correlation function.

As an example we select from (5-4) as our $\mathscr{H}_1(t)$ the term

$$\begin{aligned}\mathscr{H}_1(t) &= A_{\text{op}}F(t)\\ &= \tfrac{1}{2}(S_+e^{-i\phi} + S_-e^{i\phi})(\Delta g\beta H_0 + bI_z)\sin\theta\cos\theta\end{aligned} \tag{5-24}$$

Let $S = \frac{1}{2}$ for simplicity. Then the emission probability for an electron spin arises from the S_- operator. In particular, the system of electron and nucleus has a probability of going from $(m_I; m_S = \frac{1}{2})$ to $(m_I; m_S = -\frac{1}{2})$, which can be obtained from (5-23) and (5-21), using

$$K(-\tau) = \overline{(m_I; -\tfrac{1}{2}|\mathscr{H}_1(t-\tau)|m_I; \tfrac{1}{2})(m_I; \tfrac{1}{2}|\mathscr{H}_1(t)|m_I; -\tfrac{1}{2})} \tag{5-25}$$

Referring to (5-24) and (5-13),

$$\begin{aligned}K(\tau) &= \tfrac{1}{4}(\Delta g\beta H_0 + bm_I)^2|(-\tfrac{1}{2}|S_-|\tfrac{1}{2})|^2\overline{|\sin\theta\cos\theta\, e^{i\phi}|^2}e^{-|\tau|/\tau_c}\\ &= (1/30)(\Delta g\beta H_0 + bm_I)^2e^{-|\tau|/\tau_c}\end{aligned} \tag{5-26}$$

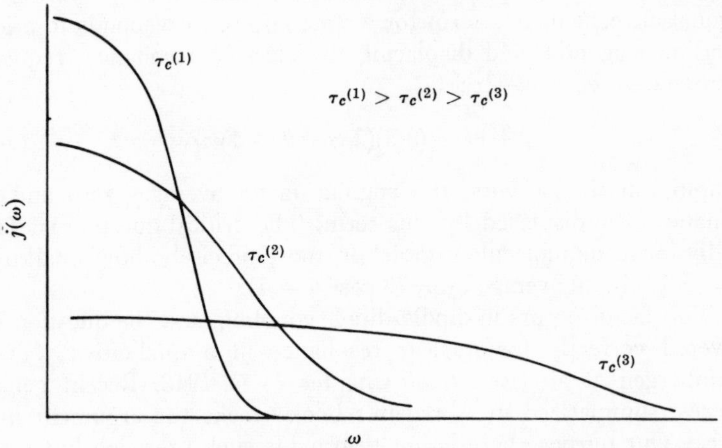

Fig. 5-2 Graphs of the correlation function (5-29) for three values of τ_c.

Finally, the contribution to the relaxation rate is found by placing (5-26) into (5-23):

$$1/2T_1 = (\hbar^2/30)(\Delta g\beta H_0 + bm_I)^2 2\tau_c/(1 + \omega^2\tau_c^2) \qquad (5\text{-}27)$$

The student can readily demonstrate that the general form (5-24) for $\mathscr{H}_1(t)$, with $k(\tau) = \exp(-|\tau|/\tau_c)$, leads to

$$(1/2T_1)_{m'm} = \hbar^{-2}(m'|A_{\text{op}}|m)|^2\overline{|F_{m'm}(t)|^2} 2\tau_c/(1 + \omega^2\tau_c^2) \qquad (5\text{-}28)$$

Figure 5-2 shows plots of the *correlation spectrum*,

$$j(\omega) = 2\tau_c/(1 + \omega^2\tau_c^2) \qquad (5\text{-}29)$$

for three different values of τ_c.

This correlation-function treatment of liquids has been extremely successful in nuclear magnetic resonance,[3] giving, in fact, far more precise quantitative agreement than the crudeness of the Stokes model would suggest. There are also a number of features of electronic paramagnetic resonance which are explained by the model. We shall describe some of these in Sec. 5-3.

5-3 Influence of Molecular Tumbling on Hyperfine Structure

Consider the effect of a term such as $(b/3)(3\cos^2\theta - 1)I_zS_z$ in (5-4). If the molecular complex is fixed in space and if the coupling

$b \ll g\beta H_0$ so that simple first-order perturbation theory applies, the diagonal element of this term for a state m_I, m_S corresponds to a local hyperfine magnetic field displacing the electron resonance frequency by an amount $\delta\nu = \delta\omega/2\pi$:

$$\hbar\delta\omega = (b/3)(3\cos^2\theta - 1)m_I \tag{5-30}$$

If rapid tumbling occurs, the angular factor averages zero and the resonance is undisplaced by this term. The critical question is: How rapidly must the molecule tumble, or, more precisely, how small must τ_c of (5-13) be to average away $(3\cos^2\theta - 1)$?

This factor occurs in dipole-dipole coupling, and the question was answered correctly for nuclear resonance in a qualitative way by Bloembergen et al. (Ref. 6 of Chapter 2) in 1948. Recent general theories, summarized in Abragam's book,[5] make the argument more precise. Our purpose here is not to provide such precision but rather to try to establish a plausible physical argument for the qualitative answer.

Both in the present example and in the picture of exchange narrowing by Anderson and Weiss (Ref. 12 of Chapter 4), narrowing is brought on by a fluctuating magnetic environment of the paramagnetic ion. Let us idealize the situation to one in which each ion, instead of resonating at ω_0, has available to it only two possible magnetic locales, which respectively shift the resonance from ω_0 either by $+\delta$ or $-\delta$ radians per second. Let us suppose that the ion jumps randomly between these two locales (or equivalently that the magnetic nature of a given locale alternates randomly) with a mean time τ_c for the existence of the ion in either kind of environment. It is now possible to deduce the effect upon the splitting or broadening of the resonance by recalling the basic definition of T_2 as the lifetime for decay of transverse components of magnetization.

Consider an assembly of these ions which may have precession frequencies $\omega_0 + \delta$ or $\omega_0 - \delta$, and suppose that somehow they have been prepared in an initial state having **M** (or total **S**) along the x' axis of a frame rotating at ω_0. Of course some spins precess at $+\delta$ and some at $-\delta$ with respect to the primed frame, and, if the environment did not fluctuate, it is clear that the vector sum of the precessing components would decay in a time $T_2^0 \approx 1/\delta$.

On the other hand, if the environment of a given spin fluctuates between $+\delta$ and $-\delta$ with a mean time τ_c, each precessing spin executes

[5] A. Abragam, "Principles of Nuclear Magnetism," Oxford University Press, New York, 1961.

a random walk in phase angle with respect to the rotating frame. By the simple properties of the random walk,[6] the mean-square phase difference $\overline{\Delta\phi^2}$ accumulated by the spins after n changes of environment is

$$\overline{\Delta\phi^2} \approx n(\tau_c\delta)^2 \tag{5-31}$$

where $\tau_c\delta$ is the magnitude of the mean phase accumulation, in radians, per step. Now the definition of the relaxation time T_2 is the time in which the spins, initially precessing in phase, get out of phase to the extent that their vector sum is decreased in magnitude by $1/e$. This requires $(\overline{\Delta\phi^2})^{1/2}$ to correspond to the order of 1 radian. If the elapsed time is T_2, we can write $n = T_2/\tau_c$, which converts (5-31) to

$$1^2 \approx (T_2/\tau_c)(\tau_c\delta)^2 \tag{5-32}$$

Thus we have for the measure of line width or splitting that

$$1/T_2 \approx \tau_c\delta^2 \qquad (\tau_c < 1/\delta) \tag{5-33}$$

This result is valid providing the environment has fluctuated before the transverse spin component will have already decayed in consequence of the $T_2{}^0 \approx 1/\delta$ decay. In other words, when $\tau_c > 1/\delta$, $1/T_2 = 1/T_2{}^0 \approx \delta$. When $\tau_c < 1/\delta$, (5-33) applies. Evidently, $\tau_c < 1/\delta$ *is the criterion for averaging away broadening effects*, and the averaging toward zero is the more complete the shorter τ_c, in accordance with (5-33).

If we return to the correlation spectrum of Fig. 5-2 and (5-29), which applies to the spherical harmonic $3\cos^2\theta - 1$ for random molecular tumbling, we can interpret (5-33) as telling us that

$$1/T_2 \approx \delta^2 j(0) \qquad (\tau_c < 1/\delta) \tag{5-34}$$

since $j(0) = 2\tau_c$. This is not surprising because the line width (that is, $1/T_2$) arises from static local fields which distribute the precession angular frequencies over an interval near ω_0. Equation (5-34) simply says that $j(0)$ is a measure of the static portion of the correlation spectrum of local fields, which is of course a truism.

The exchange-narrowing expression (4-35) is clearly a special case of (5-33) with $\omega_e = 1/\tau_c$, which is entirely consistent with the Anderson–Weiss model, in which the magnetic environment fluctuates at a rate ω_e. In this case, δ is the frequency measure of dipolar coupling.

General theories to be discussed in Chapter 7 have verified (5-33) as a quite general result, showing that δ can be taken to be the amplitude of any randomly fluctuating perturbation diagonal in m_S, which averages to zero over long times and has a correlation time τ_c. The

[6] See, for example, the Chandrasekhar paper of footnote 3.

expression does not apply to a rigid lattice (τ_c very long), for which the line width (in angular frequency units) is δ. The criterion for narrowing is that $\tau_c < 1/\delta$, where δ is the angular frequency magnitude of a diagonal term in the spin Hamiltonian.

Off-diagonal random perturbations contribute to spin-lattice relaxation, as we have already illustrated in Sec. 5-2. Under conditions of extreme narrowing $\tau_c \ll 1/\delta$, $1/T_1$ can contribute a term comparable to $1/T_2$ of (5-33) to the total line width because the finite spin state lifetime T_1 broadens energy levels in accordance with $T_1 \Delta E \approx \hbar$. We also discuss this in Chapter 7. Even including this effect, (5-33) still has order-of-magnitude validity as an expression for the narrow width.

If the molecular tumbling is very rapid, corresponding to a τ_c value much less than $1/\delta$, the averaging of the spherical-harmonic coefficients in the Hamiltonian (5-4) will be nearly complete. Rapid tumbling of the complex in effect renders the symmetry spherical by averaging away anisotropic g-factor and anisotropic hyperfine effects. The resonance lines are then located by the very simple Hamiltonian

$$\mathscr{H}^0 = g\beta H_0 S_z + a\mathbf{I}\cdot\mathbf{S} \tag{5-35}$$

assumed for the examples of Fig. 4-2.

This situation is frequently encountered in the paramagnetic resonances of the organic free radicals, molecules such as those mentioned in Sec. 4-3, that are stable even though they have unsatisfied chemical valences. These molecules are paramagnetic because they possess an odd number of electrons (except for certain of them, biradicals, having two unpaired electrons that may be located in different parts of the same molecule, and except for molecules that are readily excited into triplet states). The study of these free-radical molecules has been exceptionally fruitful for theoretical chemistry, especially when the technique of dissolving the molecule in a liquid solvent is used to "tumble away" the anisotropic hyperfine couplings. Anisotropic g values are also tumbled away, but because these organic molecules normally possess very small spin-orbit coupling, principal values of the g tensor are all very near $g_e = 2.0023$, and so, therefore, are the isotropic averages. A typical value is $g = 2.0037$. In this sense, the electrons of the organic radicals have spins that are among the "most free in captivity." Figure 5-3 shows the first of these well-resolved hyperfine splittings observed for such a molecule in a liquid.[7] Studies of the same

[7] G. E. Pake, J. Townsend, and S. I. Weissman, *Phys. Rev.*, **85**, 682 (1952).

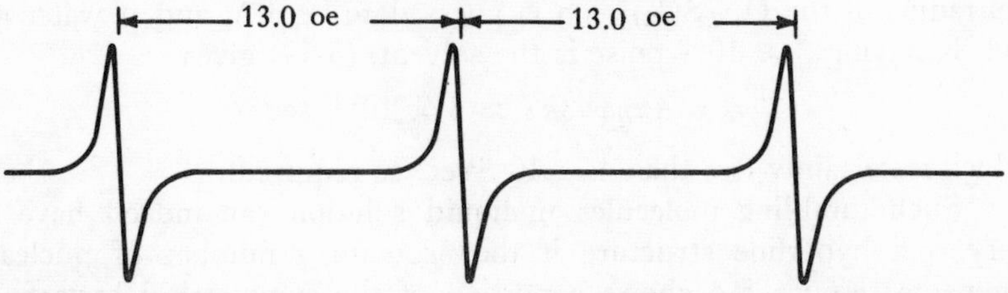

Fig. 5-3 Paramagnetic resonance of $ON(SO_3)_2^{=}$ ions in 0.01 *M* aqueous solution, observed at 10 kMc sec^{-1}. The 13-oersted splitting between adjacent lines arises from hyperfine interaction with the N^{14} nucleus $(2I+1 = 3)$. $T = 300°K$.

molecule-ion in solid solutions have shown an anisotropic hyperfine coupling comparable to the isotropic coupling responsible for the liquid spectrum in Fig. 5-3.

As an example, we can check to see whether the criterion $\tau_c \ll 1/\delta$ is met. The anisotropic splitting is comparable[8] to the isotropic splitting of 13 oersteds and corresponds, for a g near 2, to 36 Mc sec^{-1}, or to $\delta = 2.3 \times 10^8$ sec^{-1}; then $1/\delta = 4 \times 10^{-9}$ sec. If the equivalent spheri-

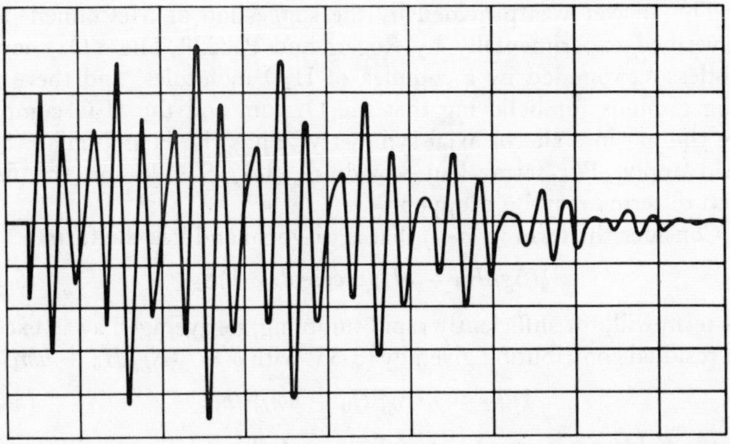

Fig. 5-4 Partial spectrum[9] of Wurster's blue ion $[(CH_3)_2N(C_6H_4)N(CH_3)_2]^+$ in 6×10^{-4} *M* aqueous solution at 20°C. The complete pattern of lines is symmetrical and arises from hyperfine interaction of the sixteen hydrogen nuclei with the unpaired electron spin. The horizontal magnetic field scale is 7 oersteds per division.

[8] S. I. Weissman and D. Banfill, *J. Am. Chem. Soc.*, **75**, 2534 (1953).
[9] K. H. Hausser, *Z. Naturforsch.*, **14a**, 425 (1959).

cal radius of the $ON(SO_3)^=$ ion is guessed to be 3 A, and if water at 300°K having $\eta \approx 10^{-2}$ poise is the solvent, (5-14) gives

$$\tau_c = 4\pi\eta a^3/3kT \approx 3 \times 10^{-11} \text{ sec}$$

which is certainly less than 4×10^{-9} sec, as required.

Such tumbling molecules in liquid solution can indeed have a very rich hyperfine structure if they contain a number of nuclear moments. Figure 5-4 shows a portion of the symmetrical hyperfine structure arising at 20°C from the sixteen hydrogen nuclei of Wurster's blue ion $[(CH_3)_2N(C_6H_4)N(CH_3)_2]^+$, in an aqueous solution of the perchlorate.[9] In methanol at lower temperatures, even greater resolution is achieved, showing splittings from the nitrogen nuclei.

Another illustration of correlation spectrum effects is provided by VO^{++} ion in aqueous solution. Figure 5-5 presents the resonance observed at about 10,000 Mc sec^{-1}. The presence of eight lines is in accordance with the nuclear spin of V^{51}, $I = \frac{7}{2}$. However, there is a puzzling feature, namely, the variation of line width from line to line of the spectrum. It is also remarkable that the width variation lacks symmetry with respect to the center of the pattern. Why should a line off the center of the spectrum be the sharpest?

The answer was provided by the suggestion of McConnell[2] and was verified experimentally by Rogers and Pake.[10] The VO^{++} ion is doubtless surrounded by a complex of H_2O molecules, and there are strong grounds for believing that the O atom and the H_2O complex place the ion in a site of axial symmetry. Thus the Hamiltonian (5-4) should apply. For tetravalent vanadium, $3d^1$, $S = \frac{1}{2}$, and the fine-structure terms may be dropped.

Consider the term in (5-4) that is diagonal and has the form

$$\tfrac{1}{3}(\Delta g\beta H_0 + bI_z)(3\cos^2\theta - 1)S_z \tag{5-36}$$

This term will, for sufficiently rapid tumbling, be averaged away except for a residual contribution given by (5-33) with $\delta = \frac{1}{3}(\Delta g\beta H_0 + bm_1)/\hbar$:

$$1/T_2 \approx \tau_c(\Delta g\beta H_0 + bm_I)^2/\hbar^2 \tag{5-37}$$

In large fields the isotropic coupling is $a\mathbf{I}\cdot\mathbf{S} \rightarrow aI_zS_z$. It thus splits the resonance into $2I + 1$ lines, and the expression (5-37) predicts a different width contribution in general for each hyperfine line. The minimum width from (5-36) should occur for that m_I which most nearly makes the bracket zero. Of course $\Delta g = g_\parallel - g_\perp$ and $b = A_\parallel - A_\perp$ are fixed by the nature of the VO^{++} complex. However, the

[10] R. N. Rogers and G. E. Pake, *J. Chem. Phys.*, **33,** 1107 (1960).

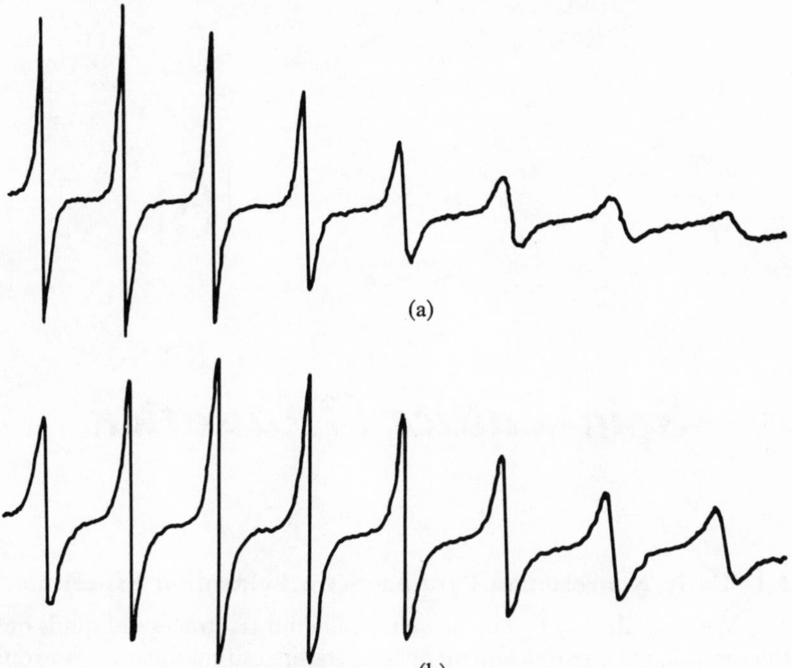

Fig. 5-5 Hyperfine splitting of the paramagnetic resonance of VO^{++} ion in aqueous solution[8]: (a) 24.3 kMc sec^{-1}, (b) 9.25 kMc sec^{-1}. The concentration in VO^{++} is 0.05 *F*. There are about 120 oersteds between adjacent resonance lines.

external field can be varied and, if (5-37) describes the situation, one should be able to shift the point of narrowest width from one line to another within the pattern by observing the resonance in higher or lower fields. This is exactly what is demonstrated by Fig. 5-5.

Again we must keep the record straight by reiterating that T_1 processes arising from off-diagonal terms of (5-4) may also contribute to the total observed line width if τ_c has the proper magnitude. One of these terms has the same dependence upon $(\Delta g\beta H_0 + bI_z)$ as does (5-36). The effect of all terms was taken into account in the work of Ref. 9. General theoretical discussion of the many interactions that may influence the magnetic resonance in liquids and how they are to be taken into account is given by Kivelson.[11]

[11] D. Kivelson, *J. Chem. Phys.*, **27,** 1087 (1957); **33,** 1094 (1960).

[6]

Spin-Lattice Relaxation

6-1 Early Nonresonant Paramagnetic Relaxation Experiments

We have already had occasion to see in our treatment of liquids how the tumbling of a paramagnetic microcystallite can modulate anisotropic interactions and thus provide a spin-lattice relaxation mechanism. In that example, energy of spin orientation is transformed to energy of lattice motion. This chapter examines paramagnetic relaxation more generally, discussing several relaxation mechanisms for solids.

Study of spin-lattice relaxation in solids has a longer history than magnetic resonance. The technique of achieving low temperatures by adiabatic demagnetization quite early focused attention on the tightness of coupling between spin and lattice degrees of freedom. Of course, the time required for the spin system and lattice to come to equilibrium with one another is a very practical matter in such cooling experiments. In addition, these so-called spin-lattice relaxation times are measurable properties of paramagnetic materials, and spin-lattice relaxation constitutes a physical phenomenon of interest in its own right.

The earliest experiments to investigate the coupling between spins and the lattice were nonresonant radiofrequency absorption and dispersion measurements pioneered by Gorter in the mid 1930s.[1,2]

[1] A summary of the nonresonance studies is provided by C. J. Gorter, "Paramagnetic Relaxation," Elsevier, Amsterdam, 1947.

[2] A. H. Cooke, *Repts. Progr. in Phys.*, **13,** 276 (1950), surveys theory and some experimental work for nonresonant paramagnetic relaxation.

Most present-day students find these nonresonance experiments conceptually more difficult to understand than the resonance investigations. We shall make an effort here to tie as closely as possible the theoretical structure developed for resonance experiments to the nonresonance dispersion and absorption investigations.

Because microwave techniques were in 1935 far from their present state of development, Gorter and his co-workers had to content themselves with radiofrequency magnetic fields as a means for coupling energy to the spin system of a paramagnetic crystal. Heating the spin system in turn transfers energy to the lattice. This heating effect was observed by monitoring the temperature of the sample while it was otherwise thermally isolated. Even though the absorption is nonresonant the result (2-41) gives generally for any imaginary susceptibility the power absorbed:[3]

$$A = 2\omega\chi'' H_1^2 \qquad (\text{ergs cm}^{-3}\,\text{sec}^{-1}) \tag{6-1}$$

If the heat capacity of the sample is known, the rise in temperature determines the amount of energy given to the sample via (6-1) during the time of heating. The Kronig-Kramers relations (2-59) enable one to find, from the frequency dependence of the χ'' measured in this way, the frequency variation of χ'. Another method used in the Dutch low-frequency experiments was to investigate relaxation phenomena by a heterodyne beat technique, which detects $\chi'(\nu)$ through the change in frequency of circuit resonance when the paramagnetic sample is inserted into a coil that is the inductance of the *LC* circuit.

From the nature of this early experimental approach it is not surprising that the theoretical analysis, by Casimir and Du Pré[4] and Debye,[5] was from a thermodynamic point of view. Before we obtain their results from the phenomenological equations, it is useful to sketch the thermodynamic treatment. Suppose that the spins are in equilibrium with each other even though they may not be so with the lattice; in other words, assume we can define a spin temperature T_S which may differ from the lattice temperature T_L. Further, assume that heat flows from the spins to the lattice at a rate proportional to the temperature difference, much as for macroscopic heat flow through a slab with its

[3] Our use of H_1 as the half-amplitude of the oscillating field is dictated by resonance considerations. The literature of nonresonant studies usually employs the full amplitude in equations such as (6-1).

[4] H. B. G. Casimir and F. K. Du Pré, *Physica*, **5**, 507 (1938).

[5] P. Debye, *Phys. Z.*, **39**, 616 (1938).

two parallel faces at different temperatures:

$$dQ/dt = \alpha\,\Delta T \tag{6-2}$$

If one now applies a constant field $\mathbf{H}_0$, plus a parallel oscillating field, so that

$$H = H_0 + he^{i\omega t} \tag{6-3}$$

the energy of the spins, which depends upon their magnetization and upon the magnitude of **H**, will in general oscillate. Oscillations of the spin temperature with the field oscillations will be reduced by the tightness of coupling of the spins to the lattice, i.e., the larger α in (6-2) the smaller will be the oscillations in spin temperature. We have seen (Sec. 1-2) that the magnetization M is a function of H/T_S. Therefore we can take M as a measure of the spin temperature in a given H. Letting

$$\begin{aligned} \Delta T &= (\theta' - i\theta'')e^{i\omega t} \\ M &= M_0 + (\sigma' - i\sigma'')e^{i\omega t} \end{aligned} \tag{6-4}$$

one can eliminate the change in temperature from the first law of thermodynamics and (6-2) to find[2]

$$\Delta M/\Delta H = (\sigma' - i\sigma'')/h = \chi' - i\chi'' \tag{6-5}$$

as

$$\begin{aligned} \chi' &= (\chi_T - \chi_S)/(1 + \omega^2\tau^2) + \chi_S \\ \chi'' &= (\chi_T - \chi_S)\omega\tau/(1 + \omega^2\tau^2) \end{aligned} \tag{6-6}$$

where $\tau = C_H/\alpha$ is the spin-lattice relaxation time. The spin-system specific heat in constant field is $C_H = (\partial U/\partial T)_H$, and $\chi_T = (\partial M/\partial H)_T$ and $\chi_S = (\partial M/\partial H)_S$ are the isothermal and adiabatic susceptibilities, respectively. Use of an imaginary temperature component in (6-4) involves nothing daring in a thermodynamic sense; it is merely the usual method for describing an out-of-phase component of a physical response resulting from a sinusoidal stimulus. The shape of the susceptibility curves from (6-6) is often called the Debye form, just as we use the term Lorentz form for (2-58) and (2-42).

There is an extensive literature on the thermodynamical quantities important in the analysis of spin-lattice relaxation, much of which can be found from the references in the reviews by Gorter[1] and Cooke[2] and in these reviews themselves. For a substance that obeys the Curie law, $M = \chi_0 H$, with $\chi_0 = C/T$, we readily see that

$$\chi_T = (\partial M/\partial H)_T = \chi_0 \tag{6-7}$$

From the discussion by Cooke[2] one can deduce

$$\chi_S = \chi_T H_{\text{int}}^2/(H_0^2 + H_{\text{int}}^2) \tag{6-8}$$

where H_{int} is a measure of rms internal fields within the paramagnetic material. For example, we know that dipolar fields contribute an amount of order βr^{-3} to H_{int}.

We have thus far merely sketched the derivation of the thermodynamic results (6-6). Let us now see whether we can obtain these same results from our phenomenological equations, and at the same time establish the relationship between τ and T_1 or T_2. Suppose the applied magnetic fields are indeed only

$$H_z = H_0 + he^{i\omega t} \tag{6-9}$$

We wish to find the M_z response to the applied oscillating field along z using the phenomenological equation (2-16). Furthermore, since H_0 values are often chosen which are not large compared to internal fields, we should use the form (2-17), in which the magnetization relaxes toward the instantaneous field. Because we have only z components, we seem at first to need only the z equation:

$$dM_z/dt = \gamma(\mathbf{M} \times \mathbf{H})_z + [\chi_0(H_0 + he^{i\omega t}) - M_z]/T_1 \tag{6-10}$$

Letting $M_z = M_0 + \sigma e^{i\omega t}$ as in (6-4), we obtain from (6-10), since H has no x or y components,

$$i\omega\sigma = (1/T_1)(\chi_0 h - \sigma) \tag{6-11}$$

which is quickly solved for $\chi' - i\chi'' = (\sigma' - i\sigma'')/h$ to give

$$\begin{aligned} \chi' &= \chi_0/(1 + \omega^2 T_1^2) \\ \chi'' &= \chi_0 \omega T_1/(1 + \omega^2 T_1^2) \end{aligned} \tag{6-12}$$

Comparison with (6-6) shows that there is not complete agreement with the thermodynamic result. But we note from (6-7) and (6-8) that the thermodynamic form (6-6) approaches (6-12) if $H_0^2 \gg H_{\text{int}}^2$. This conclusion is not surprising, for H_{int}^2 corresponds to local fields which, in our Bloch phenomenological equations, were related to T_2 processes. Our use of (6-10) alone allowed no opportunity for T_2 to enter. Furthermore, the assumption that M_z relaxes toward $\chi_0(H_0 + he^{i\omega t})$ is tantamount to the assumption that the instantaneous field at each spin is precisely along z.

Let us try to include an internal field $\mathbf{H}_{\text{int}}$. Those components of $\mathbf{H}_{\text{int}}$ along $\mathbf{H}_0$ simply have the effect of adding to or subtracting from $\mathbf{H}_0$, which, since $\mathbf{H}_0$ does not enter explicitly into our result (6-12), is

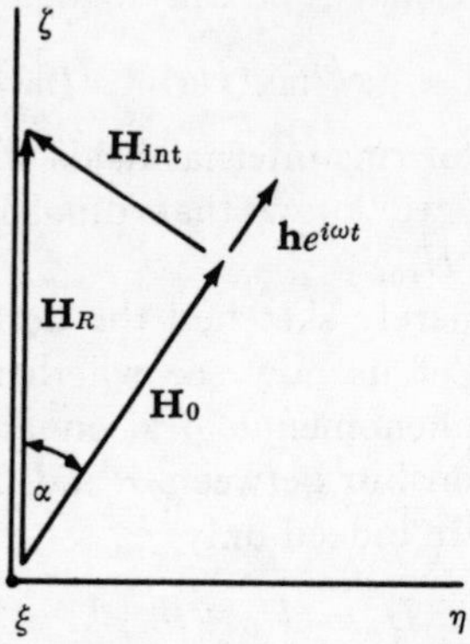

Fig. 6-1 Definition of magnetic field directions at the site of a paramagnetic ion which experiences an external field $\mathbf{H}_0$ and an internal local field $\mathbf{H}_{\text{int}}$ having a different direction from $\mathbf{H}_0$, here taken perpendicular to it.

not the essential effect of $\mathbf{H}_{\text{int}}$. To examine the effect of $\mathbf{H}_{\text{int}}$ perpendicular to $\mathbf{H}_0$, we refer to the diagram of Fig. 6-1. The total magnetic field before application of $\mathbf{h}e^{i\omega t}$ parallel to $\mathbf{H}_0$ is $\mathbf{H}_R = \mathbf{H}_0 + \mathbf{H}_{\text{int}}$, defining the ζ direction. We anticipate that the magnetization will experience longitudinal relaxation at a rate $1/T_1$ toward the ζ direction and that components perpendicular to H_R will undergo transverse relaxation and decay at a rate $1/T_2$. The effect of applying a small oscillating field $\mathbf{h}e^{i\omega t}$ along the $\mathbf{H}_0$ direction will be to introduce sinusoidally varying components into the total magnetization, so that

$$\begin{aligned} M_\zeta &= \chi_0 H_\zeta + \sigma_\zeta e^{i\omega t} \\ &= \chi_0(H_0 \cos\alpha + H_{\text{int}} \sin\alpha) + \sigma_\zeta e^{i\omega t} \\ M_\xi &= \sigma_\xi e^{i\omega t} \\ M_\eta &= \sigma_\eta e^{i\omega t} \end{aligned} \tag{6-13}$$

The time-varying part of total magnetization along the direction of $\mathbf{h}$ is, since $M_z = M_\zeta \cos\alpha + M_\eta \sin\alpha$,

$$\sigma e^{i\omega t} = (\sigma_\zeta \cos\alpha + \sigma_\eta \sin\alpha)e^{i\omega t} \tag{6-14}$$

Since we shall let $|\mathbf{H}_0|$ possibly be as small as $|\mathbf{H}_{\text{int}}|$, or even smaller, it is again necessary to take the form (2-17) in which T_1 relaxation is toward the magnetization corresponding to the instantaneous ζ component of magnetic field. The equation corresponding to (6-10), which now describes longitudinal relaxation of ζ components, is

$$dM_\zeta/dt = \gamma(\mathbf{M} \times \mathbf{H})_\zeta + [\chi_0(H_\zeta + h \cos \alpha \, e^{i\omega t}) - M_\zeta]/T_1 \quad (6\text{-}15)$$

There is an η component of $\mathbf{h}e^{i\omega t}$, but the only ξ component of $\mathbf{M}$ is a small one introduced by $\mathbf{h}e^{i\omega t}$; therefore the cross-product term is of second order in small quantities and may be dropped. Equation (6-15) becomes

$$i\omega\sigma_\zeta = (1/T_1)(\chi_0 h \cos \alpha - \sigma_\zeta) \quad (6\text{-}16)$$

which is readily solved as was (6-11) to give

$$\begin{aligned}\sigma_\zeta &= \sigma_\zeta' - i\sigma_\zeta'' \\ &= \chi_0 h \cos \alpha \left(\frac{1}{1 + \omega^2 T_1{}^2} - \frac{i\omega T_1}{1 + \omega^2 T_1{}^2}\right)\end{aligned} \quad (6\text{-}17)$$

By (6-14), this contributes to the total σ, before η components of σ are considered, as follows:

$$\sigma = \chi_0 h \cos^2 \alpha \left(\frac{1}{1 + \omega^2 T_1{}^2} - \frac{i\omega T_1}{1 + \omega^2 T_1{}^2}\right) + \sigma_\eta \sin \alpha \quad (6\text{-}18)$$

Even before calculating the σ_η contribution, we observe from (6-18) that the contribution of ζ magnetization to $\chi = \sigma/h$ is

$$\begin{aligned}(\chi')_\zeta &= \chi_0 \cos^2 \alpha/(1 + \omega^2 T_1{}^2) \\ (\chi'')_\zeta &= \chi_0 \cos^2 \alpha \, \omega T_1/(1 + \omega^2 T_1{}^2)\end{aligned} \quad (6\text{-}19)$$

Now Fig. 6-1 defines $\cos^2 \alpha = H_0{}^2/(H_0{}^2 + H^2_{\text{int}})$, permitting us to re-express the thermodynamic results (6-7) and (6-8) as

$$\begin{aligned}\chi_0 \cos^2 \alpha &= \chi_T - \chi_S \\ \chi_0 \sin^2 \alpha &= \chi_S\end{aligned} \quad (6\text{-}20)$$

We see that (6-19) and (6-20) have already provided the thermodynamic result (6-6), except for the χ_S term in χ'.

The η components of magnetization will next be shown to provide not only the χ_S term in the expression (6-6) for χ', but also the spin-spin absorption from which the early nonresonant experiments determined what we now call T_2. To find σ_η, we examine the coupled phenomenological equations for M_ξ and M_η as they undergo transverse relaxation.

$$\begin{aligned}dM_\xi/dt &= \gamma(\mathbf{H} \times \mathbf{M})_\xi - M_\xi/T_2 \\ dM_\eta/dt &= \gamma(\mathbf{H} \times \mathbf{M})_\eta - M_\eta/T_2\end{aligned} \quad (6\text{-}21)$$

Keeping only terms to first order in the small quantities σ and h, substitution of $M_\xi = \sigma_\xi e^{i\omega t}$ and $M_\eta = \sigma_\eta e^{i\omega t}$ into (6-21) and removing the common factor $e^{i\omega t}$ leads to

$$\begin{aligned} (1 + i\omega T_2)\sigma_\xi &= \gamma T_2 H_R(\chi_0 h \sin\alpha - \sigma_\eta) \\ (1 + i\omega T_2)\sigma_\eta &= \gamma T_2 H_R \sigma_\xi \end{aligned} \tag{6-22}$$

We define $\epsilon = \gamma T_2 H_R$ and solve for σ_η by eliminating σ_ξ:

$$\sigma_\eta = \chi_0 h \sin\alpha\, \epsilon^2/[(1 + i\omega T_2)^2 + \epsilon^2] \tag{6-23}$$

Finally we can place this result in (6-18) to obtain the complete complex magnetization $\sigma = (\chi' - i\chi'')h$. The complete susceptibility expressions are obtained by breaking (6-23) into its real and imaginary parts, which are added to (6-19):

$$\chi' = \chi_0 \cos^2\alpha \frac{1}{1 + \omega^2 T_1^2} + \chi_0 \sin^2\alpha \frac{\epsilon^2(1 + \epsilon^2 - \omega^2 T_2^2)}{(1 + \epsilon^2 - \omega^2 T_2^2)^2 + 4\omega^2 T_2^2} \tag{6-24}$$

$$\chi'' = \chi_0 \cos^2\alpha \frac{\omega T_1}{1 + \omega^2 T_1^2} + \chi_0 \sin^2\alpha \frac{2\omega T_2 \epsilon^2}{(1 + \epsilon^2 - \omega^2 T_2^2)^2 + 4\omega^2 T_2^2}$$

First, we consider χ' as observed in the low-frequency limit. Since T_2 for nondilute paramagnetics is perhaps 10^{-9} or 10^{-10} sec, which is often shorter than T_1 (especially at low temperatures), the early nonresonant experimental frequencies were often capable of $\omega T_1 > 1$ but kept $\omega T_2 < 1$. For $\omega T_2 < 1$, (6-24) reduces to a χ' of the form

$$\chi' = \chi_0 \cos^2\alpha/(1 + \omega^2 T_1^2) + \chi_0 \sin^2\alpha\, \epsilon^2/(1 + \epsilon^2) \qquad (\omega T_2 < 1) \tag{6-25}$$

With (6-20), this agrees with the thermodynamic result (6-6) if the factor $\epsilon^2/(1 + \epsilon^2)$ is unity. For $H_0 > 1/\gamma T_2$, such is the case. Note that, as H_0 becomes small, $\epsilon = \gamma T_2 H_R$ approaches something near unity, as there is an approximate equality between $(\gamma T_2)^{-1}$ and H_{int}. The absence of a precise relation between these two quantities is the weakest point of this entire discussion. In view of such imprecision, we must expect to give or take factors of 2 or so in comparisons with the thermodynamic treatment. To this accuracy, the phenomenological equation (2-17) does reproduce the χ' of Casimir and Du Pré's analysis.

Within the condition $\omega T_2 \ll 1$, χ'' in (6-24) does not differ from (6-19), which already agreed with the thermodynamic result (6-6).

However, the early nonresonant experiments could approach from the low-frequency side the condition $\omega T_2 \lesssim 1$. For ωT_2 appreciable but still less than unity, the second χ'' term in (6-24) leads to an additional absorption. Using $A = \frac{1}{2}\omega h^2 \chi''$ [the appropriate form of (6-1) with $2H_1 = h$], we find that when $\epsilon = 1$, the additional absorption is

$$A = \tfrac{1}{4}\omega^2 T_2 \chi_S h^2 \tag{6-26}$$

This is to be compared with the expression [Eq. (11) of Cooke[2]] used in the nonresonant experiments to describe the spin-spin absorption:

$$A = \tfrac{1}{2}\omega^2 \tau_S \chi_S h^2 \tag{6-27}$$

In addition to the inaccuracy inherent in our result because H_{int} is not precisely defined, there is of course the complicated dependence of our spin-spin relaxation term on $\epsilon = \gamma T_2 H_R$ and upon ωT_2 if it increases

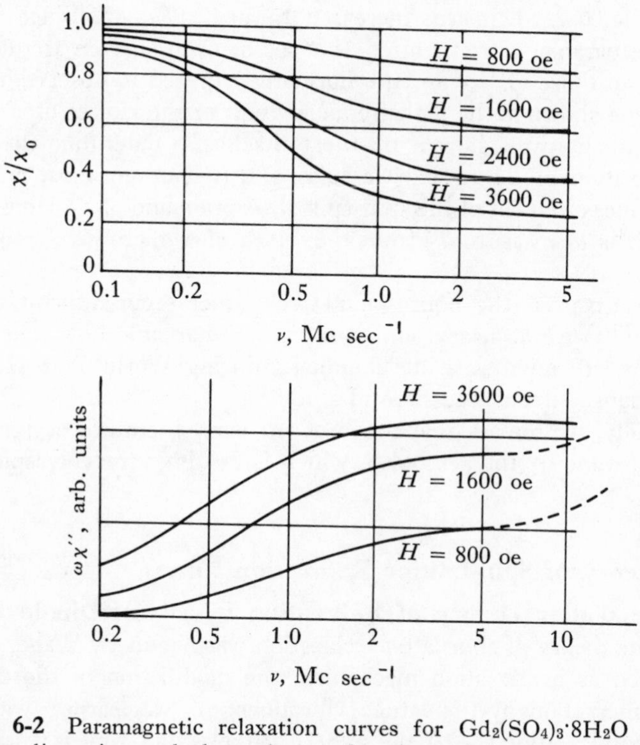

Fig. 6-2 Paramagnetic relaxation curves for $Gd_2(SO_4)_3 \cdot 8H_2O$ at 77°K, showing dispersion and absorption as functions of frequency for indicated values of external parallel fields. The dashed curves at higher frequencies show the onset of spin-spin absorption.

toward unity. For the conditions of the early Dutch experiments, however, it is clear from (6-24), (6-26), and (6-27) that we may associate the spin-spin time τ_s with our T_2.

We now turn to comparison of experimental results with the foregoing formulas developed for their analysis. Figure 6-2 shows experimental data[1] for paramagnetic relaxation in $Gd_2(SO_4)_3 \cdot 8H_2O$ at 77°K (in parallel $\mathbf{H}_0$ and $\mathbf{h}$ fields, of course). These particular data do not extend above 10 Mc sec^{-1}. From (6-6) and the form of the curves we conclude that $T_1 = 5 \times 10^{-7}$ sec at 2400 oersteds. The resonant absorption line at g near 2 (Gd^{3+} is an S-state ion and should have g near the spin-only value) would occur in a perpendicular field of 2400 oersteds at a frequency near 6700 Mc sec^{-1}. Thus the perpendicular-field main-resonance line occurs at frequencies well out along the frequency axis of Fig. 6-2.

The spin-spin absorption will be added to the spin-lattice absorption of Fig. 6-2 when ω is increased toward $\omega T_2 \to 1$. Since T_2 for nondilute paramagnetics is often 10^{-9} sec or even shorter, frequencies higher than those of Fig. 6-2 are normally required to observe it. The dashed line shown at the high-frequency end of the curves of Fig. 6-2 suggests qualitatively how it manifests itself. To determine the spin-spin relaxation time from such a curve and (6-27), one must make an absolute measurement of the spin-spin absorption and of χ_s. How much simpler it is to measure T_2 from the width of a microwave-frequency resonance!

In retrospect, the nonresonant techniques seem difficult to use with quantitative accuracy, and it is truly remarkable how much was learned before microwave developments during World War II made the resonance effects accessible to study.

Finally, we remark that much of the early literature designates a relaxation time by the symbol ρ, which is 2π times the corresponding T_1 or T_2.

6-2 Theory of Spin-Lattice Relaxation Times

The Waller Theory of Relaxation by Dipole-Dipole Coupling. The theory of spin-lattice relaxation was begun by Waller,[6] who considered as a relaxation mechanism the modulation of the dipole-dipole interaction by the lattice vibrations. As we learned with the fundamental relation (2-70), the spin-lattice relaxation time is essentially the reciprocal of the probability per unit time that a spin will make an

[6] I. Waller, *Z. Physik*, **79**, 370 (1932).

emissive transition under the perturbing influence of the relaxing mechanism.

$$1/T_1 \sim W \tag{6-28}$$

Although, for $S = \frac{1}{2}$, W is multiplied by a factor dependent upon temperature and lying between 1 and 2 [see (2-70)], no such general and precise statement can be made for higher S, and we therefore use the order-of-magnitude relation (6-28).

We can think of the mechanism Waller used as follows: When the lattice vibrates, the interionic distances are modulated at the frequency of the lattice vibration. An oscillatory magnetic-field component thus arises from the motion of the neighboring magnetic dipoles, and those lattice vibrations with frequency at the Larmor frequency $h\nu = g\beta H_0$ have a certain probability per unit time W for flipping a moment from "up" to "down." A more proper picture, however, must also allow for the quantum nature of the lattice oscillators. We can thus picture the process as in Fig. 6-3, which schematically describes the flip of a spin from "up" (energy $\frac{1}{2}g\beta H_0$) to "down" (energy $-\frac{1}{2}g\beta H_0$) with the accompanying emission or creation of a phonon having $h\nu = g\beta H_0$. This single phonon process is called a *direct process*.

The matrix element for the transition probability is determined from the dipole interaction (4-2), which clearly has matrix elements of such operators as $S_{-j}S_{zk}$ that will take spin j from "up" to "down." The part of the dipolar interaction that will create the phonon arises from the $1/r^3$ factor in each term of (4-2). Thus, if the lattice vibrates

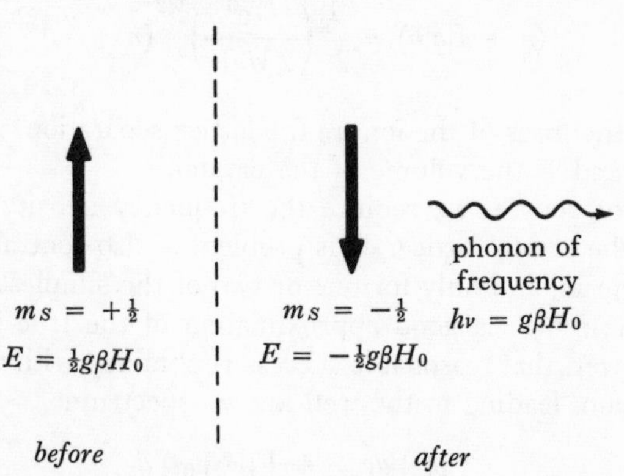

Fig. 6-3 Schematic illustration of spin-lattice relaxation by the direct process. There may, of course, be other phonons of frequency ν present. Only the newly created phonon is shown.

so that a particular ion is displaced $\mathbf{q}$ from its equilibrium position, we can write, for long wavelengths,

$$r^{-3} = (r^{-3})_0 + \mathbf{\Delta r} \cdot (\mathbf{grad}\, r^{-3})_0 \tag{6-29}$$

in which $\mathbf{\Delta r} \approx (2\pi r_0/\lambda)\mathbf{q}$ is the relative change in position between two interacting dipoles as they participate in an elastic wave of wavelength λ.

To obtain an order-of-magnitude expression for the relaxation time, we use the interaction

$$V_1 = \beta^2 S_{-j} S_{kz} \left[\frac{\partial}{\partial r}\left(\frac{1}{r^3}\right)\right]_{r=r_0} \left(\frac{2\pi r_0}{\lambda}\right) q \tag{6-30}$$

This neglects numerous geometrical factors of order unity, such as the angular dependence in (4-2) and the polarization factors arising from the vector nature of q. There are also terms in (4-2) that flip two spins and create correspondingly a phonon of twice the energy. However (6-30) is adequate to exemplify the theory. If we let m_j be the magnetic quantum number before the spin flips, the order of magnitude of the transition probability becomes

$$1/T_1 \approx W = \hbar^{-2} |(m - 1, n + 1 | V | m,n)|^2 \rho(\nu) \tag{6-31}$$

The spin matrix element is of order unity. The matrix element of q is, from harmonic oscillator theory,

$$(n + 1 | q | n) = \frac{1}{2\pi}\left(\frac{h r_0^3}{2M\nu V}\right)^{1/2} (n + 1)^{1/2} \tag{6-32}$$

Here M is the mass of the ion, r_0 the lattice separation, ν the oscillator frequency, and V the volume of the crystal.

Next, of course, we require the frequency density of oscillation modes for the crystal lattice. This problem is also central to the theory of specific heats, and only for one or two of the simplest solid types is there available even a good approximation of the true spectrum. We know, however, that reasonable success is obtained with the continuum approximation, leading to the well-known spectrum

$$\rho(\nu)\, d\nu = 4\pi V (\nu^2/v_0^3)\, d\nu \tag{6-33}$$

Here $\rho(\nu)$ is the number of oscillation modes of a particular polarization between ν and $\nu + d\nu$, and v_0 is the velocity of sound in the crystal. This spectrum, as sketched in Fig. 6-4, is cut off at a maximum frequency

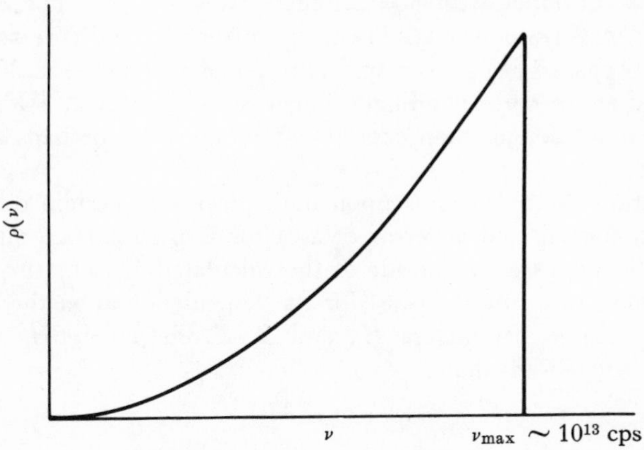

Fig. 6-4 Continuum approximation to the acoustic vibration spectrum (6-33) of a crystal. The typical paramagnetic resonance frequency of 10^{10} cps is almost at the origin of this plot.

given by the requirement that the total number of modes of a particular polarization is N, the number of atoms in the crystal:

$$\nu_{\max} = v_0(3N/4\pi V)^{1/3} = k\theta_D/h \tag{6-34}$$

The Debye temperature of specific-heat theory is denoted θ_D. Representative θ_D values are a few hundred degrees Kelvin, corresponding to a representative $\nu_{\max}$ of $\sim 10^{13}$ cps.

Using the foregoing expressions in (6-31) and multiplying by 3 for the possible polarization directions we obtain

$$1/T_1 \approx \hbar^{-2}(3\beta^2/r_0^4)^2(r_0^2/\lambda^2)(hr_0^3/2M\nu)(12\pi\nu^2/v_0^3)(n+1) \tag{6-35}$$

Letting the mass density be $\rho \cong M/r_0^3$ and $\lambda = v_0/\nu$, and employing for lattice temperature T the average

$$\overline{n+1} = e^{h\nu/kT}/(e^{h\nu/kT} - 1) \tag{6-36}$$

provides the result

$$1/T_1 \approx (108\pi^2/\hbar)(\beta^2/r_0^3)^2(\nu^3/\rho v_0^5)e^{h\nu/kT}/(e^{h\nu/kT} - 1) \tag{6-37}$$

For temperatures larger than $h\nu/k$, which means at typical microwave magnetic frequencies $T \geqslant 5°$K, (6-37) can be simplified by expanding the exponentials to give

$$1/T_1 \approx (54\pi\nu^2/\hbar^2\rho v_0^5)(\beta^2/r_0^3)^2kT \tag{6-38}$$

Consider a substance with $\rho = 2\ \text{g cm}^{-3}$, $v_0 = 2 \times 10^5\ \text{cm sec}^{-1}$, and $r_0{}^3 = 10^{-22}\ \text{cm}^3$ ($r_0 = 4.6$ A). Then, in a magnetic field corresponding to $\nu = 10^{10}$ cps, (6-38) gives a typical order of magnitude at 300°K as $T_1 \sim 1$ sec and a correspondingly longer $T_1 \sim 100$ sec at 4°K. These times are much longer than experimental values, by perhaps a factor of 10^8.

Equation (6-38) depends upon high powers of certain quantities such as r_0 and v_0, and an error of a factor 2 or so in such quantities greatly influences the magnitude of the calculated T_1. For this reason it is common to examine (6-38) for its dependence upon the experimentally variable parameters H_0 and T. From $h\nu = g\beta H_0$ we can conclude from (6-38) that

$$1/T_1 \propto H_0{}^2 T \tag{6-39}$$

There are two features to note in the weakness of the direct process. One is, of course, the fact that the acoustic spectrum (Fig. 6-4) is woefully weak at 10^{10} cps. The other is that acoustic waves of this frequency have a long wavelength $\lambda = v_0/\nu$, and the relative displacement of two neighboring dipoles is only the very small fraction $2\pi r_0/\lambda$ of q, which leads to very small modulation of the local magnetic fields.

Waller considered a second process, called *indirect*, in which a higher frequency phonon is inelastically scattered by the flipping spin. Figure 6-5 schematically presents the idea. The indirect or Raman process of Fig. 6-5 is evidently a higher-order process than the direct one, but it may dominate the direct process because it utilizes all the modes of the spectrum in pairs, thus bringing into play the energetic and far more plentiful higher frequency modes up toward the cutoff in Fig. 6-4. Of course, only at high-enough temperatures will these modes be excited, and therefore at very low temperatures the indirect process should be dominated by the direct process.

For the indirect process, Waller finds essentially that

$$\frac{1}{T_1} \approx \frac{163\pi^2}{\rho^2 v_0{}^{10}} \left(\frac{\beta^2}{r_0{}^3}\right)^2 \int_0^{k\theta_D/h} \frac{\nu^6 e^{h\nu/kT}\, d\nu}{(e^{h\nu/kT} - 1)^2} \tag{6-40}$$

The integral of (6-40) occurs, with various powers of ν in the integrand, in all two-phonon relaxation calculations using the Debye spectrum. It can be approximated[7] in two extremes of temperature relative to

[7] J. H. Van Vleck, *Phys. Rev.*, **57**, 426 (1940).

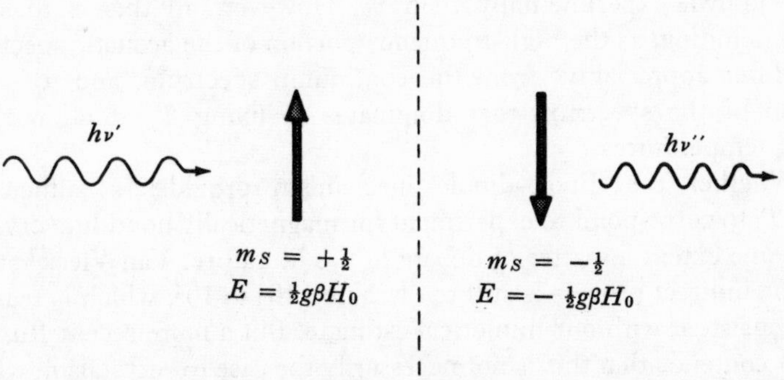

Fig. 6-5 Schematic illustration of spin-lattice relaxation by the indirect process. A phonon of frequency ν' is absorbed and one of frequency ν'' emitted as the electron spin flips (Van Vleck called this a Raman process). For energy conservation we must have $h\nu' + g\beta H_0 = h\nu''$.

the Debye θ_D:

$$\int \nu^n \cong n!(kT/h)^{n+1} \qquad (T \ll \theta_D)$$

$$\cong \left(\frac{k\theta_D}{h}\right)^{n+1} \frac{e^{\theta_D/T}}{(n+1)(e^{\theta_D/T}-1)^2} \qquad (T \gtrsim \theta_D) \qquad (6\text{-}41)$$

In the lower temperature region $T \ll \theta_D$, the result is

$$1/T_1 \approx [163\pi^2(6!)/(\rho^2 v_0^{10})](\beta^2/r_0^3)^2(kT/h)^7 \qquad (6\text{-}42)$$

which predicts that $T_1 \sim 10^7$ sec for 4°K and $T_1 \sim 10^{-2}$ sec for $T = 77$°K, using again $\rho = 2$ g cm^{-3}, $r_0^3 = 10^{-22}$ cm^3, and $v_0 = 2 \times 10^5$ cm sec^{-1}. Room-temperature values are to some extent more simply estimated if (6-34) is used with (6-40) and (6-41) ($T \sim \theta_D$) to eliminate the ratio $(\theta_D/v_0)^7$ in favor of the density of ions: $(N/V)^{7/3}$. One obtains a somewhat shorter T_1 of perhaps 10^{-3} sec at 300°K.

In terms of dependence upon experimental parameters, we see that (6-42) provides

$$1/T_1 \propto H_0^0 T^7 \qquad (T \ll \theta_D) \qquad (6\text{-}43)$$

Of course, the high power of v_0 in (6-42) means that small errors in estimating it can grossly influence the magnitude of a calculated T_1. Actually the velocity of sound enters via the Debye approximation, and v_0 can be replaced through (6-34) by an equal power of the Debye temperature. For many substances, the Debye temperature may be better known experimentally than v_0. However, all this is to some extent deluding, as the high-frequency portion of the acoustic spectrum may differ appreciably[8] from the continuum spectrum, and it is this portion of the spectrum that dominates in fixing T_1 at all but the lowest temperatures.

Whether the dipole-dipole mechanism provides a sufficiently short T_1 to correspond to experiment for magnetically nondilute crystals is to some extent a matter of debate in the literature. Van Vleck[7] states that the indirect process is still too weak by 10^2 to 10^4, which is reasonably consistent with our numerical estimate. But a more recent Russian paper[9] contends that this is not necessarily the case for crystals in which ions of large spin S lie reasonably close to one another.

The Van Vleck Theory of Relaxation by Spin-Orbit Coupling. There are, however, experimental examples of short T_1 values for magnetically dilute crystals. Clearly the Waller mechanism will be inadequate to explain these results. Kronig[10] suggested that lattice vibrations can influence T_1 by modulating the crystalline electric field, which effect is then felt by the spins through spin-orbit coupling. Although Kronig made order-of-magnitude estimates of this effect, Van Vleck in a *tour de force*[11] made numerical calculations of T_1 for Ti^{3+} and Cr^{3+} ions. This classic calculation builds upon an earlier paper in which Van Vleck analyzes the Jahn-Teller effect in clusters of the form $X \cdot 6H_2O$. Van Vleck first studied the normal modes of such a cluster,[11] and then expanded their normal coordinates in terms of the Debye elastic waves of the entire lattice.[7] For titanium alum, $CsTi(SO_4)_2 \cdot 12H_2O$, the levels are split by an axially distorted octahedral field much as shown in our Fig. 3-4. The upper $d\epsilon$ levels (which are split from the ground level by the axial component of electric field) enter into the calculation as intermediate states of the higher-order perturbation. Both the spin-orbit interaction $\lambda \mathbf{L} \cdot \mathbf{S}$ and the orbit-lattice interaction (as determined by the vibrational modulation of the electric splitting of the cluster) are the perturbing interactions. As in the Waller calculation, both direct (one-phonon) and indirect or Raman (two-phonon) processes are considered.

[8] J. de Launay, in Solid State Physics, F. Seitz and D. Turnbull (eds.), Academic Press, New York, 1956, Vol. 2, p. 219.

[9] S. A. Al'tshuler, *Bull. Acad. Sci. USSR*, **20,** 1207 (1956). (This article appears on pp. 1098ff. of the English translation by Columbia Technical Translations, White Plains, N.Y.)

[10] R. deL. Kronig, *Physica*, **6,** 33 (1939).

[11] J. H. Van Vleck, *J. Chem. Phys.*, **7,** 72 (1939).

We present below much-simplified versions of Van Vleck's expressions for the transition probability which we identify with $1/T_1$. Van Vleck incorporates into his discussion the thermodynamic formulas[4] of Casimir and Du Pré, which are appropriate to the analysis of the Dutch nonresonant low-frequency experiments. For our purposes in obtaining the T_1 of the phenomenological equations we require simply the transition probability.

For direct processes, Van Vleck obtains[7]

$$1/T_1 \approx W \approx 10^3 \frac{\lambda^2(ep\overline{r^2}R^{-4})^2 h\nu^5 e^{h\nu/kT}}{\delta^4 \rho v_0^5 (e^{h\nu/kT} - 1)} \tag{6-44}$$

which is an algebraically simplified, order-of-magnitude version of his Eqs. (23), (24), and (25). In (6-44) the following symbols need explanation: p = the electric dipole moment of a water molecule, $\overline{r^2}$ = the mean-square radius of the Ti^{3+} electron cloud, R = the distance between the Ti^{3+} center and the center of the H_2O dipole moment, and δ = the axial field splitting (see Fig. 3-4).

Van Vleck took $R = 2 \times 10^{-8}$ cm, $ep\overline{r^2}R^{-4} = 10^{-12}$ erg, and δ and λ corresponding to 1000 cm^{-1} and 154 cm^{-1}, respectively. In the limit $h\nu/kT \ll 1$, we find that (6-44) predicts

$$1/T_1 \approx 10^3 \lambda^2 (ep\overline{r^2}R^{-4})^2 \nu^4 kT/\delta^4 \rho v_0^5 \tag{6-45}$$

Evidently

$$1/T_1 \sim (\text{const}) H_0^4 T \tag{6-46}$$

At $T = 300$°K, (6-45) gives $T_1 \sim 10^{-2}$ sec, and at 4°K $T_1 \sim 1$ sec. These times are of course too long, but they are shorter than the Waller mechanism gave. And we still have the indirect process, which, from our experience with the Waller calculation, we expect will give considerably shorter T_1 values.

As above, we give an algebraically simplified form for Van Vleck's calculation of relaxation through spin-orbit coupling and inelastic phonon scattering (the Raman or indirect process):

$$\frac{1}{T_1} \approx 10^6 \frac{\lambda^2(ep\overline{r^2}R^{-4})^4 h^2}{\delta^6 \rho^2 v_0^{10}} \int_0^{k\theta_D/h} \frac{\nu^8 e^{h\nu/kT}\, d\nu}{(e^{h\nu/kT} - 1)^2} \tag{6-47}$$

Using (6-41) we can express (6-47) in two temperature regions:

$$\frac{1}{T_1} \approx 10^6 \frac{\lambda^2(ep\overline{r^2}R^{-4})^4 h^2 (8!)}{\delta^6 \rho^2 v_0^{10}} \left(\frac{kT}{h}\right)^9 \qquad (T \ll \theta_D) \tag{6-48}$$

$$\frac{1}{T_1} \approx 10^6 \frac{\lambda^2(ep\overline{r^2}R^{-4})^4 h^2}{\delta^6 \rho^2 v_0^{10} \times 9} \left(\frac{k\theta_D}{h}\right)^9 \qquad (T \gtrsim \theta_D) \qquad (6\text{-}49)$$

Numerically, one can obtain almost any result he wishes with (6-48), which is certainly the applicable form for the helium region. It is possible, for example, to give or take a factor 2 in the velocity of sound, which changes the result by a factor $2^{10} \simeq 10^3$. And there are 16 powers of R. Van Vleck states that his form corresponding to (6-48) leads to a $T_1 \cong 10^3 T^{-9}$. The author estimates, using the parameters we have previously employed in this section, that $T_1 \cong 10T^{-9}$. If this estimate were correct, the 1°K region would be where the indirect process gives way to the direct process with its much weaker rate of T_1 increase as temperature decreases: $T_1 = 10T^{-9}$ gives $T_1 \cong 10$ sec at 1°K and $T_1 \cong 10^{-4}$ sec at 4°K. (The direct process gave 1 sec at 4°K.)

An interesting feature of the high-temperature form (6-49) is that the very large dependence upon the velocity of sound is largely removed because the Debye temperature appears in the numerator to the ninth power; $(\theta_D/v_0)^9$ can be evaluated with reasonable certainty from (6-34), which relates it to the numerical density of paramagnetic ions. Thus we can write

$$\frac{1}{T_1} \approx \frac{10^6 \lambda^2(ep\overline{r^2}R^{-4})^4 h^2}{9\delta^6 \rho^2 v_0} \left(\frac{3N}{4\pi V}\right)^3 \qquad (T \gtrsim \theta_D) \qquad (6\text{-}50)$$

This is still sensitive to errors in R, but Van Vleck evaluates $ep\overline{r^2}R^{-4} \cong 10^{-12}$ erg from the static crystal splitting, thus helping avoid a piling of errors in R, $\overline{r^2}$, etc. For $CsTi(SO_4)_2 \cdot 12H_2O$, N/V is about 2×10^{21} cm^{-3}. Thus the limiting high-temperature value of T_1 is temperature-independent and given by (6-50) as $T_1 = 10^{-10}$ sec. This time is, if anything, perhaps an order of magnitude too short to compare well with experimental numbers at room temperature for substances with θ_D near $T = 300$°K. Nonetheless, it is refreshing indeed to encounter, for the first time in this discussion, a situation in which the proposed relaxation mechanism seems to be more than adequately potent.

Although the numerical difficulties in determining an absolute value of T_1 are evidently great, we conclude that spin-orbit coupling is in many cases capable of providing the observed relaxation mechanism for iron-group elements.

As we have done previously, we note that (6-48) provides a dependence on external field and on temperature as follows:

$$\begin{aligned} 1/T_1 &= (\text{const}) H_0^0 T^9 \qquad (T \ll \theta_D) \\ &= (\text{const}) H_0^0 T^0 \qquad (T \gtrsim \theta_D) \qquad (6\text{-}51) \end{aligned}$$

The Orbach Process of Relaxation via a Real Intermediate State. It sometimes happens, as in rare earth salts with their weaker crystal field interactions with the paramagnetic ion, that electric splittings are smaller than the energy of some phonons. This probably occurs for certain 3*d* ions, and it definitely obtains for shallow donors and acceptors in silicon. In this situation it is possible for an ion in the upper Zeeman level of the ionic ground state to absorb a phonon and thus be excited into the low-lying crystal-field excited state, thence dropping back into the lower Zeeman level of the ground state. A similar mechanism for relaxation transitions among hyperfine levels of a paramagnetic complex in low magnetic fields was visualized by Lloyd and Pake (Ref. 10 of Chapter 2), but Orbach[12] and co-workers independently conceived the mechanism for Ce^{3+} in cerium magnesium nitrate and carried out both experimental and theoretical evaluations of the resulting T_1.

In this substance the Debye temperature is about 60°K, whereas the crystal-field level lies above the ground level by only about 24 cm^{-1}, which corresponds to 34°K. Evidently it will be energetically quite possible for phonons to excite the ion directly to this level. Orbach[12] calculates

$$1/T_1 \approx (3G^2/h\rho v_0^5)(\Delta/\hbar)^3 e^{-\Delta/kT} \qquad (6\text{-}52)$$

where Δ corresponds to 34°K and $G \approx 1.2 \times 10^{-14}$ erg is a coefficient which, multiplying the strain, gives the change in ionic crystal-field energy under lattice strain. The result for Ce^{3+} in cerium magnesium nitrate is

$$T_1 \sim 10^{-10} \exp(34°/T) \text{ sec} \qquad (6\text{-}53)$$

in good agreement with experiment.

Another paper of Orbach[13] discusses a more succinct approach to such calculations as Van Vleck pursued for Ti^{3+}, showing that certain conclusions reached in the Van Vleck calculation are more generally applicable than his special cases lead one to suppose.

Cross Relaxation. A number of interesting relaxation effects have been observed in recent years which involve communication between two different species of spins within the same sample by means of the spin-spin or dipole-dipole interaction. Bloembergen et al.[14] have

[12] C. B. P. Finn, R. Orbach, and W. P. Wolf, *Proc. Phys. Soc.* (*London*), **A77,** 261 (1961).

[13] R. Orbach, *Proc. Phys. Soc.* (*London*), **A77,** 821 (1961).

[14] N. Bloembergen, S. Shapiro, P. S. Pershan, and J. O. Artman, *Phys. Rev.*, **114,** 445 (1959).

called these processes *cross relaxation*, but the term is now used to cover such a multitude of effects that it has to some degree lost its utility. In this section we shall give examples of a number of processes that fall under the heading of cross relaxation. Whether the terminology in precise or not, some interesting physics is involved in these processes.

Perhaps the simplest process conceptually is one exemplified in the nuclear resonance spin calorimetry experiments of the type performed by Abragam and Proctor[15] in their investigation of the validity of the spin-temperature concept. The requirement is that two species of spins be present in the sample, and for present purposes we suppose that one relaxes much more slowly, by whatever interaction it may have directly with the lattice, than does the other species. If one can experimentally arrange for the resonance curves for these two species to overlap partially, mutual spin flips between the two species can take place, conserving energy. Let G be the species in good contact with the lattice and let P be that in poor contact. Then system P can, under these favorable experimental conditions, cool off by having an "up" P spin flip down while a "down" G spin flips up, via their dipole-dipole coupling. We shall call this a double flip process. Spin G can now flip back down as it originally was by means of its good contact with the lattice. Thermodynamically speaking, energy has flowed from spin system P to the lattice via system G.

Abragam and Proctor arranged to turn on or off the "cross communication" between different spin species simply by decreasing or increasing the external H_0 field. This process depends upon the fact that line widths are essentially independent of the external field value (apart from an esoteric effect, to be discussed in Chapter 7, which varies the width by at most a factor of $\frac{10}{3}$ between low and high fields). If one has a sample with spins P and G initially in a large H_0 field, so that their resonances do not overlap, he can achieve overlap by lowering the external H_0 until the two resonance frequencies differ by perhaps only two or three line widths. Even if the difference is greater, the small overlap of frequencies in the tails of the resonances may measurably facilitate relaxation for the P spins. Figure 6-6 sketches the effect.

Such effects could occur in electron resonance because two different species of paramagnetic ions in the crystal have, for example, quite different spin-orbit coupling, λ. If λ_P is small, we see from Sec. 6-2 that T_{1P} will be long. If the second species G has large λ, its T_{1G} will be short, but from our discussion of Sec. 3-2 its g value will depart

[15] A. Abragam and W. G. Proctor, *Phys. Rev.*, **109**, 1441 (1958).

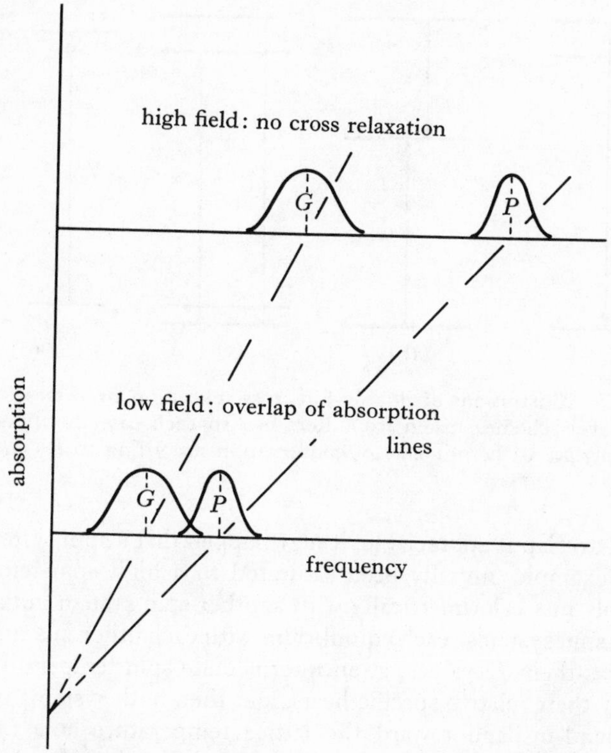

Fig. 6-6 A schematic illustration of one kind of cross relaxation. In the upper curve the magnetic field is high and no appreciable resonance overlap occurs. Spins P, with poor spin-lattice contact, have a very long T_1. In the lower curve the resonance tails overlap, and spins P relax more readily by mutual flips with spins G, which have good lattice contact.

appreciably from g_e. Therefore we expect no resonance overlap in large enough magnetic fields, but in lower fields, where the resonance tails would overlap, species P could relax via spin-spin flips with G spins.

When λ is large for the G spins, lower-than-cubic symmetry will lead to a highly anisotropic g tensor. In this event, one may be able to turn on or off the P–G spin-spin contact by rotating the crystal to a position in the magnetic field which facilitates or minimizes overlap in the resonance tails.

Theoretical analysis of this double-flip cross-relaxation process is presented by Bloembergen et al.[14] and by Pershan.[16] If both T_1's are

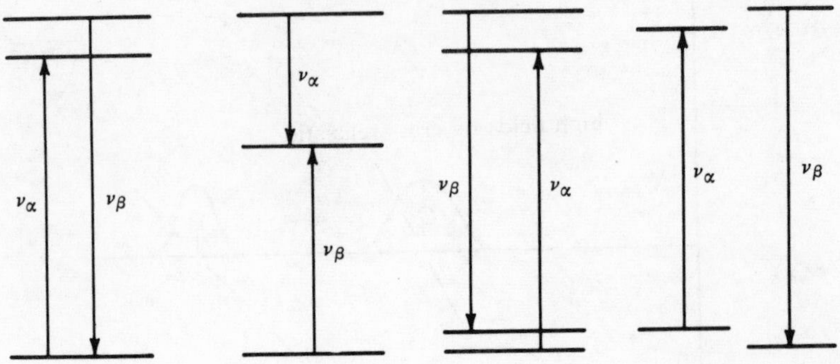

Fig. 6-7 Illustrations of double-flip cross-relaxation processes for several types of level schemes, taken from Ref. 14. In each case the dipole energy must supply $h\nu_d$ to permit energy conservation according to $h\nu_\alpha + h\nu_d = h\nu_\beta$.

long and overlap is appreciable, it may happen that a spin system which has, for example, initially been saturated to a high spin temperature will simply mix calorimetrically with another spin system initially cool. The two spin systems reach equilibrium with each other in a time nearly as short as their T_2 values, at an intermediate spin temperature determined by their relative specific heats, and then both systems will move slowly hand-in-hand toward the lattice temperature at a rate given more nearly by the shorter of their two T_1's. The Abragam and Proctor experiments were of this type. The point of mentioning this situation is to note that, in the initial relaxation to spin-spin equilibrium, the spin system may relax at something approaching its $1/T_2$. But the final relaxation toward the lattice temperature could be no more rapid than the faster T_1 will permit. Evidently fairly complex relaxation behavior can occur.

Bloembergen et al.[14] present a diagram, reproduced in Fig. 6-7, which shows a number of possible double-flip cross-relaxation processes. In each case the energy of the two transitions is not precisely balanced, as is also true in the lower part of Fig. 6-6, and the dipole-dipole interaction is necessary to cause overlap in the sense of Fig. 6-6, thus allowing the dipole-dipole coupling to take up or supply the energy necessary for energy conservation.

More exotic higher-order cross-relaxation processes can occur. Suppose the g values are such that, again for two spin species within the same crystal, $2h\nu_A \cong h\nu_B$. Then if two A spins flip down when one

[16] P. S. Pershan, *Phys. Rev.*, **117**, 109 (1960).

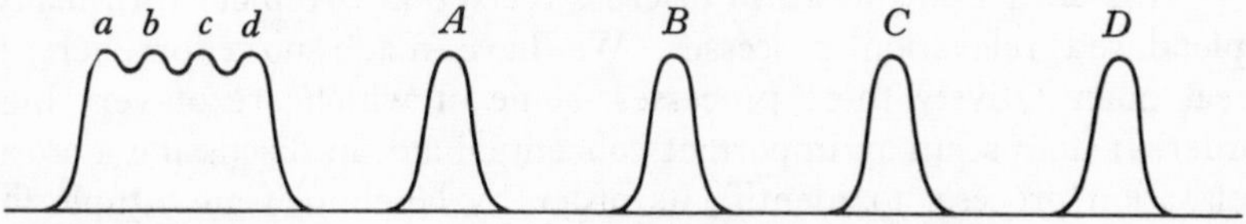

Fig. 6-8 Cu^{++} resonances[17] for a particular orientation of the crystal $Cu(NH_4)_2(SO_4)_2 \cdot 6H_2O$. The two quartets *abcd* and *ABCD* are hyperfine patterns for the copper nuclear spin of $\frac{3}{2}$ arising from two nonequivalent Cu^{++} sites in the crystal. The anisotropic *g* values prevent overlapping of the two quartets.

B spin flips up, energy will nearly be conserved, and it may be precisely so with the aid of dipolar interaction. We call this a triple-flip cross-relaxation process. One's imagination need not be held back. If we have $3h\nu_A \cong 2h\nu_B$, there is the possibility of a quintuple-flip process. And so it goes.

Of course, when we refer to *A* spins and *B* spins, they can also arise from but one kind of ion which, however, occupies two non-equivalent sites within the crystal. An interesting and provocative example of this was provided by the Cu^{++} ions in $Cu(NH_4)_2(SO_4)_2 \cdot 6H_2O$, first studied by Giordmaine et al.[17] and discussed by Bloembergen et al.[14] Figure 6-8 reproduces the absorption spectrum for a particular crystal orientation.

The interesting question posed by the experiments on this crystal was why saturation of, for example, line *A* would lead quickly to saturation of the resonances *abcd*. (Since the *abcd* resonances overlap each other closely, it is necessary only to find a means for any one of the *abcd* resonances to communicate with the *A* resonance.) Bloembergen et al.[14] point out that the *Ad* spacing is very nearly the same as the *AB* spacing. Therefore energy will be conserved if two *A* spins flip down while a *d* spin and a *B* spin flip up. This quadruple-flip process communicates spin-temperature information from one kind of Cu^{++} site to the other. It is also clear that a quadruple-flip cross-relaxation process which flips two *B* spins one way and an *A* and a *C* spin the other will communicate spin-temperature information through the entire *ABCD* spectrum, even though the individual resonances do not overlap as in the *abcd* spectrum, where double-flip processes can communicate the information.

[17] J. A. Giordmaine, L. E. Alsop, F. R. Nash, and C. H. Townes, *Phys. Rev.*, **109**, 302 (1958).

It is clear that the world of cross relaxation is replete with many-splendored relaxation processes. We have made no effort here to treat quantitatively these processes, some of which are of very high order. It does seem an important conceptual aid, in discussing a cross-relaxation process, to identify its order by labeling it an *n*-tuple flip process or, as other authors have done,[18] as an *n*-spin process. For quantitative theoretical estimates of cross-relaxation times, one should consult the literature.[14–16,18,19]

Note that, in our theories of T_1 in Sec. 6-2, every process visualized was a single-flip or one-spin process, although multiple phonon processes occurred.

Cross-relaxation processes are of great practical importance for the solid-state masers to be discussed in Chapter 8.

[18] R. W. Roberts, J. H. Burgess, and H. D. Tenney, *Phys. Rev.*, **121,** 997 (1961).

[19] W. J. Caspers, *Physica*, **26,** 778, 798 (1960).

[7]

General Theories of Line Shapes and Relaxation

7-1 The Relation of the Line Shape to the Relaxation Function

A detailed excursion into one or several of the formulations of the theory of line shapes and relaxation would be out of place in this book which is designed to give the reader with at least a graduate student's physics background a first over-all view of paramagnetic resonance. However, in such a first view it is important to understand what the general theories try to do as well as to see something of their method of attack. Once the reader has achieved that degree of orientation, he can turn to any of the original papers or—perhaps the best procedure—examine the composite discussion of these theories presented in Abragam's book (Ref. 5 of Chapter 5), which treats the subject in a consistent and clear way, if not quite in consecutive sections of text following directly upon one another. The fact that Abragam has in mind only nuclear magnets is no real restriction on the formalism. However, where the high-temperature approximation is used, $g\beta H_0 \ll kT$, it is evidently more of a restriction for the larger magnetic moments with which we deal in electron resonance.

It is useful to preface our discussion with some simple statements about the magnetic resonance line shape, its Fourier transform, and its moments. As before, we find it convenient to measure frequency on the scale of $\omega = 2\pi\nu$. Let ω_0 be the resonance center,

$$\hbar\omega_0 = g\beta H_0 \tag{7-1}$$

We define, as in Sec. 4-2, $\Omega = \omega - \omega_0$ to be the frequency measured from the resonance center. Let $f(\omega)$ and $F(\Omega)$ be the normalized resonance shapes on the two angular frequency scales, illustrated in Fig. 7-1. Note that it is assumed that $F(\Omega)$ vanishes for Ω extending to points where the $|\Delta m| \neq 1$ satellites would occur, and we suppose $F(\Omega)$ normalized, excluding the satellites, as

$$\int_{-\infty}^{\infty} F(\Omega)\, d\Omega = 1 \tag{7-2}$$

where the lower limit is properly $-\omega_0$ but we assume the resonance sharp enough to extend this limit to $-\infty$.

The nth moment of $F(\omega)$ is

$$\mu_\Omega{}^n = \int_{-\infty}^{\infty} \Omega^n F(\Omega)\, d\Omega \tag{7-3}$$

The Fourier transform of $F(\Omega)$ is $\Gamma(t)$ defined by

$$\Gamma(t) = \int_{-\infty}^{\infty} F(\Omega) e^{i\Omega t}\, d\Omega \tag{7-4}$$

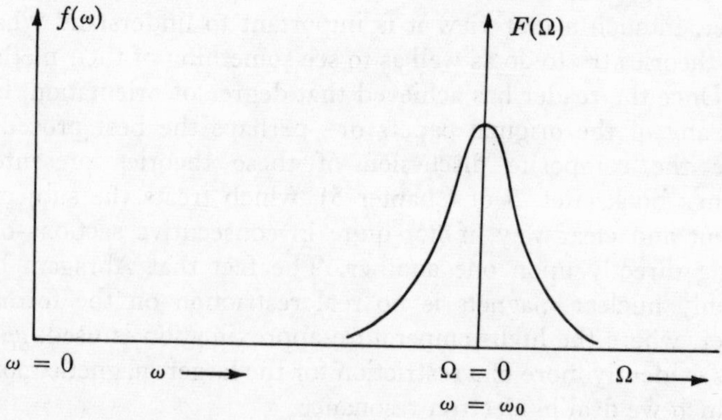

Fig. 7-1 A sketch illustrating the shape functions $f(\omega)$ and $F(\Omega)$ on the scales of ω and $\Omega = \omega - \omega_0$. If the line is assumed sharp, the normalizing condition $\int_0^\infty f(\omega)\, d\omega = 1$ becomes $\int_{-\infty}^{\infty} F(\Omega)\, d\Omega = 1$ to good approximation.

which is real if $F(-\Omega) = F(\Omega)$. Inversion of this equation gives

$$F(\Omega) = \frac{1}{2\pi} \int_{-\infty}^{\infty} \Gamma(t) e^{-i\Omega t}\, d\Omega \qquad (7\text{-}5)$$

Differentiation of (7-4) gives

$$d^n\Gamma(t)/dt^n = i^n \int_{-\infty}^{\infty} \Omega^n F(\Omega) e^{i\Omega t}\, dt \qquad (7\text{-}6)$$

Evidently, from (7-3) and (7-6),

$$\mu_{\Omega}{}^n = i^{-n}[d^n\Gamma(t)/dt^n]_{t=0} \qquad (7\text{-}7)$$

So far the foregoing appears to be little more than some kind of elementary Fourier calisthenics. But there is an important reason for introducing $\Gamma(t)$; we shall find that it is essentially a quantum mechanical correlation function for the time-dependent Heisenberg magnetic moment operator $M_x(t) = g\beta S_x(t) = \gamma\hbar S_x(t)$. If we could use the system Hamiltonian equation of motion for $M_x(t)$ to find $\Gamma(t)$, (7-7) would give us the moments. And, even better, the line shape would be obtainable from (7-5). The reader may well guess that this program takes some doing, and that it has thus far only been attempted with serious and questionable approximations. This ambitious program is, nonetheless, precisely that of the general theories of line shape.

First we shall establish the relationship of $\Gamma(t)$ to the correlation function for the Heisenberg operator $M_x(t)$. Let the sample have volume V and let E_n be the energy of a total eigenstate n of the sample. If P_n is the probability that eigenstate n is occupied and w_{nm} is the probability per unit time of a transition from state n to m, the energy absorption per unit volume per unit time is

$$A = V^{-1} \sum_{m,n}{}' [P_n(1 - P_m)(E_m - E_n)w_{nm} - P_m(1 - P_n)(E_m - E_n)w_{mn}] \qquad (7\text{-}8)$$

The notation Σ' means that only states n and m, for which $E_m - E_n = \hbar\omega$, are to be summed over, since the H_1 field in the x direction has just the one frequency, ω. The negative term in the bracket represents emissive transitions. Now w_{nm} is an induced transition probability and has the property $w_{nm} = w_{mn}$. This permits simplification of the expression (7-8) to

$$A = V^{-1} \sum_{m,n}{}' (P_n - P_m)(E_m - E_n)w_{nm}$$

The restriction on the summing procedure can be incorporated by means of a δ function to rule out nonconserving transitions if we simply use for w_{nm} the form (2-56) with a δ function as the shape function for an individual transition between n and m. Since the present discussion is on the ω scale, we replace $g(\nu)$ in (2-56) by $2\pi\delta[(E_n - E_m)\hbar^{-1} - \omega]$. We also convert to the operator $M_x = \gamma\hbar S_x = \gamma\hbar \sum_j S_{xj}$. The resulting form of w_{nm} is, since the perturbing energy for the entire sample is $-(VM_x)(2H_1 \cos \omega t)$ instead of $\mathscr{H}_1$ in (2-44),

$$w_{nm} = 2\pi\hbar^2 H_1{}^2 V^2 |(m|M_x|n)|^2 \delta[(E_m - E_n)\hbar^{-1} - \omega] \tag{7-9}$$

The absorption A becomes

$$A = 2\pi\hbar^2 H_1{}^2 V \sum_{m,n} (P_n - P_m)(E_m - E_n) \times |(m|M_x|n)|^2 \delta[(E_m - E_n)\hbar^{-1} - \omega] \tag{7-10}$$

It is convenient to use the functional representation of the δ function provided by the Fourier integral theorem:

$$\delta(x) = \frac{1}{2\pi} \int_{-\infty}^{\infty} e^{ixt}\, dt \tag{7-11}$$

Incorporating the fact that the line is sharp, we replace the multiplicative factor $E_m - E_n$ by $\hbar\omega$ and obtain from (7-11) and (7-10) the form

$$A(\omega) = V\hbar H_1{}^2 \omega \int_{-\infty}^{\infty} e^{-i\omega t} \sum_{m,n} (P_n - P_m) \times |(m|M_x|n)|^2 e^{i(E_m - E_n)t/\hbar}\, dt \tag{7-12}$$

The probability P_n that state n is occupied is simply the diagonal element of the statistical matrix or density matrix ρ,

$$P_n = e^{-E_n/kT} / (\sum_l e^{-E_l/kT}) = \rho_{nn} \tag{7-13}$$

Whatever terms may be included in the system Hamiltonian, it is true that states E_m and E_n, between which transitions occur, differ only by a frequency $\hbar\omega$, which we take to be smaller than kT. Thus

$$\begin{aligned} P_n - P_m &= (e^{-E_n/kT} - e^{-E_m/kT}) / \sum_l e^{-E_l/kT} \\ &= Z^{-1} e^{-E_m/kT} (e^{\hbar\omega/kT} - 1) \\ &\approx (\hbar\omega/kT) Z^{-1} e^{-E_m/kT} \end{aligned} \tag{7-14}$$

Here we use the abbreviation $Z = \Sigma_l\, e^{-E_l/kT}$, as it is the partition function of statistical mechanics. Incorporating (7-14) into (7-12), we write the matrix product in the following form:

$$A(\omega) = H_1{}^2\omega^2 V(ZkT)^{-1} \int_{-\infty}^{\infty} e^{-i\omega t} \sum_{m,n} e^{-E_m/kT} \times e^{iE_m t/\hbar}(m|M_x|n)e^{-iE_n t/\hbar}(n|M_x|m)\, dt$$

$$= H_1{}^2\omega^2 V(ZkT)^{-1} \int_{-\infty}^{\infty} e^{-i\omega t} \times \mathrm{tr}(e^{-\mathscr{H}/kT}\, e^{i\mathscr{H}t/\hbar} M_x e^{-i\mathscr{H}t/\hbar} M_x)\, dt \qquad (7\text{-}15)$$

where $\mathscr{H}$ is the system Hamiltonian having eigenvalues E_m. Now (2-41) relates $A(\omega)$ to χ'': $A = 2\omega H_1{}^2\chi''$. Thus we conclude from (7-15) that

$$\chi''(\omega) = (\omega V/2kTZ) \int_{-\infty}^{\infty} e^{-i\omega t}\, \mathrm{tr}(e^{-\mathscr{H}/kT} M_x(t) M_x)\, dt \qquad (7\text{-}16)$$

where $M_x(t)$ is the Heisenberg operator,

$$M_x(t) = e^{i\mathscr{H}t/\hbar} M_x e^{-i\mathscr{H}t/\hbar} \qquad (7\text{-}17)$$

Recalling that $e^{-i\omega t} = e^{-i\omega_0 t - i\Omega t}$, we can compare with (7-5) to find the form for $\Gamma(t)$:

$$\Gamma(t) = Ce^{-i\omega_0 t}\, \mathrm{tr}(e^{-\mathscr{H}/kT} M_x(t) M_x)/\mathrm{tr}(e^{-\mathscr{H}/kT}) \qquad (7\text{-}18)$$

However, it will be equally convenient for our present purposes in dealing with sharp resonances to work with $G(t)$:

$$G(t) = e^{i\omega_0 t}\Gamma(t)$$

$$= C\, \mathrm{tr}(e^{-\mathscr{H}/kT} M_x(t) M_x)/\mathrm{tr}(e^{-\mathscr{H}/kT}) \qquad (7\text{-}19)$$

Evidently, from (7-16), $G(t)$ is essentially the Fourier transform for $f(\omega)$, whereas $\Gamma(t)$ corresponds to $F(\Omega)$. The constant C is chosen so that $\Gamma(0) = G(0) = 1$, which is demanded by (7-4) since $F(\Omega)$ is normalized to unity. Because the ordinary operator M_x is equal to the Heisenberg operator at $t = 0$,

$$G(t) = \frac{C\, \mathrm{tr}(e^{-\mathscr{H}/kT} M_x(t) M_x(0))}{\mathrm{tr}(e^{-\mathscr{H}/kT})}$$

$$= C\langle M_x(t) M_x(0)\rangle \qquad (7\text{-}20)$$

and it follows from $G(0) = 1$ that

$$C = \langle M_x(0) M_x(0) \rangle^{-1}$$

The bracket $\langle \rangle$ means a statistical average as defined by (7-20). $G(t)$ is evidently [cf. (5-11)] a kind of quantum mechanical correlation function for the Heisenberg operator $M_x(t)$. $G(t)$ is variously called the correlation function, the autocorrelation function, or the relaxation function of the system magnetization.

In principle, one finds $G(t)$ from (7-19) after solving the equation of motion for the operator $M_x(t)$,

$$i\hbar \dot{M}_x(t) = [M_x(t), \mathscr{H}] \tag{7-21}$$

Throughout the discussion it is assumed that there is no explicit time dependence in the Hamiltonian $\mathscr{H}$. Section 7-2 illustrates some of the practical problems encountered in attempting solution of (7-21).

7-2 The Kubo–Tomita Approach Applied to Exchange Narrowing

The Interaction Representation for $M_x(t)$. In this section we shall sketch briefly the theory of Kubo and Tomita[1,2] as they formulated it for a description of exchange narrowing. There are a number of formulations of the theory, and we choose this one because historically it was the first of the ambitious attempts to approximate $G(t)$. It also serves to illustrate several other points of interest.

For this problem we take as the total Hamiltonian

$$\mathscr{H} = \mathscr{H}_Z + \mathscr{H}_e + \mathscr{H}_d \tag{7-22}$$

where $\mathscr{H}_Z$, $\mathscr{H}_e$, and $\mathscr{H}_d$ are our old friends, defined in (4-1) and (4-6). An important point about (7-22) is that it includes all N interacting spins of the sample, where N may be a large number such as 10^{22}. A feature of (7-22) is that it does not include the lattice. Hence it operates only on spin coordinates, and the orbital coordinates of $\mathscr{H}_d$ enter only as parameters. To calculate $G(t)$ we need at least approximate solutions to

$$i\dot{M}_x(t) = [M_x(t), \mathscr{H}] \tag{7-23}$$

(In this section we drop $\hbar$, which is equivalent to measuring all energies

[1] R. Kubo and K. Tomita, *Proc. Intern. Conf. Theoret. Phys.*, Kyoto and Tokyo, 1953, p. 779.

[2] R. Kubo and K. Tomita, *J. Phys. Soc. Japan*, **9**, 888 (1954).

in units of $\hbar$.) As a first step we transform to the interaction representation, regarding $\mathscr{H}_d$ as the perturbing interaction.

Calling $\mathscr{H}_Z + \mathscr{H}_e = \mathscr{H}_T$, we transform to M_t, defined through

$$M_x(t) = e^{it\mathscr{H}_T} M_t e^{-it\mathscr{H}_T} \tag{7-24}$$

Differentiation of (7-24) for $M_x(t)$ and substitution into (7-23) provides

$$i\dot{M}_t = [M_t, \mathscr{H}'(t)] \tag{7-25}$$

where $\mathscr{H}'(t)$ signifies

$$\mathscr{H}'(t) = e^{-it\mathscr{H}_T} \mathscr{H}_d e^{it\mathscr{H}_T} \tag{7-26}$$

If it were not for $\mathscr{H}_e$, this would simply be a transformation to the rotating frame. Thus the rapid Larmor frequencies are removed and we can focus attention on the slow perturbing frequencies.

The Iteration Approximation Solution for M_t and $G(t)$. We now use a successive approximation procedure for (7-25), subject to $M_{t=0} \equiv M_0 = M_x(0) = M_x$, as given for $t = 0$ by (7-24) and (7-17). From (7-25),

$$M_t - M_0 = i^{-1} \int_0^t [M_t, \mathscr{H}'(t')]\, dt' \tag{7-27}$$

The first approximation to (7-27) is

$$M_t^{(1)} - M_0 = i^{-1} \int_0^t [M_0, \mathscr{H}'(t')]\, dt'$$

which, when placed for M_t in (7-27), gives a second approximation,

$$M_t^{(2)} = M_0 + i^{-1} \int_0^t [M_0, \mathscr{H}'(t')]\, dt' + i^{-2} \int_0^t dt' \int_0^{t'} dt'' \{[M_0, \mathscr{H}'(t'')], \mathscr{H}'(t')\} \tag{7-28}$$

It may be mentioned in passing that, through (7-28) and an expansion such as (7-30) below for $\Gamma(t)$, the nth iteration approximation gives the nth moment exactly. Equation (7-28) is as far as we shall go in the successive approximations to M_t, although it is clear that the process can be continued indefinitely. By inverting $M_t^{(2)}$ through (7-24) we can, from (7-28), find, term for term,

$$M_x^{(2)}(t) = M_x^0(t) + M_x'(t) + M_x''(t) \tag{7-29}$$

which leads in turn through (7-20) to

$$G^{(2)}(t) = C[\langle M_x^0(t)M_x\rangle + \langle M_x'(t)M_x\rangle + \langle M_x''(t)M_x\rangle + \cdots] \tag{7-30}$$

where the average brackets are used in the sense defined by (7-20).

The High-Temperature Approximation.[3] Equation (7-30) is an expansion of $G(t)$ in the perturbation $\mathscr{H}_d$, which enters succeeding terms in successively higher "powers" through higher orders of commutation with $\mathscr{H}'$. Temperature enters each term of the perturbation expansion (7-30) through the definition (7-20) of the brackets $\langle\rangle$. We wish now to consider the expansion of any bracket $\langle\rangle$ in powers of $1/kT$.

It is generally assumed that high temperatures, defined by

$$\gamma\hbar H_0 = g\beta H_0 \ll kT \tag{7-31}$$

permit use of a simple expansion of the statistical matrix $e^{-b\mathscr{H}}$. Some explanation of this expansion is desirable. Abragam, for example, writes the equilibrium density matrix ρ_0 as[4]

$$\rho_0 \equiv e^{-b\mathscr{H}}/\mathrm{tr}\,(e^{-b\mathscr{H}}) \approx (1 - b\mathscr{H} + \cdots)/\mathrm{tr}\,1 \tag{7-32}$$

where 1 denotes the unit operator and $\mathscr{H}$ is the Hamiltonian for the entire crystal. Since $\mathscr{H}$ is the many-particle Hamiltonian, its eigenvalues E_n are proportional to the total number of spins N in the crystal. The expansion (7-32) might at first seem to require a temperature some 10^{22} times higher than the condition (7-31) specifies! But, of course, e^{-bE_n} is not explicitly involved in the evaluation of the bracket (7-20). Consider the bracket for any operator A,

$$\langle A\rangle \equiv \mathrm{tr}(e^{-b\mathscr{H}}A)/\mathrm{tr}\,(e^{-b\mathscr{H}}) = f(b) \tag{7-33}$$

and regard it as a function $f(b)$ of $b = \hbar/kT$. Making a Taylor's expansion of $f(b)$, one has

$$f(b) = f(0) + bf'(0) + b^2f''(0)/2! + \cdots \tag{7-34}$$

[3] The author is indebted to J. Dreitlein, R. B. Griffiths, and Baldwin Robertson for helpful discussions on this subject.

[4] Ref. 5 of Chapter 5, pp. 100–101.

where differentiation of (7-33) shows that

$$\begin{aligned} f(0) &= \mathrm{tr}\, A/\mathrm{tr}\, 1 \\ f'(0) &= [(\mathrm{tr}\, A)(\mathrm{tr}\, \mathscr{H}) - (\mathrm{tr}\, 1)(\mathrm{tr}\, \mathscr{H}A)]/(\mathrm{tr}\, 1)^2 \\ f''(0) &= \{(\mathrm{tr}\, 1)[(\mathrm{tr}\, \mathscr{H}^2 A)(\mathrm{tr}\, 1) - (\mathrm{tr}\, A)(\mathrm{tr}\, \mathscr{H}^2)] \\ &\quad + 2(\mathrm{tr}\, \mathscr{H})[(\mathrm{tr}\, A)(\mathrm{tr}\, \mathscr{H}) - (\mathrm{tr}\, 1)(\mathrm{tr}\, \mathscr{H}A)]\}/(\mathrm{tr}\, 1)^3 \end{aligned} \tag{7-35}$$

etc.

For a large class of operators A and $\mathscr{H}$ of interest, at least one of the quantities tr A and tr $\mathscr{H}$ vanishes. The expansion (7-33) then becomes

$$\begin{aligned} \langle A \rangle &= \mathrm{tr}(e^{-b\mathscr{H}} A)/\mathrm{tr}\, e^{-b\mathscr{H}} \\ &= \mathrm{tr}\, A/\mathrm{tr}\, 1 - b\, \mathrm{tr}(\mathscr{H}A)/\mathrm{tr}\, 1 + \cdots \end{aligned} \tag{7-36}$$

which explains the sense in which (7-32) is valid.

We can now illustrate this expansion in temperature by calculating its first two terms for the zero-order *perturbation* term in (7-30). Then the operator A is, from (7-30), (7-28), and (7-24),

$$A = e^{it\mathscr{H}_T} M_x e^{-it\mathscr{H}_T} M_x = M_x{}^0(t) M_x \tag{7-37}$$

Because $\mathscr{H}_e$ in $\mathscr{H}_T$ commutes with $\mathscr{H}_Z$ or any component of $\mathbf{M}$, we commute $\exp(-it\mathscr{H}_e)$ through M_x on its left and out of the problem. The remaining $\exp(-it\mathscr{H}_Z)$ simply provides a unitary transformation rotating M_x about z at the frequency ω_0. Therefore

$$M_x{}^0(t) M_x = (M_x \cos \omega_0 t - M_y \sin \omega_0 t) M_x \tag{7-38}$$

where $\mathbf{M} = -\gamma\hbar\, \Sigma_j\, \mathbf{S}_j$. It is readily shown (Ref. 2 of Chapter 4) that $\mathrm{tr}\, S_y S_x = 0$. This leaves for the first term of the expansion (7-36)

$$\mathrm{tr}\, M_x{}^2 \cos \omega_0 t = \gamma^2 \hbar^2 \cos \omega_0 t\, \mathrm{tr}\, S_x{}^2 \tag{7-39}$$

Now $\mathrm{tr}\, S_x{}^2 = \mathrm{tr}\, S_y{}^2 = \mathrm{tr}\, S_z{}^2$, and it will be noted that $\mathrm{tr}\, S_y^2 = \mathrm{tr}\, \Sigma_j\, S_{yj}{}^2$ has already been evaluated in Sec. 4-2 as $\frac{1}{3}NS(S+1)(2S+1)^N$. Therefore the leading term in (7-36) is, since $\mathrm{tr}\, 1 = (2S+1)^N$,

$$\mathrm{tr}\, A/\mathrm{tr}\, 1 = (N/6)\gamma^2\hbar^2 S(S+1)(e^{i\omega_0 t} + e^{-i\omega_0 t}) \tag{7-40}$$

The next term in (7-36) is

$$\begin{aligned} &- b\, \mathrm{tr}(\mathscr{H}A)/\mathrm{tr}\, 1 \\ &\quad = - b\, \mathrm{tr}[(\mathscr{H}_Z + \mathscr{H}_e)(M_x \cos \omega_0 t - M_y \sin \omega_0 t) M_x]/\mathrm{tr}\, 1 \end{aligned} \tag{7-41}$$

[Note that $\mathscr{H}_T = \mathscr{H}_Z + \mathscr{H}_e$ is traceless, thus permitting us to use the second-term form of (7-36).] To aid evaluation of the required traces, there are discussions[5] of useful theorems and tabulations[6] in the literature. Using the form (4-6) for $\mathscr{H}_e$ and recalling that $\mathscr{H}_Z = +\gamma\hbar H_0 S_Z$ and $\mathbf{M} = -\gamma\hbar\mathbf{S}$, one finds upon evaluating the traces that (7-41) becomes

$$- b\,\mathrm{tr}(\mathscr{H}A)/\mathrm{tr}\,1$$
$$= -(\gamma\hbar H_0/kT)(\gamma\hbar)^2(N/12)S(S+1)(e^{i\omega_0 t} - e^{-i\omega_0 t})$$
$$- (J/kT)(\gamma\hbar^2(\hbar z N/18)[S(S+1)]^2(e^{i\omega_0 t} + e^{-i\omega_0 t}) \qquad (7\text{-}42)$$

Here z is the number of nearest-neighbors exchange-coupled through exchange integral J to a given spin. Collecting (7-40) and (7-42) we find the expansion (7-36) in $1/kT$ for $\langle M_x{}^0(t)M_x\rangle$ to be

$$\langle M_x{}^0(t)M_x\rangle = (N/6)(\gamma\hbar)^2 S(S+1)\{e^{i\omega_0 t}[1 - \tfrac{1}{2}(\gamma\hbar H_0/kT)$$
$$- \tfrac{1}{3}zS(S+1)J/kT + \cdots] + e^{-i\omega_0 t}[1 + \tfrac{1}{2}(\gamma\hbar H_0/kT)$$
$$- \tfrac{1}{3}zS(S+1)J/kT + \cdots]\} \qquad (7\text{-}43)$$

Equation (7-43) illustrates that even so far as the many-particle Zeeman interaction is concerned, the pertinent expansion parameter is $\gamma\hbar H_0/kT$, and (7-31) still gives properly the high-temperature condition. But (7-43) also shows that when the exchange interaction is present there is a second high-temperature condition analogous to (7-31), $J \ll kT$. If this condition is not met, we know from the theory of ferromagnetism that we may be dealing with a ferromagnet or antiferromagnet rather than a paramagnetic sample.

Comparing (7-43) with (7-30) indicates that the leading term in $G(t)$ has a Fourier transform giving a δ-function line shape at $\omega = \omega_0$ and at $\omega = -\omega_0$. This is to be expected, as the dipolar interaction $\mathscr{H}_d$ did not enter the zero-order perturbation approximation.

Kubo and Tomita's Approximation to $G(t)$. In calculating $G(t)$, we use, from this point on, the high-temperature approximation and denote it by

$$\langle A\rangle_{b=0} \equiv \mathrm{tr}\,A/\mathrm{tr}\,1 \qquad (7\text{-}44)$$

To proceed beyond the zero-order perturbation approximation in (7-30) Kubo and Tomita[1] must of course invoke the form of $\mathscr{H}_d$, the dipolar interaction of (4-2), which they write as

$$\mathscr{H}_d = \sum_{j>k}\sum_{\alpha=-2}^{2}\{jk\}_\alpha \Phi_{jk}{}^\alpha \qquad (7\text{-}45)$$

[5] J. Dreitlein and H. Kessemeier, *Phys. Rev.*, **123**, 835 (1961).
[6] G. S. Rushbrooke and P. J. Wood, *Mol. Phys.*, **1**, 257 (1958).

where

$$\begin{aligned}\{jk\}_{-2} &= S_{-j}S_{-k}\\ \{jk\}_{-1} &= S_{-j}S_{zk} + S_{zj}S_{-k}\\ \{jk\}_0 &= S_{zj}S_{zk} - \tfrac{1}{4}(S_{+j}S_{-k} + S_{-j}S_{+k})\\ &\text{etc.}\end{aligned} \tag{7-46}$$

and (recall that $\mathscr{H}_d$ is in units of $\hbar$),

$$\begin{aligned}\Phi_{jk}{}^{-2} &= -\tfrac{3}{4}\gamma^2\hbar r_{jk}{}^{-3}\sin^2\theta_{jk}\, e^{2i\phi_{jk}}\\ \Phi_{jk}{}^{-1} &= -\tfrac{3}{2}\gamma^2\hbar r_{jk}{}^{-3}\sin\theta_{jk}\cos\theta_{jk}\, e^{i\phi_{jk}}\\ \Phi_{jk}{}^{0} &= -\gamma^2\hbar r_{jk}{}^{-3}(3\cos^2\theta_{jk}{}^{-1})\\ &\text{etc.}\end{aligned} \tag{7-47}$$

Kubo and Tomita show that the form of $\mathscr{H}_d$ leads to

$$\langle M'_x(t)M_x\rangle_{b=0} = 0 \tag{7-48}$$

With much complicated evaluation of commutators and traces, they find the next approximation to be

$$\begin{aligned}\langle M''_x(t)M_x\rangle_{b=0} = &-\tfrac{1}{8}N[S(S+1)]^2 e^{i\omega_0 t}\int_0^t dt_1 \int_0^{t_1} dt_2 [K^{00}(\tau)\\ &+ \tfrac{16}{9}e^{i\omega_0\tau}K^{-1,1}(\tau) + \tfrac{8}{3}e^{-i\omega_0\tau}K^{1,-1}(\tau)\\ &+ \tfrac{16}{9}e^{-2i\omega_0\tau}K^{2,-2}(\tau)] + \text{c.c.}\end{aligned} \tag{7-49}$$

where $\tau = t_1 - t_2$. Here $K^{\alpha\alpha'}(t_1 - t_2)$ is the correlation function for dipolar terms as they are randomly modulated by the exchange interaction. However, we must think of the angular factors $\Phi_{jk}{}^{\alpha}$ as fixed parameters (we shall later average over all orientations as for a powder sample) and regard the operator portions of $\mathscr{H}_d$ as being modulated rapidly by $\mathscr{H}_e$ in accordance with the Heisenberg equation for $\mathscr{H}_d$. In the simple case of $\{jk\}_0$, which commutes with $\mathscr{H}_Z$, we have

$$\begin{aligned}K_{jk}{}^{00}(\tau) &= \mathrm{tr}[e^{-b\mathscr{H}}(e^{i\mathscr{H}_e\tau}\{jk\}_0 e^{-i\mathscr{H}_e\tau}\{jk\}_0)]/\mathrm{tr}\, e^{-b\mathscr{H}}\\ K^{\alpha\alpha'}(\tau) &= \sum_k K_{jk}{}^{\alpha\alpha'}(\tau)\end{aligned} \tag{7-50}$$

As the reader may suspect, we shall usually guess the form of these correlation functions, although Moriya[7] has made a calculation to order $1/T^2$.

[7] T. Moriya, *Progr. Theoret. Phys.* (*Kyoto*), **16,** 23 (1956).

Now (7-49) is simplified by a change of variable. We have a form

$$I(t) = \int_0^t dt_1 \int_0^{t_1} dt_2\, f(t_1 - t_2) \tag{7-51}$$

Upon letting $t_1 - t_2 = x$, $dt_2 = -dx$ for t_2 integration. Define $g(t_1) = \int_0^{t_1} f(x)\, dx$. Then

$$I(t) = \int_0^t dt_1\, g(t_1) = t_1 g(t_1)\Big]_0^t - \int_0^t t_1(dg/dt_1)\, dt_1$$

But $dg/dt_1 = f(t_1)$. Then shifting to variable τ instead of t_1,

$$I(t) = tg(t) - \int_0^t \tau f(\tau)\, d\tau$$

$$= \int_0^t (t - \tau) f(\tau)\, d\tau \tag{7-52}$$

We can use (7-52) as we collect (7-42) with (7-49) to give our approximate form $G^{(2)}(t)$ as in (7-30):

$$G^{(2)}(t) = (CN/6kT)S(S+1)e^{i\omega_0 t}\{1 - \tfrac{3}{4}S(S+1)\int_0^t d\tau(t-\tau)$$

$$\times [K^{00}(\tau) + \tfrac{16}{9}e^{i\omega_0\tau}K^{-1,1}(\tau) + \tfrac{8}{3}e^{-i\omega_0\tau}K^{1,-1}(\tau)$$
$$+ \tfrac{16}{9}e^{-2i\omega_0\tau}K^{2,-2}(\tau)]\} + \text{c.c.} \tag{7-53}$$

Since the factor unity inside the braces gives the unperturbed motion (7-40) for noninteracting spins, and the next term is presumably a correction term due to the perturbation, Kubo and Tomita now make an *assumption*, based upon $G^{(2)}(t)$, as to the form of $G(t)$. They suppose (7-53) to be an expansion of an exponential. No justification can be given for this, although Kubo and Tomita cite stringent integrability conditions on $G(t)$ with which this assumption is consistent. Thus they assume

$$G(t) = (CN/6kT)S(S+1)e^{i\omega_0 t}\exp\{-\tfrac{3}{4}S(S+1)\int_0^t d\tau(t-\tau)[\cdots]\} + \text{c.c.} \tag{7-54}$$

where the bracket integrand is that of (7-53). The complex conjugate in (7-54) refers to the resonance at $-\omega_0$. Because we considered linearly polarized magnetic excitations, this resonance arises from the "wrong-rotating" component of the linear field. Henceforth, we neglect this resonance at $-\omega_0$.

Rigid-Lattice Second Moment from the Kubo–Tomita $G(t)$. Without yet assuming a form for $K^{\alpha\alpha'}(\tau)$, a number of interesting conclusions can be drawn from (7-53) or (7-54) for a rigid lattice with no exchange, which implies $K^{\alpha\alpha'}(\tau) = \text{const} = K^{\alpha\alpha'}(0)$, as there is then no random modulation of $\mathscr{H}_d$. Consider the integrand term $K^{00}(\tau)$:

$$\int_0^t (t-\tau)K^{00}(0)\,d\tau = K^{00}(0)(t^2/2)$$

Then the exponential form (7-54) becomes, neglecting the complex conjugate and therefore the lines at $-\omega_0$,

$$G(t) = e^{i\omega_0 t}\exp\{-\tfrac{1}{2}[\tfrac{3}{4}S(S+1)K^{00}(0)]t^2\} \tag{7-55}$$

where the other terms in the bracket are neglected because the factor $e^{\pm i\omega_0\tau}$ or $e^{\mp 2i\omega_0\tau}$ causes them to oscillate rapidly to zero average value. From (7-55) and (7-19) we obtain

$$\Gamma(t) = \exp\{-\tfrac{1}{2}[\tfrac{3}{4}S(S+1)K^{00}(0)]t^2\}$$

which clearly gives $\Gamma(0) = 1$ as required by (7-4). It is interesting to verify from (7-7) and the above $\Gamma(t)$ the following relations:

$$\begin{aligned}\mu_\Omega{}^2 &= -\,d^2\Gamma(t)/dt^2|_{t=0}\\ &= \tfrac{3}{4}S(S+1)K^{00}(0)\end{aligned} \tag{7-56}$$

$$\Gamma(t) = \exp(-\tfrac{1}{2}\mu_\Omega{}^2t^2)$$

The student can readily calculate classically the powder average $K^{00}(0)$ and show that these relations agree with Van Vleck's second-moment expression. In this approximation the rigid lattice line, without exchange effects, is a Gaussian with the proper Van Vleck second moment, since the Fourier transform $F(\Omega)$ obtained by (7-5) from a Gaussian $\Gamma(t)$ is a Gaussian in frequency.

The Subsidiary Non-Larmor Lines for a Rigid Lattice. Consider, for example, the integrand term in $K^{-1,1}(\tau)$ in (7-53). For $K^{-1,1}(\tau) = \text{const} = K^{-1,1}(0)$, it becomes

$$\begin{aligned}&-\tfrac{4}{3}S(S+1)\int_0^t (t-\tau)e^{i\omega_0\tau}K^{-1,1}(0)\,d\tau\\ &= -\,\tfrac{4}{3}S(S+1)K^{-1,1}(0)\omega_0{}^{-2}[e^0 - e^{i\omega_0 t} + i\omega_0 t]\end{aligned} \tag{7-57}$$

As (7-56) shows, $K^{\alpha\alpha'}(0)$ is of magnitude comparable to the dipolar second moment, and the factor in front of the bracket in (7-57) is of order μ_Ω^2/ω_0^2, which is usually much less than unity. The e^0 term thus provides a small correction to the Larmor line at ω_0 given by the $e^{i\omega_0 t}$ factor in front of the braces of (7-53). The $e^{i\omega_0 t}$ term in (7-57) combines with the $e^{i\omega_0 t}$ factor in front of the braces to give $e^{2i\omega_0 t}$, corresponding in its Fourier transform to a line at $2\omega_0$ but of relative intensity $K^{-1,1}(0)/\omega_0^2 \approx \omega_d^2/\omega_0^2$, where ω_d is an angular-frequency measure of the strength of dipolar interaction. Thus the subsidiary resonances and intensities as deduced in Sec. 4-1 and sketched in Fig. 4-2 are provided by our approximate $G(t)$. The other integrand terms in (7-53) will give the lines at 0 and $3\omega_0$.

The last term in (7-57) is something we have not heretofore encountered and is strictly a product of the refined theories. Placed in the assumed exponential form (7-54), it gives a frequency shift of the Larmor line by an amount

$$\delta\omega = -\,4S(S+1)K^{-1,1}(0)/3\omega_0 \approx -\,\omega_d^2/\omega_0 \qquad (7\text{-}58)$$

which is small and normally unmeasurable or, at best, measurable with difficulty. The larger ω_d is, the broader is the line within which the shift must be found.

Exchange Narrowing. Here we can no longer avoid assuming a form for $K^{\alpha\alpha'}(\tau)$. For simplicity we assume all $K^{\alpha\alpha'}(\tau)$ to have the same functional dependence on τ, and we use a Gaussian correlation function as first suggested in this connection by Anderson and Weiss (Ref. 12 of Chapter 4),

$$K^{\alpha\alpha'}(\tau) = K^{\alpha\alpha'}(0)\exp(-\tfrac{1}{2}\omega_e^2\tau^2) \qquad (7\text{-}59)$$

where ω_e corresponds to $1/\tau_c$ in Sec. 4-3. This form is consistent with Moriya's calculation[7] in the high-temperature approximation, which gives the form (7-59) with $\hbar^2\omega_e^2 = (8/3)J^2zS(S+1)$, where z is the number of nearest-neighbors.

First we shall consider what is called the *adiabatic* broadening. Returning to the bracket of (7-53), we shall define this kind of broadening to occur when $\omega_0 > \omega_e$. This means that $K^{-1,1}(\tau)$, for example, will persist through at least several oscillations of $e^{i\omega_0\tau}$, thus carrying the integral to a much smaller value than that over $K^{00}(\tau)$, which has no oscillatory multiplicative factor. The *adiabatic* broadening thus arises only from $K^{00}(\tau)$, i.e., from the diagonal perturbations in (7-45). Then, from (7-54) and (7-19),

$$\Gamma(t) = C' \exp[-\tfrac{3}{4}S(S+1)\int_0^t (t-\tau)K^{00}(0)e^{-\omega_e^2\tau^2/2}\,d\tau] \tag{7-60}$$

Let us examine the tails of the line. Recall that the tails [i.e., $F(\Omega)$ for large Ω] are determined through the Fourier transform by small values of t. In order to have narrowing, we suppose $\omega_e^2 > \omega_d^2 \approx \mu_\Omega^2$. From (7-56) we can write (7-60) as

$$\Gamma(t) = C' \exp[-\mu_\Omega^2 \int_0^t (t-\tau)e^{-\omega_e^2\tau^2/2}\,d\tau] \tag{7-61}$$

and expand $e^{-\omega_e^2\tau^2/2}$ as $1 - \frac{1}{2}\omega_e^2\tau^2$. Then we obtain

$$\Gamma(t \to 0) \approx \exp(-\tfrac{1}{2}\mu_\Omega^2 t^2 + \tfrac{1}{24}\mu_\Omega^2\omega_e^2 t^4) \tag{7-62}$$

From (7-62) and (7-7) we find $\mu_\Omega^4 = \mu_\Omega^2\omega_e^2$, in order-of-magnitude agreement with (4-30), as obtained from Van Vleck's calculation when $J > E_d$ (or, in angular frequency terms, when $\omega_e > \omega_d$).

Now we consider the center of the line $F(\Omega)$. This means consider large t. For large t, the exponent in (7-61) is proportional to

$$t\int_0^{t\to\infty} e^{-\omega_e^2\tau^2/2}\,d\tau - \int_0^{t\to\infty} \tau e^{-\omega_e^2\tau^2/2}\,d\tau = \sqrt{(\pi/2)}\,t/\omega_e - \tfrac{1}{2}\omega_e^{-2}$$

Then (7-61) becomes, with $t > 1/\omega_e$, which means for $F(\Omega)$ with $\Omega < \omega_e$,

$$\Gamma(t) = \exp(-\sqrt{(\pi/2)}\,\mu_\Omega^2|t|/\omega_e) \tag{7-63}$$

as $\Gamma(t)$ must be an even function of t. The transform of (7-63) is, for $\Omega < \omega_e$,

$$F(\Omega) = \text{const}/(\Omega^2 + R^2) \tag{7-64}$$

where

$$R = 1/T_2 = \sqrt{(\pi/2)}\,\mu_\Omega^2/\omega_e \tag{7-65}$$

This gives a good confirmation of the Anderson line-shape model and its predictions (4-34) and (4-35).

Nonadiabatic broadening can occur when we relax our condition $\omega_e < \omega_0$ imposed at the beginning of this subsection. In the event

$\omega_e > \omega_0$, $K^{-1,1}(\tau)$ will decay so rapidly that the oscillations of $e^{i\omega_0\tau}$ in the integrand of (7-53) or (7-54) will not have had time to occur, and, for integration purposes, $e^{i\omega_0\tau} \approx 1$. Then the terms in $K^{-1,1}(\tau)$, $K^{2,-2}(\tau)$, etc., will contribute amounts comparable to that from $K^{00}(\tau)$ to the exponent in (7-54). Of course, if ω_e is large, we see from (7-63) [which arose from $K^{00}(\tau)$ only] and the reasoning leading to (7-65) that $K^{00}(\tau)$ provides a smaller adiabatic width contribution of order $\mu_\Omega{}^2/\omega_e$. But the other $K^{\alpha,\alpha'}(\tau)$ terms contribute comparable amounts and it is found that, under assumption of an isotropic powder sample, the total width from all these sources is

$$1/T_2|_{\text{extreme narrowing}} = \tfrac{10}{3}\sqrt{(\pi/2)}\mu_\Omega{}^2/\omega_e \qquad (\omega_e > \omega_0) \qquad (7\text{-}66)$$

The additional 7/3 of the broadening (7-66) as compared to (7-65) arises from $K^{\alpha\alpha'}(\tau)$ other than $K^{00}(\tau)$ and is called the *nonadiabatic broadening*. Inclusion of the nonadiabatic broadening to give the result (7-66) is what was called after (4-36) "the esoteric phenomenon of the $\frac{10}{3}$ effect."

Because of the several fundamental assumptions, this theory of Kubo and Tomita may perhaps be considered only a detailed semi-phenomenological model of the resonance line. To be critical of the theory's shortcomings, however, is to miss completely the important point. When the theory appeared in 1953 and 1954, it set the tone and the ambitious program for a number of serious and detailed examinations of the theory of magnetic resonance and magnetic relaxation for an assembly of many interacting particles. Much progress has been made, since the early work, by other authors as well as by Kubo and Tomita themselves. Section 7-3 will include references to some of these other papers.

7-3 General Theories of Spin-Lattice Relaxation Processes

Because the example of Sec. 7-2 did not involve a lattice Hamiltonian at all, it clearly could not include spin-lattice relaxation in a literal sense of the term. However, it can include an essential step in spin-lattice relaxation for some systems. When there is appreciable exchange interaction, Bloembergen and Wang[8] pointed out that energy of spin orientation may first make its way to an intermediate thermal reservoir, which is in fact the so-called exchange system having energy $\mathscr{H}_e$. This intermediate reservoir can in turn transfer energy to the

[8] N. Bloembergen and S. Wang, *Phys. Rev.*, **93**, 72 (1954).

lattice vibrations. In this two-step process, it may happen that the first step is the slower and thus the limiting step determining the over-all relaxation rate $1/T_1$. This part of the two-step relaxation process can then be calculated as done in the Kubo and Tomita articles,[1,2] where the lattice-motional Hamiltonian was used as an example instead of $\mathscr{H}_e$. This analysis shows that $1/T_1$ is comparable in magnitude to, but not precisely the same as, the nonadiabatic contribution to $1/T_2$ (whether adiabatic effects dominate $1/T_2$ or not). An interesting discussion of this two-step spin-lattice relaxation process via the intermediate exchange reservoir is given by Van Vleck.[9] Some additional experimental evidence on the model is given by Goldsborough et al.[10] A calculation of the second step in the process has been made by Griffiths.[11]

The general theories of relaxation processes begin with the paper of Wangsness and Bloch,[12] who set for themselves the task of examining the effect of a general magnetic field $H(t)$ produced by the molecular surroundings and acting upon a collection of individual spins. This theory is, of course, severely limited in applicability by its exclusion of interactions between the spins. It was, however, an important pioneering effort which, like the essentially contemporary work of Kubo and Tomita, pointed the way to the future development of the theory.

F. Bloch[13] in 1956 generalized and extended the work begun with Wangsness. This second paper includes a discussion of interacting magnetic moments and saturation effects, including some double resonance phenomena and other important time dependences in the Hamiltonian. Independently and nearly simultaneously, A. G. Redfield[14] developed a theory of relaxation processes which emphasized the problems for complicated systems without important time variations in the Hamiltonian.

In most of these general theories, the approach is approximate solution of the equation of motion for the density matrix or statistical operator ρ:

$$d\rho/dt = -(i/\hbar)[\mathscr{H},\rho] \tag{7-67}$$

The time variation of the magnetization is then to be found, of course,

[9] J. H. Van Vleck, *Nuovo cimento*, **6** (*Suppl.*), 1081 (1957).

[10] J. P. Goldsborough, M. Mandel, and G. E. Pake, *Phys. Rev. Letters*, **4,** 13 (1960). The lowest-temperature points in this study are in question because of lattice heating effects.

[11] R. B. Griffiths, *Phys. Rev.*, **124,** 1023 (1961).

[12] R. K. Wangsness and F. Bloch, *Phys. Rev.*, **89,** 728 (1953).

[13] F. Bloch. *Phys. Rev.*, **102,** 104 (1956).

[14] A. G. Redfield, *IBM J. Res. Develop.*, **1,** 19 (1957).

from $\langle \mathbf{M} \rangle = \mathrm{tr}(\rho \mathbf{M})$. The typical approach to the solution (7-67) involves techniques illustrated in Sec. 7-2. It is usual to transform away the known and rapid time dependences arising from the Zeeman Hamiltonian by shifting to the interaction representation, and integration of the equation of motion by successive approximation is carried through with as few assumptions and neglected terms as possible. In many cases a reduced density matrix, applying only to spin coordinates, is solved for quantum mechanically, whereas the lattice is treated classically.

No useful purpose would be served by going into greater detail on these topics here, since the skilful blend of the general theories in Abragam's book (Ref. 5 of Chapter 5) is available to those readers who develop a deeper theoretical interest. Before leaving the topic, two final comments are in order.

First, the approach of nuclear or electronic spin assemblies to equilibrium provides perhaps the best vehicle yet for the study of irreversible statistical mechanics. Even for 10^{22} spins, there are still only a finite—if large—number of spin states accessible to the system, and it is possible experimentally to prepare the assembly in a variety of reasonably well-defined initial nonequilibrium states. It should not be forgotten that the derivation of equations describing irreversible dissipative behavior by beginning with the Schroedinger equation is a fundamental problem of physics not yet fully understood. For a recent attempt and discussion, inspired in large measure by magnetic relaxation effects, see the work of Sher and Primakoff.[15]

Second, we have continually in this chapter spoken of theories of nuclear magnetic relaxation as if they were fully applicable to electronic magnetic relaxation. Where *g* anisotropies exist, modifications may be required to carry over a nuclear result into the electronic domain. An example is the Van Vleck second-moment expression for a powder sample. There is not, to this writer's knowledge, a calculation that incorporates the effect of appreciable *g* anisotropy into such a calculation; Pryce and Stevens[16] discuss some related situations.

[15] A. Sher and H. Primakoff, *Phys. Rev.*, **119**, 178 (1960).

[16] M. H. L. Pryce and K. W. H. Stevens, *Proc. Phys. Soc.* (*London*), **A63**, 36 (1951).

[8]

Application of Paramagnetic Resonance to Materials Having Special Properties

8-1 Introductory Remarks

In our discussion thus far of paramagnetic resonance in solids we have had in mind the resonance of unpaired electrons in paramagnetic insulators, which could either be ionic crystals, or, as at the end of Chapter 4, molecular crystals of the organic free radicals. In this chapter we turn to materials having special conduction or magnetic properties. The brevity of our discussion should not mislead the reader into thinking that these are unimportant applications of paramagnetic resonance. Quite the contrary, the importance of the subject has often been that it has helped to provide much information about these materials. The brevity is the result of the goal of this book, which is to present the physical phenomena underlying electronic paramagnetic resonance so that the students can comprehend its uses and read the periodical literature concerning its applications. We do wish at least to introduce some of the applications even though we do not dwell on them.

8-2 Conduction Electron Resonance

In a metal or other conductor, there are relatively mobile electrons within the crystal structure. In first approximation these electrons are distributed in energy in accordance with the Fermi-Dirac distribution function,

$$f(E) = 1/[e^{(E-E_F)/kT} + 1] \tag{8-1}$$

which weighs the distribution of electron energy states $g(E)$ in the material. It is, of course, a well-known property of (8-1) at low temperatures that essentially all states below E_F are filled and all states above E_F are empty. As kT is increased, the energy states in a region within about $\pm kT$ of E_F become partially occupied.

Because the lower electron momentum states have electron spins paired off, they cannot contribute to a magnetic moment for the conductor. Those states, if any, near E_F can contribute, and for a simple metal, they give the Pauli paramagnetic susceptibility.[1] In order of magnitude the Pauli susceptibility is simply obtained from the Curie static susceptibility (1-10) if one recalls that only a fraction $\sim kT/E_F$ of the electrons are in unpaired momentum states. Thus

$$\chi_P \approx N(kT/E_F)g^2\beta^2/4kT = N\beta^2/E_F \tag{8-2}$$

which is the well-known temperature-independent susceptibility.

If a fraction kT/E_F of the electrons in a simple metal contributes to paramagnetism of the metal, they should in principle exhibit paramagnetic resonance. Such a resonance was discovered by Griswold, Kip, and Kittel,[2] and other experimental results are presented by Feher and Kip[3] and Levy.[4] Resonances have been observed for Li, Na, and Be, and probably for K. Many metals have not given observable resonances, presumably because relaxation times are too short and the lines are thus too broad. There are also complications introduced by the small skin depth, which means that small particles are required to provide access of the electrons to nonvanishing microwave fields. When particles are not small, the motion of electrons in and out of the skin-layer region leads to asymmetric line shapes.[5] Of course, fewer electrons are available to provide resonance absorption if many of them are in the interior, beyond the penetration of the fields.

There is also a conduction electron resonance in semiconductors. If one considers the simple example of an intrinsic semiconductor, the

[1] C. Kittel, "Introduction to Solid State Physics," 2nd ed., Wiley, New York, 1956.

[2] T. W. Griswold, A. F. Kip, and C. Kittel, *Phys. Rev.*, **88,** 951 (1952).

[3] G. Feher and A. F. Kip, *Phys. Rev.*, **98,** 337 (1955).

[4] R. A. Levy, *Phys. Rev.*, **102,** 31 (1950).

[5] F. J. Dyson, *Phys. Rev.*, **98,** 349 (1955).

Fermi level lies in the gap between the valence band and the conduction band. Therefore the density-of-states function to be multiplied by $f(E)$ of (8-1) has no states near E_F. However, if the temperature becomes high enough, electrons will of course be excited from the valence band to the conduction band, and potentially one may observe the conduction electron resonance. This was first done by Portis et al.[6] for an impurity semiconductor.

8-3 Resonance of Donor and Acceptor Impurities in Semiconductors

When a group V element is introduced into the crystal lattice of silicon, its atoms occupy a lattice site that would otherwise have contained a Si atom, and four of the five valence electrons enter into the four bonds to the neighboring Si atoms of the site. This leaves the fifth electron to move in the coulomb field of the group V ion. Because the silicon lattice has a dielectric constant of about 12, this coulomb field is reduced by dielectric polarization effects, and the weaker electrostatic force leads to an electron orbit much like that of a large hydrogen atom with a Bohr radius of ϵa_0^*, where ϵ is the dielectric constant and a_0^* is the Bohr radius corresponding to the electron's effective mass in the semiconductor. Of course, there is a corresponding reduction in the ionization energy, by a factor ϵ^{-2}, and this energy is in fact the energy required to free the electron from the donor center, i.e., to excite it to the conduction band. The reader should consult Kittel's book[1] for an introduction to the picture of the donor impurity center.

When bound in the ground state of the large hydrogenlike electron orbits about the impurity center, the extra electron is in fact a seat of paramagnetism. Its four brothers in the valence shell of the group V atom have their spins effectively cancelled in the bonding with the four Si neighbors. The paramagnetic electron not only exhibits a paramagnetic resonance near $g = 2$, as one might expect for the S-state first Bohr orbital, but it also possesses an isotropic hyperfine structure arising from the contact hyperfine interaction term (3-28). Figure 8-1 presents resonances obtained by Feher[7] from phosphorus-doped silicon.

The number of hyperfine lines $(2I + 1)$ helps to confirm the identity of the impurity giving rise to the resonance. The magnitude of the splitting reflects, of course, $|\psi(0)|^2$ for the unpaired electron and provides

[6] A. Portis, A. F. Kip, C. Kittel, and W. Brattain, *Phys. Rev.*, **90,** 988 (1953).

[7] G. Feher, *Phys. Rev.*, **114,** 1219 (1959).

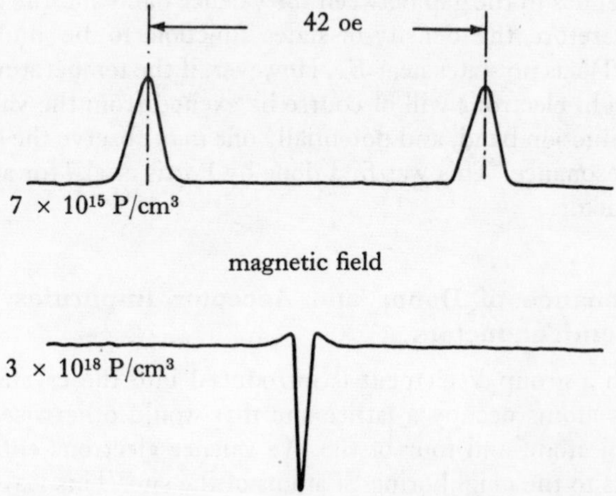

Fig. 8-1 Resonances from two samples of phosphorus-doped silicon.[7] The upper spectrum is a doublet arising from hyperfine interaction of the P^{31} nucleus of the donor with the paramagnetic fifth electron, which circulates about the donor ion in an expanded hydrogen-like orbit. The lower spectrum has a higher concentration of donors and exhibits a single electron resonance without hyperfine splitting because of exchange interactions. Spectra are observed at 8845 Mc sec^{-1} and 1.25°K.

the theoretical physicist with a sensitive test of the picture we have presented for the structure of the donor-impurity center.[8] The beautiful series of experiments described by Feher[7,9] indicates that paramagnetic resonance has afforded a superb tool indeed for studying donor impurities in semiconductors.

As is pointed out by Kohn,[8] the degeneracy of the valence band in silicon makes observation of paramagnetic resonance from acceptors difficult. Recently, however, Feher, Hensel, and Gere[10] have observed absorption by acceptors in silicon using a technique of applying a uniaxial stress to the crystal to lift the degeneracy. For boron-doped silicon, they find the hole g value to be anisotropic with respect to the stress axis.

[8] W. Kohn, Solid State Physics, F. Seitz and D. Turnbull (eds.), Academic Press, New York, 1957, Vol. 5.

[9] G. Feher and E. A. Gere, *Phys. Rev.*, **114,** 1245 (1959).

[10] G. Feher, J. C. Hensel, and E. A. Gere, *Phys. Rev. Letters*, **5,** 309 (1960).

8-4 Ferromagnetic Resonance

When paramagnetic ions in a regular crystalline three-dimensional array have a nearest-neighbor exchange integral J, the spins and therefore the magnetic moments become aligned or polarized if the temperature meets the condition $kT < |J|$. If J as defined in (4-6) is positive, the spins fall into a lowest-energy state which is characterized by parallel spins and which is, of course, called the ferromagnetic state. Can one observe magnetic resonance in such a material?

An affirmative answer was provided by Griffiths[11] and Yager and Bozorth.[12] But it was apparent that the resonance condition was not simply $\omega = \gamma H_0$. For example, Yager and Bozorth used a microwave cavity with one wall made of a magnetic material, Supermalloy, so arranged that the microwave magnetic field and the externally applied static magnetic field were perpendicular to each other in the plane of the cavity magnetic wall. A sharp resonance occurred at 5000 oersteds, with a frequency of 24,000 Mc sec^{-1}, which is quite at variance with the 2.80 Mc (sec oersted)$^{-1}$ characterizing spin-only paramagnetic resonance.

Kittel[13] showed that this dilemma arises because of the demagnetizing fields, which are of course appreciable for a specimen of magnetized ferromagnetic material. (In fact, for ordinary paramagnetic materials at low-enough temperature, even the Curie susceptibility can occasionally lead—for crystals dense in paramagnetic ions—to measurable demagnetizing effects.) Kittel's development of the resonance conditions, which we give below, is entirely classical; Van Vleck[14] has presented a quantum mechanical discussion yielding the same result.

Consider the macroscopic magnetization **M** and the angular momentum density **J** of the ferromagnet,

$$\mathbf{M} = \gamma \mathbf{J} \tag{8-3}$$

The equation of motion for unit volume of the sample is

$$d\mathbf{J}/dt = \mathbf{M} \times \mathbf{H} \tag{8-4}$$

[The reader who wants to worry about whether (8-4) should contain **H** or **B** should note that the $4\pi\mathbf{M}$ part of **B** will give a vanishing cross product with **M**.] If the sample shape is ellipsoidal, the demagnetizing

[11] J. H. E. Griffiths, *Nature*, **158**, 670 (1946).
[12] W. A. Yager and R. M. Bozorth, *Phys. Rev.*, **72**, 80 (1947).
[13] C. Kittel, *Phys. Rev.*, **73**, 155 (1948).
[14] J. H. Van Vleck, *Phys. Rev.*, **78**, 266 (1950).

fields in a uniform external field will also be uniform. If x, y, z is a principal axis system of the ellipsoid, the effective internal magnetic field for H_0 along z and the rf field along x is

$$\begin{aligned} H_x{}^i &= 2H_1e^{i\omega t} - N_xM_x \\ H_y{}^i &= -N_yM_y \\ H_z{}^i &= H_0 - N_zM_z \end{aligned} \tag{8-5}$$

The equation of motion is, using $\mathbf{H}^i$ for $\mathbf{H}$ in (8-4),

$$\begin{aligned} dM_x/dt &= \gamma[H_0+(N_y - N_z)M_z]M_y \\ dM_y/dt &= \gamma[M_z(2H_1e^{i\omega t}) - (N_x - N_z)M_xM_z - M_xH_0] \\ dM_z/dt &\cong 0 \end{aligned} \tag{8-6}$$

The right member of the dM_z/dt equation is taken zero because it is second order in the small quantities M_x and M_y (the N's are of order unity). Solution of these equations for $\chi_x = M_x/2H_1e^{i\omega t}$, assuming the time-dependence $e^{i\omega t}$ for M_x and M_y, gives

$$\chi_x = \frac{\chi_0}{1 - (\omega/\omega_0)^2} \tag{8-7}$$

where χ_0 is *not* the Curie susceptibility but is instead

$$\chi_0 = \frac{M_z}{H_0 + (N_x - N_z)M_z} \tag{8-8}$$

The resonance frequency is

$$\omega_0 = \gamma\{[H_0 + (N_y - N_z)M_z][H_0 + (N_x - N_z)M_z]\}^{1/2} \tag{8-9}$$

Several special cases occur frequently in experimental practice. First is the plane corresponding to the experiment discussed in the second paragraph of this section. For it, $N_x = N_z = 0$ and $N_y = 4\pi$. Then (8-9) reduces to

$$\omega_0 = \gamma(B_0H_0)^{1/2} \quad \text{(plane)} \tag{8-10}$$

which combines with the data of Yager and Bozorth to give a g value not too far from 2.0 (see Ref. 3).

For a sphere, $N_x = N_y = N_z = 4\pi/3$, and (8-9) becomes

$$\omega_0 = \gamma H_0 \quad \text{(sphere)} \tag{8-11}$$

For an infinite circular cylinder with axis along the static field direction,

$N_x = N_y = 2\pi$ and $N_z = 0$. The resonance condition is

$$\omega_0 = \gamma(H_0 + 2\pi M) \qquad \text{(cylinder)} \qquad (8\text{-}12)$$

An interesting feature of (8-12) which is also true for general ellipsoids other than the limiting case of the sphere and the plane, is the prediction of nonzero resonance frequency in zero external field when the specimen is magnetized. However, unless the magnetized specimen is magnetized as a single domain, inhomogeneous magnetization may cause damping effects that mask observation of the resonance.

For most samples, the condition (8-9) derived for the resonance is too simple, because anisotropy effects are also present within the crystal which influence the resonance frequency. The effect manifests itself as a dependence upon the relative directions of crystal axes and principal axes of the macroscopic specimen shape. Kittel[13] discusses methods of including these effects in the resonance condition.

A sample having extreme magnetic uniformity and low anisotropy can give a very sharp resonance, much as (8-7) predicts. Yager and Bozorth[12] used a logarithmic plot to follow the steep rise of the resonant susceptibility χ_x. In general, however, there are relaxation and damping effects in ferromagnetics which must be included.[15,16]

Finally, it should be noted that χ_x is not the imaginary susceptibility χ'' we have discussed earlier. Kittel discusses in a section of his paper[13] the relation between the eddy-current losses, the susceptibility χ_x, and the measured cavity Q.

8-5 Antiferromagnetic Resonance

Students unfamiliar with the salient properties of antiferromagnetic materials will find it advantageous to read an introductory discussion, such as that in Kittel's book.[17] The fundamental feature of the antiferromagnetic ground state is the ordered array of spins, which alternate spatially such that, as one proceeds along a row, successive spins point in one direction and then in the opposite. In effect there are two interpenetrating lattices having opposite magnetizations because the exchange integral J in (4-6) is negative instead of positive, as for ferromagnetic arrays. At first, such a structure was hypothesized to explain

[15] H. Suhl, *J. Phys. Chem. Solids*, **1,** 209 (1956).

[16] H. B. Callen, *J. Phys. Chem. Solids*, **4,** 256 (1958).

[17] C. Kittel, "Introduction to Solid State Physics," 2nd ed., Wiley, New York, 1956, Chap. 15.

observed susceptibility behavior. Subsequently the technique of neutron diffraction has provided beautiful direct confirmation of this picture.[18] In MnO, for example, Shull, Strauser, and Wollan[19] find the face-centered cubic lattice of Mn^{++} to have spins, lying in any line parallel to any cube axis, alternately pointing along and against some one cube axis. In MnF_2, the Mn^{++} ions are on a tetragonal lattice such as would be obtained by squeezing a body-centered cubic lattice along one cubic axis. The resulting cell is 3.31 A by 4.87 A square.[20]

Early studies of paramagnetic resonances in such materials were rewarded with the not especially satisfying result that the resonance disappeared as temperature was lowered through the transition temperature or Neel temperature from the paramagnetic region into the antiferromagnetic region.[21] The subsequent phenomenological theory of Kittel[22] and Keffer and Kittel[23] explained why this was so and pointed the way to experiments that indeed have observed resonance in the antiferromagnetic state.

The phenomenological theory begins by extending the idea of the molecular field or exchange field to antiferromagnets. Here, however, spins on the sublattice 1 experience an exchange field $-\lambda \mathbf{M}_2$ arising from the (oppositely pointed) magnetization on sublattice 2, and vice versa:

$$\begin{aligned} \mathbf{H}_{1E} &= -\lambda \mathbf{M}_2 \\ \mathbf{H}_{2E} &= -\lambda \mathbf{M}_1 \end{aligned} \tag{8-13}$$

It is further necessary to take into account the anisotropy forces. The anisotropy energy is described by an energy-density constant K, giving the energy necessary to turn the spin systems relative to the crystal axes. For small deflections of the magnetization, we may use an effective anisotropy field $H_A = K/M$, where M is the sublattice magnetization. The sublattice magnetization is treated as depending upon T/T_N, where T_N is the Néel temperature, just as the molecular field treatment finds it to depend upon T/T_C for the ferromagnetic case.[17]

Suppose now that $\mathbf{H}_0$ is along the preferred direction (z). Then $-\lambda \mathbf{M}_1$ and $-\lambda \mathbf{M}_2$ are the exchange fields. The anisotropy fields are $\mathbf{H}_A$ and $-\mathbf{H}_A$, acting respectively on sublattices 1 and 2. If $\mathbf{H}$ is the

[18] C. G. Shull and J. S. Smart, *Phys. Rev.*, **76,** 1256 (1949).
[19] C. G. Shull, W. A. Strauser, and E. O. Wollan, *Phys. Rev.*, **83,** 333 (1951).
[20] R. A. Erickson, *Phys. Rev.*, **90,** 779 (1953).
[21] L. R. Maxwell and T. R. McGuire, *Rev. Mod. Phys.*, **25,** 279 (1953).
[22] C. Kittel, *Phys. Rev.*, **82,** 565 (1951).
[23] F. Keffer and C. Kittel, *Phys. Rev.*, **85,** 329 (1952).

microwave magnetic field perpendicular to $\mathbf{H}_0$, the equations of motion are as follows:

$$\begin{aligned} d\mathbf{M}_1/dt &= \gamma\mathbf{M}_1 \times [(H_x - \lambda M_{2x})\mathbf{i} \\ &\quad + (H_y - \lambda M_{2y})\mathbf{j} + (H_0 + H_A + H_E)\mathbf{k}] \\ d\mathbf{M}_2/dt &= \gamma\mathbf{M}_2 \times [(H_x - \lambda M_{1x})\mathbf{i} \\ &\quad + (H_y - \lambda M_{1y})\mathbf{j} + (H_0 - H_A - H_E)\mathbf{k}] \end{aligned} \tag{8-14}$$

Here we denote $H_E = \lambda M_{1z} = -\lambda M_{2z}$. For our antiferromagnetic case, λ is positive.

The normal-mode frequencies of (8-14) may be found by putting $\mathbf{H} = 0$. If M_{1z} and M_{2z} are replaced by H_E/λ, the equations (8-14) become essentially a set of four homogeneous equations in M_{1x}, M_{1y}, M_{2x}, and M_{2y}. (Products of small quantities, such as $M_{1x}M_{2y}$, are dropped because the magnetizations are essentially along z.) The secular determinant for these four homogeneous equations may be solved[23] to give the four modes

$$\begin{aligned} \omega_1 &= -\,\omega_2 = \gamma H_0 + \gamma[H_A(2H_E + H_A)]^{1/2} \\ \omega_3 &= -\,\omega_4 = \gamma H_0 - \gamma[H_A(2H_E + H_A)]^{1/2} \end{aligned} \tag{8-15}$$

When there is zero external field,

$$\omega(H_0 = 0) = \gamma(2H_EH_A)^{1/2} \qquad (H_A \ll H_E) \tag{8-16}$$

Whether or not this frequency will be in the ordinary microwave range depends upon H_E. For substances with low T_N (e.g., $CuCl_2{\cdot}2H_2O$ with $T_N = 4.3°K$), it falls in this range and has been extensively studied at Leiden.[24]

For substances with larger T_N, H_E will be 10^5 or 10^6 oersteds, and H_A may be perhaps 10^3 or 10^4. Thus $(2H_EH_A)^{1/2}$ ranges from 10^4 up to or beyond 10^5 oersteds, corresponding to large microwave frequencies. Because of the minus sign in the second of equations (8-15), application of a large-enough magnetic field can bring ω_4 down toward easier microwave frequencies. This technique has been used by Foner.[25]

Johnson and Nethercot[26] used high frequencies in the region 96 to 247 kM sec^{-1} to study both branches of the frequency condition (8-15). Their paper gives a discussion of the experimental technique, as well as extensive data on frequency and line-width variation with temperature for MnF_2. For example, Fig. 8-2 shows the curve Johnson

[24] H. J. Gerritsen, thesis, University of Leiden, 1955. See H. J. Gerritsen and M. Garber, *Physica*, **22,** 197, 213, and 481 (1956).

[25] S. Foner, *Phys. Rev.*, **107,** 683 (1957).

[26] F. M. Johnson and A. H. Nethercot, *Phys. Rev.*, **114,** 705 (1959).

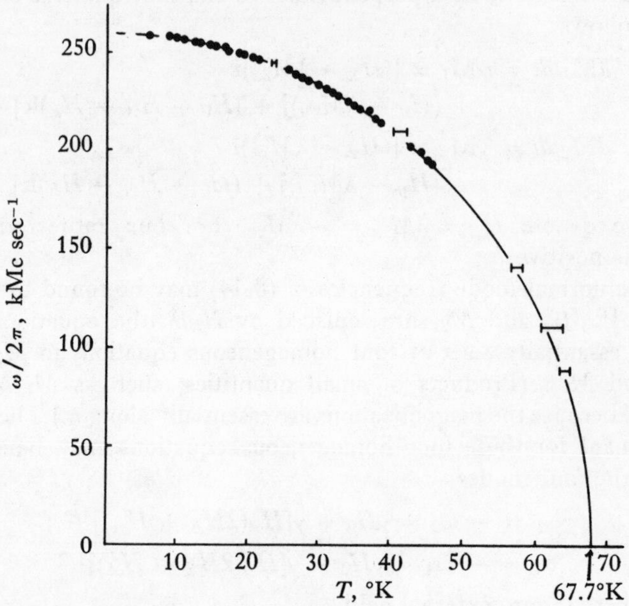

Fig. 8-2 Variation of $\omega = \gamma(2H_EH_A)^{\frac{1}{2}}$ with temperature as determined experimentally for a MnF_2 crystal in the antiferromagnetic state.

and Nethercot obtain for $\gamma(2H_EH_A)^{1/2}$ versus T showing clearly the effect of the decline of H_E as each such sublattice demagnetizes on approaching T_N from below. According to calculations of the anisotropy energy by Oguchi,[27] it can be concluded that $H_A \propto [M(T)]^{1.9}$. Thus we expect $(2H_EH_A)^{1/2}$ to vary as $[M(T)]^{1.45}$. Johnson and Nethercot use nuclear resonance frequency data for F^{19} to measure $M(T)$ and find good agreement with this predicted exponent of 1.45. In this way, considerable detail is learned about exchange and anisotropy fields within these antiferromagnets.

8-6 Electronic and Nuclear Population Rearrangements by Saturation of Electronic Transitions

Much of the recent interest in paramagnetic resonance has been elicited by the so-called solid-state maser, which provides new means

[27] T. Oguchi, *Phys. Rev.*, **111**, 1063 (1958).

for low-noise amplification, and by the various schemes for achieving nuclear polarization through saturation of electronic magnetic dipole transitions. Both of these experimental developments can be treated in introductory fashion by a rate-equation approach, although intense-enough saturation irradiation can lead to coherence effects not describable by rate equations.

The Three-Level Solid-State Maser. To illustrate the simplest form of this device one must consider a system having at least three levels not uniformly spaced (Fig. 8-3). The levels might arise from a combination of crystal-field and magnetic-field effects, as in the crystal, $NiSiF_6{\cdot}6H_2O$. Levels for a particular crystal orientation are shown in Fig. 3-8. As a consequence, the selection rules will in general permit transitions coupling all possible pairs of levels in Fig. 8-3. Suppose, as an illustration, that transition $1 \leftrightarrow 3$ is intensely irradiated, so that the population difference $N_3 - N_1$ is reduced to zero by saturation. After steady state has been reached in this nonequilibrium situation,

$$\begin{aligned} 0 = dN_1/dt &= -N_1(W_{12} + W_{13}) + N_2W_{21} + N_3W_{31} \\ = dN_2/dt &= N_1W_{12} - N_2(W_{21} + W_{23}) + N_3W_{32} \\ = dN_3/dt &= N_1W_{13} + N_2W_{23} - N_3(W_{32} + W_{31}) \end{aligned} \tag{8-17}$$

These three equations are linearly dependent because $N_1 + N_2 + N_3 = N$. Here W_{ij} is the probability per unit time of a transition from i to j, arising from all causes, including relaxation mechanisms and laboratory excitation. If transition $1 \leftrightarrow 3$ is saturated, then $N_3 = N_1$,

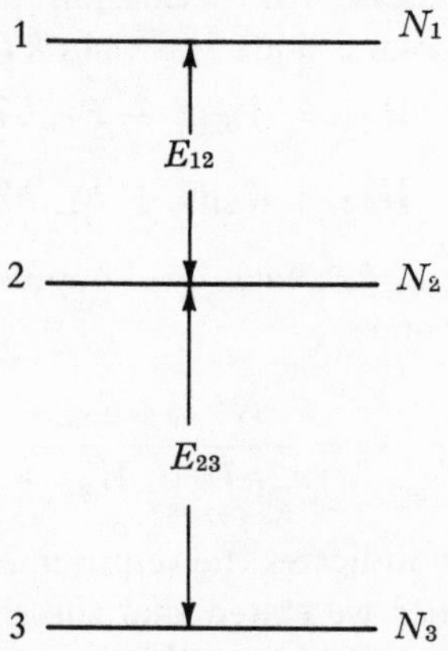

Fig. 8-3 Level scheme for discussion of the three-level maser.

and the first and third of equations (8-17) may be added and solved for N_2/N_1:

$$N_2/N_1 = (W_{12} + W_{32})/(W_{21} + W_{23}) \tag{8-18}$$

The population difference $N_1 - N_2$ may be found by subtracting (8-18) from $N_1/N_1 = 1$:

$$N_1 - N_2 = N_1 \frac{(W_{23} - W_{32}) - (W_{12} - W_{21})}{W_{21} + W_{23}} \tag{8-19}$$

Now N_1 and each W_{ij} are inherently positive. Furthermore, each bracket in the numerator of (8-19) is positive, because it represents an emission probability minus an absorption probability [recall (2-61) and (2-63)]:

$$\begin{aligned} W_{23} &= W_{32} \exp(E_{23}/kT) \\ W_{12} &= W_{21} \exp(E_{12}/kT) \end{aligned} \tag{8-20}$$

Depending upon the relative magnitudes of the W's and of E_{12} and E_{23}, the numerator in (8-19) *could* vanish, but in general it will not. Furthermore, it may even be *positive*, which puts a larger population N_1 in level 1 than that (N_2) occupying level 2. This is called a population inversion, and it has the property that, so long as energy of the proper frequency is supplied to saturate transition $1 \leftrightarrow 3$, the sample can supply energy at the frequency E_{12}/h. Such energy can be used to amplify or even to generate oscillations at the frequency E_{12}/h.

A simple special case for discussion purposes arises when all energy separations of Fig. 8-3 are less than kT. Then

$$\begin{aligned} W_{23} &= W_{32}(1 + E_{23}/kT) \\ W_{12} &= W_{21}(1 + E_{12}/kT) \end{aligned} \tag{8-21}$$

and, within a fraction E_i/kT, each level population is $N/3$. Under these conditions, (8-19) becomes

$$N_1 - N_2 = \frac{N}{3kT} \frac{W_{32}E_{23} - W_{21}E_{12}}{W_{21} + W_{23}} \tag{8-22}$$

The numerator clearly indicates the requirements to be met if $N_1 - N_2$ is to be positive. Earlier we stated that the three levels should not be uniformly spaced. In point of fact, this is not a proper phrasing of the restriction. The point is that, for many systems, if $E_{12} = E_{23}$, then it is likely—although far from a certainty—that $W_{32} = W_{21}$. Clearly the proper requirement for population inversion in the high-temperature case is

$$W_{32}E_{23} - W_{21}E_{12} > 0 \qquad (8\text{-}23)$$

Whenever $N_1 - N_2$ can be made positive, there is the potentiality of maser action permitting amplification. The advantage of such a preamplifier functioning in the microwave region with a paramagnetic crystal as the working substance is that the crystal may be kept cold, and, although there are many sources of noise that may make themselves felt, a much lower amplifier noise temperature can be achieved than with more conventional microwave preamplification techniques involving hot cathodes.

Even when there is not complete saturation, a population inversion between some pair of levels may occur in a multilevel system. The techniques of Lloyd and Pake (Ref. 10 of Chapter 2) may be used to calculate such population effects for any degree of partial saturation, provided rate equations give an adequate description of the system.

The first proposal along the lines of the foregoing argument was made by Bloembergen,[28] and the first experimental demonstration of such a device operating in the microwave range was made by Scovil, Feher, and Seidel.[29] A lanthanum ethylsulfate crystal containing 0.5 per cent gadolinium was used as the working substance. For a more detailed discussion of solid-state masers, some of the standard references on the subject should be consulted.[30–32]

It is of considerable scientific interest that the three-level maser preamplifier has been used quite successfully in radio-telescope applications. The 1421 Mc $\sec^{-1}$ emission line from galactic hydrogen (arising from relative reorientation of the nuclear and electronic magnetic moments that are in hyperfine interaction) is at a frequency which lends itself extremely well to maser amplification using common microwave sources for the saturating power. Since there is no opportunity to increase the power available from a galactic source, optimum signal-to-noise in the preamplification is the only possible approach to weak source regions of the galaxy.

[28] N. Bloembergen, *Phys. Rev.*, **104,** 324 (1956).

[29] H. E. D. Scovil, G. Feher, and H. Seidel, *Phys. Rev.*, **105,** 762 (1957).

[30] J. R. Singer, "Masers," Wiley, New York, 1959.

[31] A. A. Vuylsteke, "Elements of Maser Theory," Van Nostrand, Princeton, N.J., 1960.

[32] A. E. Siegman, "Microwave and Optical Masers," McGraw-Hill, New York, to be published.

The Overhauser Nuclear Polarization Effect. Another fascinating example of population rearrangement in consequence of saturating a paramagnetic resonance transition is the Overhauser effect, which was first proposed on theoretical grounds for metals[33] and which was shortly thereafter observed by Carver and Slichter.[34] We begin, however, with a discussion of the effect as observed for a nonconducting paramagnet, such as the phosphorus-doped silicon mentioned in Sec. 8-3. In consequence of the hyperfine interaction, the energy levels available to the system in a magnetic field are determined by the spin Hamiltonian

$$\mathscr{H} = g\beta H_0 S_z + a\mathbf{S}\cdot\mathbf{I} - g_N\beta_N H_0 I_z \tag{8-24}$$

Under typical experimental conditions, $g\beta H_0 > a > g_N\beta_N H_0$, we can neglect the nuclear Zeeman term. Then the energy levels will be given by simple first-order perturbation theory as

$$E(m_S,m_I) = g\beta H_0 m_S + a m_S m_I \tag{8-25}$$

which levels we show in Fig. 8-4 for a particular value of H_0. Defining $\frac{1}{2}g\beta H_0 = \Delta$ and $a/4 = \delta$, we give the energy of each level on the figure. Also labeled on the figure are certain transition probabilities.

W_e^e and W_e^a are, respectively, emission and absorption probabilities for a single electron flip, $|\Delta m_s| = 1$. The probabilities with subscript x refer to mutual flips of electron and nucleus, $\Delta m_s = \pm 1$, $\Delta m_I = \mp 1$, with superscripts a and e for absorption and emission. The heavy vertical arrow identifies the transition that we consider to be intensely irradiated—in this example, the electron resonance hyperfine component corresponding to $m_I = +\frac{1}{2}$. For the present, we suppose that no relaxation mechanism couples levels 1 and 4.

Of course, if there is no intense radiation of any transition and thermal equilibrium exists, the ratio of nuclear population having $m_I = +\frac{1}{2}$ to that having $m_I = -\frac{1}{2}$ will be given simply by the nuclear Boltzmann factor as

$$\frac{N_0(m_I = \frac{1}{2})}{N_0(m_I = -\frac{1}{2})} = \exp(g_N\beta_N H_0/kT)$$

$$\cong 1 + (g_N\beta_N H_0/kT) \tag{8-26}$$

where, in typical experiments, $g_N\beta_N H_0/kT \approx 10^{-5}$.

[33] A. W. Overhauser, *Phys. Rev.*, **92,** 411 (1953).
[34] T. R. Carver and C. P. Slichter, *Phys. Rev.*, **102,** 975 (1956).

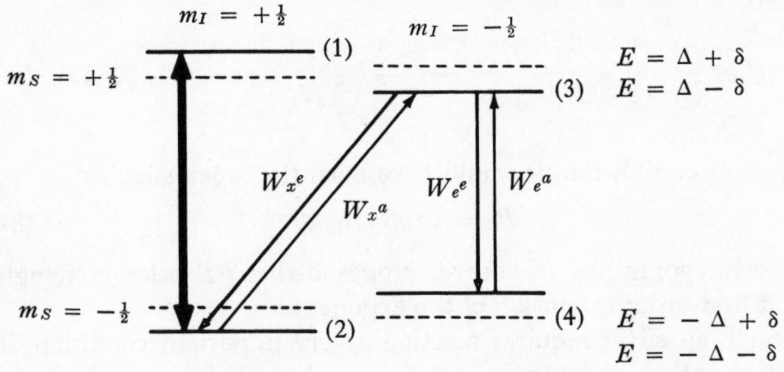

Fig. 8-4 Levels and relaxation probabilities (arrows) for discussion of the Overhauser polarization. The broad double arrow identifies the transition to which saturating radiation is applied.

When the transition $1 \leftrightarrow 2$ indicated in Fig. 8-4 is saturated, the levels it connects assume equal populations, $N_1 = N_2$. But if there is a relaxation mechanism causing $W_x{}^a$ and $W_x{}^e$, it follows from $W_x{}^a \cong W_x{}^e \exp(-2\Delta/kT) = W_x{}^e(1 - 2\Delta/kT)$ that there will be at steady state an excess of systems in the state 2 as compared to state 3:

$$N_3 \cong N_2(1 - 2\Delta/kT) \tag{8-27}$$

Finally, $W_e{}^e$ and $W_e{}^a$ will assure that

$$N_4 \cong N_3(1 + 2\Delta/kT) \tag{8-28}$$

where we neglect δ against Δ, $\delta \ll \Delta$. The polarization of the nuclei now corresponds to

$$\frac{N(m_I = \frac{1}{2})}{N(m_I = -\frac{1}{2})} = \frac{N_1 + N_2}{N_3 + N_4} = \frac{2N_2}{N_3(2 + 2\Delta/kT)}$$
$$= \frac{2(1 + 2\Delta/kT)}{2 + 2\Delta/kT} \cong 1 + \Delta/kT \tag{8-29}$$

But $2\Delta = g\beta H_0$ is the electron transition energy in a field H_0, and the population ratio (8-29) corresponds to a Boltzmann factor with Δ as the relevant energy instead of $g_N\beta_N H_0$, which is of order 300 to 1000 times or more smaller, depending upon the nucleus. In effect the nucleus is tricked into polarizing in an external field according to a Boltzmann factor with the much larger energy Δ. This leads to a far-greater-than-normal nuclear polarization. In fact, the polarization P, as usually defined, is

$$P = \frac{N(+) - N(-)}{N(+) + N(-)} = \frac{N_1 + N_2 - (N_3 + N_4)}{\sum_i N_i} = \tfrac{1}{2}\Delta/kT \quad (8\text{-}30)$$

whereas at equilibrium it would have been the much smaller

$$P_0 = \tfrac{1}{2}g_N\beta_N H_0/kT \quad (8\text{-}31)$$

All the foregoing has, of course, supposed that kT is large enough to permit first-order expansion of the exponentials.

Such an effect requires meeting a very important condition. The condition is that we must find a system with negligible relaxation, compared to W_x, between levels 1 and 4, as well as negligible nuclear relaxation (between levels 1 and 3 or 2 and 4). In fact our example above was tailored to impurity-doped silicon, for which lattice modulation of the hyperfine interaction is the probable W_x relaxation mechanism.[35] The hyperfine coupling should be quite isotropic, and if one writes it as

$$a\mathbf{I}\cdot\mathbf{S} = a[I_zS_z + \tfrac{1}{2}(I_+S_- + I_-S_+)] \quad (8\text{-}32)$$

it is evident that the off-diagonal part can provide only W_x processes, as there are no matrix elements of (8-32) connecting the states $m_S = +\frac{1}{2}$, $m_I = +\frac{1}{2}$ and $m_S = -\frac{1}{2}$, $m_I = -\frac{1}{2}$. Appreciable polarizations can be obtained in impurity-doped semiconductors, but one finds that there generally are competing relaxation processes.

It sometimes happens that the hyperfine coupling (8-32) will be sufficiently weak that the electron transitions $1 \leftrightarrow 2$ and $3 \leftrightarrow 4$ of Fig. 8-4 are unresolved. If so, it may be possible to saturate both electron transitions simultaneously. It is then a simple matter to show that one obtains twice the polarization of (8-30), namely,

$$P = \Delta/kT \quad (8\text{-}33)$$

This is a good exercise with which the student can verify that he has learned how to play the polarization game with level structures such as Fig. 8-4.

When it happens that the relaxation processes coupling levels 1 and 4 in Fig. 8-4 dominate W_x, the polarization of nuclei under full saturation of $1 \leftrightarrow 2$ will build up in the reverse direction and P will be negative. This is colloquially called the "Underhauser effect." It has been pointed out by Abragam[36] that the dipole-dipole interaction in a

[35] D. Pines, J. Bardeen, and C. P. Slichter, *Phys. Rev.*, **106**, 489 (1957).
[36] A. Abragam, *Phys. Rev.*, **98**, 1729 (1955).

liquid between paramagnetic solute molecules and nuclei of the solvent leads to an Underhauser effect. Both $1 \leftrightarrow 4$ and $2 \leftrightarrow 3$ relaxation processes arise from the dipolar interaction, as well as $1 \leftrightarrow 3$ and $2 \leftrightarrow 4$ processes. However, the net effect of the competition is a reverse polarization (for nuclei with positive nuclear moments) just half as great in magnitude as the pure Overhauser effect would provide.

Finally, it should be noted in closing this section that Overhauser's prediction of the effect for saturation of the conduction electron resonance in a metal cannot be calculated quite so simply as could be done for Fig. 8-4. The interaction of all conduction electrons with each nucleus must be considered. The Fermi distribution inserts a small complication into the calculation, which the one-to-one correspondence of interacting nucleus and electron avoids for the impurity center in a semiconductor.

The So-called Solid-State Effect. A polarization effect closely similar to the Overhauser effect has been called the solid-state effect.[37] Consider a nuclear moment and a nearby electron coupled weakly by the magnetic dipole interaction in a solid placed in a laboratory magnetic field. The level scheme might be as shown in Fig. 8-5, where ϵ arises from the nuclear Zeeman energy $-g_N \beta_N H_0 I_z$,

$$\epsilon = \tfrac{1}{2} g_N \beta_N H_0 \tag{8-34}$$

and the isotropic hyperfine coupling is taken to be negligible. The only purpose to be served by the weak anisotropic hyperfine coupling (dipole-dipole coupling between nucleus and electron) is to break down to a small degree the selection rule forbidding simultaneous flips of both the nucleus and electron (transitions $b \leftrightarrow c$ or $a \leftrightarrow d$ in Fig. 8-5). If either of these transitions is saturated, a polarization occurs, the sign of which depends upon whether saturation of $b \leftrightarrow c$ or $a \leftrightarrow d$ dominates. It is again a simple matter for the student to show that the greatest polarizations theoretically obtainable in this way are, respectively, $P = -\Delta/kT$ for the irradiation shown in Fig. 8-5 and $P = +\Delta/kT$ for irradiation of $a \leftrightarrow d$. The thermal-equilibrium nuclear polarization would be $+\ \epsilon/kT$, and we thus have a theoretically possible *enhancement* of $\pm\Delta/\epsilon$.

For protons and electrons this factor is 657, exactly the same as Overhauser predicted for electrons in metals. Abragam's book[38] and a

[37] A. Abragam and W. G. Procter, *Comp. rend.*, **246,** 2253 (1958).

[38] A. Abragam, "Principles of Nuclear Magnetism," Oxford University Press, New York, 1961, Chap. IX.

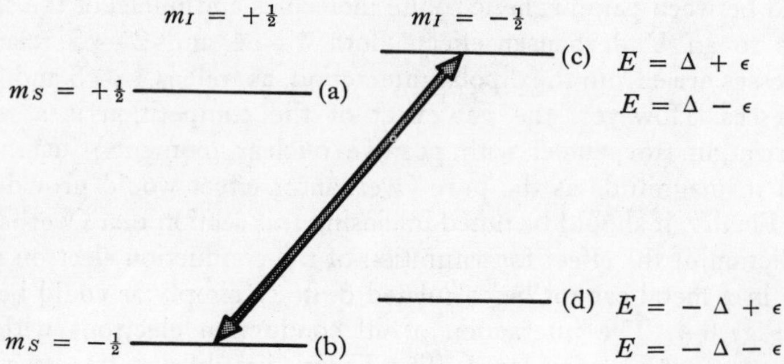

Fig. 8-5 Levels for illustration of the solid-state effect. The double arrow shows the transition that is saturated.

recent review paper[39] describe the enhancements or polarizations that have been achieved experimentally in various materials at various temperatures. At low temperatures, where P should be greatest, the enhancement is usually well below the theoretical maximum, because of competing effects. Because the nuclear resonance frequency is often quite small compared with the width of the electron line ($\Delta m_S = \pm 1$), it is difficult to saturate $b \leftrightarrow c$, for example, without irradiating to some degree $a \leftrightarrow d$, as well as the pure electron flips $a \leftrightarrow b$ and $c \leftrightarrow d$. As a consequence, the polarization may not be as large experimentally as one estimates from simple analysis of Fig. 8-5 with, e.g., $b \leftrightarrow c$ the only saturated transition. This is a competing effect for the solid effect, just as other relaxation processes were for the Overhauser effect.

Figure 8-6 illustrates how the solid-state-effect polarization changes sign as the external magnetic field is swept through the various transitions near the electron resonance frequency.

Both the Overhauser and solid-state effects are often referred to as dynamic nuclear polarizations.

The ENDOR Technique. A combination of microwave and radio-frequency techniques was devised by Feher[40] to permit study of nuclear resonances under conditions of appreciable hyperfine coupling that is, however, unresolved in the electron resonance spectrum. The

[39] R. H. Webb, *Am. J. Phys.*, **29**, 428 (1961). This review contains a superb bibliography, up to early 1961, on the various nuclear polarization effects obtainable by saturation of electron resonances.

[40] G. Feher, *Phys. Rev.*, **114,** 1219 (1959).

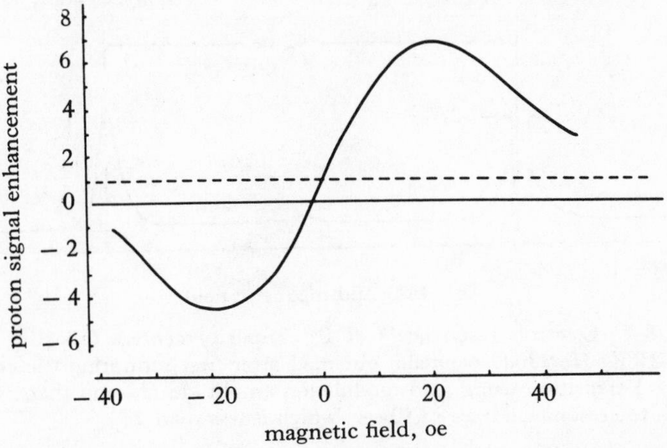

Fig. 8-6 Enhancement of the proton nuclear resonance at 4.2°K by the solid-state effect in the crystalline organic radical, Wurster's blue perchlorate [R. H. Webb, *Phys. Rev. Letters*, **6**, 611 (1961)]. The zero of magnetic field is taken at the center of the electron resonance for a microwave frequency of 9.7 kMc sec^{-1}. This resonance is exchange-narrowed to about 3 oersteds width and has a *g* very near 2.002.

electron resonance is then said to be *inhomogeneously* broadened,[41] meaning that each electron resonance occurs in a relatively static local hyperfine field corresponding to the spin orientations of the interacting nuclei; the ratio of each line width to the hyperfine splitting is large enough to prevent resolution and instead leads to one bell-shaped curve, the envelope of the individual lines. Saturation of such a resonance alters the profile of the envelope by "burning a hole," so to speak, in the resonance curve. This occurs because the saturating microwave field affects only those component lines of the envelope near the applied microwave frequency. The opposite effect occurs for a line with *homogeneous* broadening, for application of a saturating field anywhere within such a resonance simply reduces the line intensity uniformly throughout the entire curve (provided H_1 is not extremely large, thus introducing certain coherence effects[42]). A superb textbook example of a hole burned in an electron resonance is given by Feher,[40] who observes it in one line of the P^{31} doublet in an *n*-type silicon (Fig. 8-7).

[41] A. M. Portis, *Phys. Rev.*, **91,** 1071 (1953).
[42] W. I. Goldburg, *Phys. Rev.*, **122,** 831 (1961).

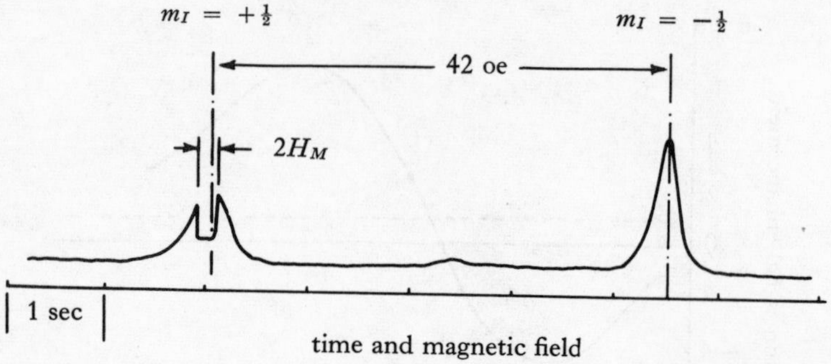

Fig. 8-7 Electron resonance[40] of P^{31} impurity centers (5×10^{16} P cm^{-3}, $T = 1.25°K$, $\mathbf{H}_0 \simeq 3000$ oersteds) obtained after first saturating the center of the $m_I = \frac{1}{2}$ transition using field-modulation amplitude H_m and then sweeping through the resonance trace in 10 sec, which is less than T_1.

The essence of the ENDOR technique is to hold the H_0 field on the electron resonance, using ample microwave intensity to saturate, while sweeping slowly the frequency of a radiofrequency field applied simultaneously to the sample. This can be done either by placing a coil in the cavity interior or by wrapping the rf coil about the outside of a cavity made from a nonconductor with walls plated to a thickness of a few microwave skin depths. When this radiofrequency reaches a value corresponding to one of the nuclear transitions possible in the electron's hyperfine coupling magnetic field at the nuclei, some nuclei will be flipped into the orientation corresponding to the hole that has been burned in the electron line. This should cause the electron absorption to rise, and thus a change in deflection of the electron resonance output meter occurs. Note that ENDOR is caused by the rf field but is detected by its effect on the microwave absorption. No rf detection equipment is used.

A careful experimental study of ENDOR in ruby by Lambe et al.,[43] includes examination of both the electron χ' and χ'' and has shown that under certain circumstances the picture of ENDOR given above is inadequate. They propose a model in which certain nuclei of the sample polarize via the solid effect but are then depolarized when the ENDOR rf field has the proper frequency to saturate a purely nuclear transition. Nuclei more distant from the paramagnetic center probably feel polarizing effects by means of nuclear spin diffusion, and application of the rf frequency to either the distant or local nuclei can ultimately effect

[43] J. Lambe, N. Laurence, E. C. McIrvine, and R. W. Terhune, *Phys. Rev.*, **122,** 1161 (1961).

the depolarization of nuclei in the unirradiated group. Clearly many effects can occur simultaneously in a given material under such double resonance conditions, and the response of the electron spectrometer is shown by Lambe et al. to depend upon a number of experimental parameters and details, including whether or not the spectrometer is sensitive, even to a small degree, to the dispersion part (χ') of the electron signal.

A beautiful example of the power of the ENDOR technique for studying incompletely resolved hyperfine structure is provided by the experiments of Holton, Blum, and Slichter,[44] who obtain hyperfine coupling constants for the first seven shells of nuclei surrounding an *F* center in crystals of LiF.

[44] W. C. Holton, H. Blum, and C. P. Slichter, *Phys. Rev. Letters*, **5**, 197 (1960).

Appendix

Representative Paramagnetic Resonance Results

The following tables (including three pages of references) are excerpts from the article by K. D. Bowers and J. Owen [*Repts. Progr. in Phys.*, **18**, 304 (1955)], reproduced with permission of the publisher, the Physical Society of London. The tables are included to give the student a number of detailed examples of paramagnetic resonance results. Supplementary tables to these, not given here, have been prepared by J. W. Orton [*Repts. Progr. in Phys.*, **22**, 204 (1959)].

Each table is headed by the symbol for the paramagnetic ion studied. Various crystals in which it has been studied are then listed. The row after the chemical formula for the crystal typically contains the temperature (T), the spectroscopic splitting factor (g), the fine structure couplings (D and E), and the hyperfine coupling (A), followed by remarks and one or more symbols denoting references given at the conclusion of the tables. When more than one isotope with a nuclear moment exists, the hyperfine coupling is preceded by a superscript giving the mass number of the isotope in question, such as ^{51}A for vanadium. Couplings P and P' measure nuclear quadrupole interactions; if the electric field gradient has axial symmetry, P' vanishes.

The coupling coefficients D, E, and A of the spin Hamiltonian are given in wave numbers (cm^{-1}). Of course, $1\ cm^{-1} = 3 \times 10^{10}$ cps.

Following are the abbreviations and symbols used in the tables:

d.	dilution, expressed as the ratio of number of ions of diluent to paramagnetic, e.g., ratio of number of Zn ions to Mn ions; in the chemical formulas, the diluent ion is in italics.
d.c.	direction cosines of the axes (x, y, z) of the magnetic complexes, with respect to mutually perpendicular crystallographic axes (a, b, c).
M	number of molecules in unit cell, as determined by X-ray methods.
M_m	number of distinct magnetic complexes in unit cell, as determined by paramagnetic resonance.
p	powder.
T	temperature in degrees Kelvin.
u	unpublished.
χ_z	temperature-dependent part of the gram ionic susceptibility of one set of ions along their z axis, in emu; it is assumed that $kT \gg$ any splitting of the ground state in zero field.
S'	effective spin, defined by equating $2S'+1$ to the degeneracy of the ground state, excluding nuclear interactions.

Occasionally other symbols will be encountered for which it will be necessary to consult the original Bowers and Owen paper to have complete understanding. The notation C.S.2, for example, may be found under the chemical formula for a crystal. It means that crystal structure information is given in Section 2 of §4.3 of Bowers and Owen.

3d[1] *Titanium* Ti^{3+}, *Vanadyl* VO^{2+}, *Manganese* Mn^{6+}.

A cubic (octahedral) field leaves an orbital triplet lowest, and this is split into three Kramers doublets by fields of lower symmetry and spin–orbit coupling (cf. figure 2.3).* For octahedral complexes which are only slightly distorted, the separation between the doublets is small (of order 100 cm^{-1}) and, since at high temperatures rapid spin–lattice relaxation broadens the lines, paramagnetic resonance can only be observed at very low temperatures.

(*a*) Ti^{3+}. The results on the two crystals which have been studied (see table below) are interpreted in terms of the following spin Hamiltonian, with $S=\frac{1}{2}$:

$$\mathcal{H}=g_{\parallel}H\beta_z S_z+g_{\perp}\beta(H_x S_x+H_y S_y).$$

The nuclear interactions have been omitted, since the hyperfine structure has not been observed. The energy levels are simply given by $\pm\frac{1}{2}g\beta H$, where $g^2=g_{\parallel}^2\cos^2\theta+g_{\perp}^2\sin^2\theta$, and θ is the angle which H makes with the axis. For the oxalate, the complex is not octahedral, and low-lying levels are not expected. The susceptibility with $H\parallel z$ is thus $\frac{3}{32}g_{\parallel}^2/T$.

Ti^{3+}

Formula	T	$g_{\parallel}$	$g_{\perp}$	Remarks	Ref.
$CsTi(SO_4)_2.12H_2O$ C.S.2	4·2 to 2·5	1·25 ±0·02	1·14 ±0·02		Bl2 55
$KTi(C_2O_4)_2.2H_2O$	90, 20	1·86	1·96	$M_m=2$	Bo2 u

(*b*) VO^{2+}, Mn^{6+}. Measurements have been made on some vanadyl compounds; the complexes are almost certainly not octahedral. The g value of MnO_3 has also been measured.

VO^{2+}

Formula	T	g	Ref.
$K_2V_2O_2(C_2O_4)_3.4H_2O$ single crystal	290, 90	$g_1=1{\cdot}95_4$ $g_2=1{\cdot}98_5$ $g_3=1{\cdot}96_7$	† Gr u
VO Cl_2	290	2·00	La 51
$VO_3(C_6H_4)_3N_2(CH)_2$	290	2·02	La 51
VO $SO_4.2H_2O$	290	1·96	Hu3 53
VO $SO_4.5H_2O$	300 70 4	$1{\cdot}990_1\pm0{\cdot}002$ $1{\cdot}998_7\pm0{\cdot}002$ $1{\cdot}994\pm0{\cdot}004$	Pa u

Mn^{6+}

Formula	T	g	Ref.
MnO_3	290	1·96	La 51

† In a powder diluted with the titanium salt, the hyperfine structure due to ^{51}V ($I=\frac{7}{2}$) was observed at 290°K, 90°K: $A=0{\cdot}010\pm0{\cdot}001$.

*Note added by GEP: Figure 3-3 in this volume, page 58.

V^{2+}

Formula	T	g	D	E	^{50}A	^{51}A	Remarks	Ref.
$(NH_4)_2\mathit{Zn}(SO_4)_2.6H_2O$ C.S. 1; d. 3	290		0·155 ±0·005				$\psi=+4°$; $\alpha=23\frac{1}{2}°$	Hu3 53
d. 1000	20	1·951 ±0·002	0·158 ±0·010	0·049 ±0·005		0·0088 ±0·0002	$\psi=+2°$; $\alpha=22°$ $^{50}A/^{51}A=0·3792±0·0008$	Bl8 51 Ki1 53
$K_4[\mathit{Fe}(CN)_6].3H_2O$ C.S. 7; d. 100	90 20	1·992	−0·0264	0·0072	0·0021	−0·0056	$^{50}A/^{51}A=0·380±0·001$	Ba4 52

d.c. of axes:	a	b	c
z	0·470	±0·737	−0·470
x	0·707	0	0·707
y	0·523	±0·676	−0·523

Paramagnetic resonance has also been observed in VSO_4, $T=290$; Ba1 48; $V(C_6H_4)_4(CN)_8$, $T=270$ to 20, $g=2·0$, In2 54.

Cr^{3+}*

Formula	T	g	D	E	A	Remarks	Ref.
$CsCr(SO_4)_2.12H_2O$ C.S. 2	290	1·98	$0·072_5$ ±0·003				Ba2 50 a Bl1 50b Ki2 51
	193	1·98 ±0·02	−0·067				
	90, 20	1·98 ±0·02	$−0·066_5$ ±0·001				

Cr^{3+*} (*contd.*)

Formula	*T*	*g*	*D*	*E*	*A*	Remarks	Ref.
$KCr(SO_4)_2.12H_2O$ C.S. 2	290	1·98	0·060 ±0·003			Two different magnetic complexes below 160°K; the crystal transition is gradual	Ba2 50a, Bl1 50b, Ha1 48, Ki2 51, Ti1 51, Wh 48
	193	1·98 ±0·02	0·027 ±0·003				
	160	1·98 ±0·02	$0{\cdot}017_5$				
	90	1·98 ±0·02	I 0·130, II 0·075 ±0·005				
	20	1·98 ±0·02	I 0·135 ±0·002, II 0·075 ±0·005				
$K\mathit{Al}(SO_4)_2.12H_2O$ C.S. 2; d. 8·5	290	1·98	$0{\cdot}045_5$				Wh 48
$(NH_3CH_3)Cr(SO_4)_2.12H_2O$ C.S. 2	290	1·98	$0{\cdot}082_5$ ±0·003			Crystal transition at (157±3)°K; below this temperature, spectrum has rhombic symmetry	Ba2 50a, Bl1 50b, Ba3 u
	90, 20	$1{\cdot}97_5$ ±0·01	0·087 ±0·002	0·009 ±0·001			
$(NH_3CH_3)\mathit{Al}(SO_4)_2.12H_2O$ C.S. 2; d. 100	90	$1{\cdot}97_5$ ±0·01	$0{\cdot}095_9$ ±0·002	0·009 ±0·001		Crystal transition at (170±3)°K; below this temperature, spectrum has rhombic symmetry	Ba3 u
$(NH_4)Cr(SO_4)_2.12H_2O$ C.S. 2	290	1·98	$0{\cdot}067_5$ ±0·003			Sudden crystal transition just above 80°K; below this temperature there are two different magnetic complexes	Ba2 50a, Bl1 50b, Bl11 48, Ha1 48, Ki2 51, Wh 48, Ya 49
	193	1·98 ±0·02	$0{\cdot}042_5$				
	90	1·98 ±0·02	$0{\cdot}017_5$				

$(NH_4)Cr(SO_4)_2.12H_2O$ C.S. 2 (*contd.*)	80	1·98 ±0·02	I 0·157 ±0·002; II 0·121 ±0·002	
	20	1·98 ±0·02	I 0·158 ±0·002; II 0·120 ±0·002	
(NH_4)*Al*$(SO_4)_2.12H_2O$ C.S. 2; d. 8·5	290	1·97	0·050	Wh 48
$RbCr(SO_4)_2.12H_2O$ C.S. 2	290	1·98	$0{\cdot}082_5$ ±0·003	Ba2 50 a, Bl1 50b, Ki2 51
	193	1·98 ±0·02	0·063	
	90, 20	1·98 ±0·02	0·054 ±0·001	
$KCr(SeO_4)_2.12H_2O$ C.S. 2	90		0·064 ±0·002	Ba3 u
	20		0·070 ±0·002	
K*Al*$(SeO_4)_2.12H_2O$ C.S. 2; d. 10	90		$0{\cdot}089_5$ ±0·001	Ba3 u
	20		0·098 ±0·001	
d. 100	90	1·976 ±0·002	0·0900 ±0·0003	Bl3 51
	20	1·976 ±0·002	0·0983 ±0·0003	

Cr^{3+} * (*contd.*)

Formula	T	g	D	E	A	Remarks	Ref.
$K\mathit{Al}(SeO_4)_2.12D_2O$ C.S. 2	90, 20	1·976 ±0·002	$0{\cdot}10_5$		$0{\cdot}0018_5$ ±0·0001		Bl3 51
$K_3[Cr(CN)_6]$ C.S. 7	90, 20	1·99 ±0·01				Only one line	Bo5 52
$K_3[\mathit{Co}(CN)_6]$ C.S. 7; d. 100 to 1000	90 to 12	1·992 ±0·002	+0·083 ±0·001	0·011 ±0·001	0·00147 ±0·00005		† Bo5 52
$K_3[\mathit{Mn}(CN)_6]$ C.S. 7; d. 100	90 to 12	1·993 ±0·002	+0·054 ±0·001	0·012 ±0·001	$0{\cdot}0014_7$ ±0·0001		‡ Bo5 52
$\mathit{Al}[(CH_3CO)_2CH]_3$ C.S. a; d. 50	290	1·983 ±0·002	0·592 ±0·002	0·052 ±0·002		$M_m=2$, $\psi=+22\frac{1}{2}°$, $\alpha=59°$	§ Si 55

† At 20°K, d.c. of axes:

	a	b	c
z	±0·994	0·104	0
x	±0·104	0·994	0
y	0	0	1

‡ At 90°K, d.c. of axes:

	a	b	c
z	1	0	0
x	0	±0·996	0·087
y	0	±0·087	0·996

* Measurements on some chromic alums have been duplicated by several different authors. Selected values are given in this table, with the most recent publication of any one group of authors.

a, § $Al[(CH_3CO)_2CH]_3$. Astbury (1926): monoclinic, $M=4$. The surroundings of the Al are probably three chelate groups arranged octahedrally. The four magnetic complexes are equivalent in pairs; description of axes as for C.S. 1. The results of Ba2 u, with $d\sim10$, show that there is a gradual transition between 290°K and 90°K. Each of the two sets of complexes is subdivided into three types at 90°K, with either (*a*) slightly differently oriented z axes, or (*b*) slightly different splittings. No further change at 20°K.

Paramagnetic resonance absorption has also been observed in the following compounds at room temperature; (apparent) g-values are given in brackets: $CrBr_3$ (1·99), Ti1 51; $Cr(C_2H_3O_2)_3.H_2O$, Ba1 48; $Cr(C_5H_5N)_2(OH)_2(H_2O)_2Cl$ (1·99), La 51; $Cr(C_7H_5O_3)_3.H_2O$ (2·07), La 51; $Cr[(CH_3)_3(CH)_2CH_2(CO)_2]_3$, $Cr[(C_6H_5)(CO)_2CH.CH_3]_3$, both $g\sim2$, $D>\sim0{\cdot}5$, Si 55; $CrCl_3$ (1·99), Ko 52; CrF_3 (2·00), Ti1 51; $[Cr(H_2O)_4Cl_2]Cl$ (1·95), La 51; $[Cr(H_2O)_4Cl_2]Cl.2H_2O$, Ko 52; $[Cr(H_2O)_5Cl]Cl_2.H_2O$, Ko 52; $[Cr(NH_3)_5Cl]Cl_2$ (1·97), $[Cr(NH_3)_6]Cl_3.H_2O$ (1·97), $[Cr(NH_3)_6](NO_3)_3.H_2O$ (1·95), all La 51; $[Cr(NH_2CH_2)_6]_2(SO_4)_3$, ($g\sim2$, $D\sim0{\cdot}15$), Si 55; $Cr(NO_3)_3.9H_2O$ (2·26), La 51; $Cr(OH)_3$, Ko 52; $Cr(OH)_3.2H_2O$ (2·00), La 51; $CrPO_4.3H_2O$, Ba1 48; $[Cr(SCN)_2\{C_2H_4(NH_2)_2\}_2](SCN)$ (1·98), La 51, 52; Cr_2O_3, Ko 52; $Cr_2(SO_3)_3$ (2·00), Ti1 51; $Cr_2(SO_4)_3$ (1·98), Ti1 51; $Cr_2(SO_4)_3.5H_2O$, Ba1 48; $Cr_2(SO_4)_3.15H_2O$, Ba1 48; $Cr_2(SO_4)_3.18H_2O$ (2·00), La 51; $K_3Cr(C_2O_4)_3.3H_2O$ ($g\sim2$, $D\sim0{\cdot}4$), Si 55.

Fe^{3+}

Formula	T	g	D	a	F	Remarks	Ref.
$KAl(SeO_4)_2.12H_2O$ C.S. 2; d. 300	90	2·003 ±0·003	−0·0103 ±0·0001	−0·0127 ±0·0002	−0·0002 ±0·0002	$\phi=(10·5±0·5)°$	Bl15 54
	20	2·003 ±0·001	−0·0115 ±0·0001	−0·0127 ±0·0001	−0·0002 ±0·0001		
$(NH_3CH_3)Al(SO_4)_2.12H_2O$ C.S. 2; d. 200	90		(−)0·188 ±0·014	(−)0·010 ±0·004			Bl15 54
$NH_4Al(SO_4)_2.12H_2O$ C.S. 2; d. 80	4		0·016 ±0·001	(−)0·0128 ±0·0004			Ub2 51 Me 51
$RbAl(SO_4)_2.12H_2O$ C.S. 2; d. 300	90	2·003 ±0·003	+0·0022 ±0·0002	−0·0134 ±0·0002	−0·0003 ±0·0002	$\phi=(7·5±0·5)°$	Bl15 54
	20	2·003 ±0·001	+0·0031 ±0·0001	−0·0134 ±0·0001	$-0·0003_3$ ±0·0001		

Paramagnetic resonance absorption has also been observed in the following compounds (room temperature, unless stated otherwise); the (apparent) g-values are given in brackets: $Fe(C_5H_7O_2)_3$ (1·95), La 51; $Fe(C_7H_5O_2)_3$, Ba1 48; $Fe(C_{17}H_{35}COO)_3$ (2·00), Ab3 53a; $FeCl(C_6H_4)_4(CN)_8$, $T=270$–20, (3·8, 2·0), In2 54; $FeCl_3$, Ba1 48; $Fe(NH_4)_3$ $(C_6H_5O_7)_2.2H_2O$ (1·98), La 51; $FeOH(C_2H_3O_2)_2$, $Fe(PO_4).4H_2O$, $Fe_2(C_2O_4)_3$, $Fe_2[C_3H_5(OH)_2OPO_3]_3$, all Ba1 48; $(FeF_3)_2.9H_2O$ (2·02), La 51; $Fe_2(SO_4)_3.3H_2O$ (2·01), Ti1 51; $Fe_2(SO_4)_3.9H_2O$ (2·01), La 51; $Fe_3(CH_3COO)_6(OH)_2NO_3.6H_2O$, $T=15$ (2·0), Ge u; $Fe_4[Fe(CN)_6]_3$, Ba1 48.

Mn^{2+}

Formula	T	g	D	E	a	A	Remarks	Ref.
$(NH_4)_2Mg(SO_4)_2.6H_2O$ C.S. 1;	290		0·0231 ±0·0002	0·006	0·0003	0·0090 ±0·0002	$\psi=+60°$; $\alpha=30°$	In1 53a
d. 250	290		$0·022_0$	$0·004_1$		0·0095	$\psi=+59°$; $\alpha=30\frac{1}{2}°$	Br 53

Mn^{2+} (*contd.*)

Formula	T	g	D	E	a	A	Remarks	Ref.
$(NH_4)_2Zn(SO_4)_2.6H_2O$ C.S. 1;	290	2·000 ±0·005	0·0238	0·007$_5$	0·0005	0·0091		Ha2 53
d. 1000	230		+0·0243 ±0·0005	0·010 ±0·002	+0·0005 ±0·0001	−0·0091$_1$ ±0·0001	ψ=+58°; α=32°	Bl7 51a
	195		+0·0258 ±0·0005	0·008 ±0·001$_6$	+0·0007 ±0·0001	−0·0089$_0$ ±0·0001		
	90		+0·0275 ±0·0005	0·007 ±0·001$_4$	+0·0007 ±0·0001	−0·0089$_9$ ±0·0001		
	20	2·00	+0·0277 ±0·0005	0·005 ±0·001	+0·0008 ±0·0002	−0·0093		
$Mg_3Bi_2(NO_3)_{12}.24H_2O$ C.S. 3; d. 200	90	1·99 ±0·02	−0·0211 ±0·0001	0	+0·0008 ±0·0001	−0·0090	Magnetic complex I	Tr 53
	20	1·997 ±0·003	−0·0215 ±0·0001	0	+0·0008 ±0·0001	−0·0090		
	90	1·99 ±0·02	−0·0064 ±0·0001	0	+0·0010 ±0·0001	−0·0089	Magnetic complex II	
	20	1·997 ±0·003	−0·0080 ±0·0001	0	+0·0010 ±0·0001	−0·0090		
$MgSiF_6.6H_2O$ C.S. 4; d. 20 to 150	290		(−)0·0274	0·0030	(+)0·0007	(−)0·0092	M_m=6	Ar 54
$ZnSiF_6.6H_2O$ C.S. 4;	290	2·000 ±0·005	0·0171	0	0·0007$_5$	0·0090		Ha2 53
d. 1000	290		−0·0179 ±0·0003	0	+0·0007 ±0·0001	−0·0095		Bl7 51a
	195		−0·0161 ±0·0003	0	+0·0010 ±0·0002	−0·0092		
	90	2·000 ±0·001	−0·0141 ±0·0003	0	+0·0011 ±0·0002	−0·0092		
	20		−0·0134 ±0·0003	0	+0·0009 ±0·0002	−0·0091		

Mn^{2+} (*contd.*)

Formula	T	g	D	E	a	A	Remarks	Ref.
$MgSO_4.7H_2O$ C.S. 6	290	2·000 ±0·005	$0{\cdot}040_0$	~0		0·0088	d.c. of z axes (± ∓0·282, ±0·952, 0·122)	Ha2 53
$CaCO_3$ C.S. a; d. 2000	290	2·002	0·0075	0		0·00878	F=0·0058	Hu1 54
ZnS p hexag.; d. 10^3 to 10^5	290	2·0024 ±0·0004	0·002			0·0063		Sc 51
	290		0·001			0·0065 ±0·0001		He 52
$Zn(HCOO)_2.2H_2O$	290	1·999 $\pm 0{\cdot}001_5$	0·0485 ±0·0005	0·011	$0{\cdot}0009_5$	0·0091 ±0·0001	Monoclinic, $M_m=2$ $\psi=+97°$; $\alpha=62°$ (for ψ, α, see C.S. 1)	In1 53b
$Zn(CH_3COO)_2.3H_2O$	290		0·0235	$0{\cdot}002_5$		0·0084	Monoclinic, $M_m=1$ $z\equiv c$, $x\equiv b$	Ku2 52 Ha2 53
$Zn(CH_3COO)_2.4H_2O$ d. 100	290	2·00 ±0·01	0·0412	$0{\cdot}006_6$	0·0008	0·0087	Monoclinic, $M_m=2$ $\psi=+47°$, $\alpha=29°$ (for ψ, α, see C.S. 1)	In1 53a

a $CaCO_3$ calcite. Wyckoff (1920): hexagonal, $M=2$. The nearest neighbours to each Ca are six O, with trigonal symmetry. With Mn, the two magnetic complexes are completely equivalent.

Paramagnetic resonance absorption has also been observed in the following (room temperature):

(*a*) Phosphors containing small concentrations of Mn (He 52); in each case g is close to 2·0: cubic ZnS (A=0·0064); $ZnAl_2O_4$ ($A=0{\cdot}0076_5$); MgO [197–2] (A=0·0082); MgO [200–2] (A=0·0072); $CdSiO_3$; Mg_2GeO_4; ZnF_2; ZnS: Tb; Zn_2SiO_4; $8ZnO.BeO.5SiO_2$; Zn_2GeO_4; $Zn_3(PO_4)_2$.

(*b*) Undiluted compounds; (apparent) g-values given in brackets: $Mn(BO_2)_2$ (2·01), La 51; $Mn(CH_3COO)_2.2H_2O$ (2·00), Ko 52; $Mn(C_3H_5O_3)_2.3H_2O$, Ba1 48; $Mn(C_6H_4)_4(CN)_8$ (2·0), T down to 20, In2 54; $Mn(C_{15}H_{31}COO)_2$ (2·00), Ab3 53a; $Mn(C_{17}H_{35}COO)_2$ (2·00), Ab3 53a; $MnCO_3$ (2·00), La 51; $MnC_2O_4.2H_2O$ (2·00), La 51; $MnCl_2.4H_2O$ (2·00), La 51 and (2·09), Ko 52; MnF_2, Ba1 48; $Mn(H_2PO_2)_2.H_2O$, Ba1 48; $MnK_2(SO_4)_2.6H_2O$, Ba1 48; $MnSO_4$ (2·00), Ko 52, Ku1 51; $MnSO_4.H_2O$ (2·00) Ku1 51; $MnSO_4.4H_2O$ (2·00–2·07), Ku1 51; $MnSO_4.5H_2O$ (2·06) Ku1 51; $Mn_2Fe(CN)_6.7H_2O$, $Mn_2(P_2O_7).3H_2O$, $Mn_3(AsO_4)_2$, $Mn_3(C_6H_5O_7)_2$, $Mn_3(PO_4)_2.7H_2O$, all Ba1 48.

Co^{2+} ($S' = \frac{1}{2}$)

Formula	T	g			A			Remarks	Ref.
$K_2Zn(SO_4)_2.6H_2O$ C.S. 1; d. 500 to 10^5	20	g_z 6·56 ±0·13	g_{min} (K_1K_3) 2·50 ±0·05	g_2 3·35 ±0·07	A_z 0·0286 ±0·0006	A_{min} (K_1K_3) 0·0065 ±0·0003	A_2 0·0080 ±0·0004	$\psi = +163°$; $\alpha = 35°$	Bl7 51b
$(NH_4)_2Zn(SO_4)_2.6H_2O$ C.S. 1; d. 500 to 10^5	20	g_z 6·45 ±0·13	g_{min} (K_1K_3) 3·06 ±0·06	g_2 3·06 ±0·06	A_z 0·0245 ±0·0005	A_{min} (K_1K_3) 0·0020 ±0·0001	A_2 0·0020 ±0·0001	$\psi = +130°$; $\alpha = 34°$	Bl7 51b
$Rb_2Zn(SO_4)_2.6H_2O$ C.S. 1	20	g_z 6·6₅	g_{min} (K_1K_3) 2·7	g_2 3·3	A_z 0·0293 ±0·0003	A_{min} (K_1K_3) 0·0049 ±0·0005		$\psi = +157°$; $\alpha = 37°$	Bo3 u
$Mg_3Bi_2(NO_3)_{12}.24H_2O$ C.S. 3; d. 100	20	$g_\parallel$ 7·29 ±0·01	$g_\perp$ 2·338 ±0·004		A 0·0283 ±0·0001	$B \leqslant 0·0001$		Magnetic complex I	Tr 53
		$g_\parallel$ 4·108 ±0·003	$g_\perp$ 4·385 ±0·003		A 0·0085 ±0·0001	B 0·0103 ±0·0001		Magnetic complex II	
$ZnSiF_6.6H_2O$ C.S. 4; d. 500 to 10^5	20	$g_\parallel$ 5·82 ±0·12	$g_\perp$ 3·44 ±0·07		A 0·0184 ±0·0004	B 0·0047 ±0·0002		Main line; $g_\parallel$ axis ∥ c-axis of crystal	Bl7 51b
		6·6 ±0·1	2·62 ±0·05		0·023	0·0009		Much weaker lines with different axes (defective lattice points)	
		6·6 ±0·2	2·82 ±0·06		0·025	0·0013		Much weaker lines with different axes (defective lattice points)	
		3·58 ±0·05	4·09 ±0·05		0·01	0·01		Much weaker lines with different axes (defective lattice points)	
$ZnSO_4.7H_2O$ C.S. 6; d. 100	20	g_z 6·90 ±0·14	g_x 2·30 ±0·05	g_y 3·30 ±0·07	A_z 0·0254 ±0·0005	A_x 0·0028 ±0·0001		†	Bl7 51b

† For one complex: z in (110) with $\angle zOc = 13°$; x in (110) with $\angle xOc = 103°$; $y \parallel$ [110]. Other axes are given by reflection symmetry. Undiluted $CoSO_4.7H_2O$ has also been examined: g is anisotropic, e.g. in ab plane from 1·4 to 5·8.

Paramagnetic resonance absorption has also been observed in $Co(C_6H_4)_4(CN)_8$, $T = 270$–20; two complexes: I $g = 2·9$, II $g = 2·4 - 1·98$; ref. In2 54.

Ni^{2+}

Formula	T	g	D	E	Axes* ψ(°)	θ(°)	α(°)	Remarks	Ref
$K_2Ni(SO_4)_2.6H_2O$ C.S. 1	290	2·25 ±0·05	−3·30	−0·51$_7$	−12·5	11	~45		Gr1 52a
$(NH_4)_2Ni(SO_4)_2.6H_2O$ C.S. 1	290	2·25 ±0·05	−2·24	−0·38$_7$	−14	$3\frac{1}{2}$	45	In $(NH_4)_2$*Zn*$(SO_4)_2.6H_2O$ (d. 50) parameters and axes practically unchanged	Gr1 52a
	90	2·25 ±0·05	−1·99	−0·48$_6$					
$Tl_2Ni(SO_4)_2.6H_2O$ C.S. 1	290	2·25 ±0·05	−2·6	−0·10	−11	11	45		Gr1 52a
$K_2Ni(SeO_4)_2.6H_2O$ C.S. 1	290	2·25 ±0·05	−3	−1	−13	~0	~45		Gr1 52a
$(NH_4)_2Ni(SeO_4)_2.6H_2O$ C.S. 1	290	2·25 ±0·05	−1·89	−0·79	−28	0	50		Gr1 52a
	90	2·25 ±0·05	−1·73	−0·82					
Mg$_3La_2(NO_3)_{12}.24H_2O$ C.S. 3; d. 800	90	2·24	0·177 ±0·002	0					Tr u
$NiSiF_6.6H_2O$ C.S. 4	290	2·3	−0·50	0					Ho 49
	195	2·29	−0·32	0					Pel 50
	90	2·26	−0·17	0				In *Zn*$SiF_6.6H_2O$ (d. 4, 16), *D* is ~ 20% greater than in undiluted at all *T*	Grl 52a
	60		−0·14	0					
	20	2·29	−0·12	0					
	14		−0·12	0					

Ni^{2+} (*contd.*)

Formula	T	g	D	E	Axes* ψ(°)	Axes* θ(°)	α(°)	Remarks	Ref.
$Ni(BrO_3)_2.6H_2O$ C.S. 5	290	2·29 ±0·04	1·93 ±0·04	0					Ow1 u
$NiSO_4.7H_2O$ C.S. 6	(290)	$2{\cdot}2_0$	$-3{\cdot}5_6$	$-1{\cdot}5_0$				†	On1 53

* For the two ions, z_1 and z_2 in K_1OK_3 plane, with $\angle z_1OK_1$, $\angle z_2OK_1 = \pm\theta$, where $\angle K_1Oc = \psi$; x_1 is approx. $\parallel y_2$, both lying nearly in K_2OK_3 plane, with $\angle x_1OK_2 = \alpha$, $\angle y_2OK_2 = 90 - \alpha$.

† For one complex, d.c. are z: (0·95, 0·31, 0), y: (−0·31, 0·95, 0·09). Axes of other complexes are given by reflection symmetry.

Paramagnetic resonance absorption has also been observed in the following compounds, unless stated otherwise at room temperature; the g-values are given in brackets:

$NiBr_2$, (2·27), Ti1 51; $NiBr_2(NH_3)_6$ (2·14), La 51; $NiCl_2$ (2·21), Ti1 51; $NiCl_2.6H_2O$, Ba1 48; $NiI_2(NH_3)_6$, Ow1 u; $Ni(C_6H_4)_4(CN)_8$, $T = 270$ to 20, (2·20), In2 54.

Table A. Cu^{2+} Tutton Salts (C.S. 1)

Formula	T	g			A			P	ψ(°)	α(°)	Ref.
$Cs_2Cu(SO_4)_2.6H_2O$	90	g_z 2·43 ±0·02	g_{min} (K_1K_3) 2·08 ±0·02	g_2 2·06 ±0·02					+114	40	Bl12 49
$K_2Cu(SO_4)_2.6H_2O$	290	g_1 2·31 ±0·03	g_2 2·07 ±0·03	g_3 2·25 ±0·03					+105		Ba2 52
	90	g_z 2·36 ±0·02	g_x 2·14 ±0·02	g_y 2·04 ±0·02					+105	42	Bl12 49
$K_2Zn(SO_4)_2.6H_2O$ d. 50 to 2000	290	g_z 2·05 ±0·03	g_{max} (K_2K_3) 2·25 ±0·03	g_1 2·26 ±0·03					+15	32	Ba2 52
	90, 20	g_z 2·44 ±0·02	g_{min} (K_1K_3) 2·13 ±0·02		A_z 0·0103 ±0·0005	A_{min} (K_1K_3) 0·0034 ±0·0005		0·0011 ±0·0001	~+105	42	Bl4 55
$K_2Zn(SO_4)_2.6D_2O$ d. 200 to 1000	20	g_z 2·42 ±0·01	g_x 2·16 ±0·01	g_y 2·04 ±0·01	A_z −0·0099 ±0·0001	A_x <0·0017	A_y +0·0061 ±0·0003	+0·00110 ±0·00005 and P'= 0·00011 ±0·00005	~+105	43	† Bl4 55
$K_2Cu(SeO_4)_2.6H_2O$	90	g_z 2·38 ±0·02	g_{min} (K_1K_3) 2·07 ±0·02	g_2 2·04$_5$ ±0·02					+73	37	Bl12 49
$(NH_4)_2Cu(SO_4)_2.6H_2O$	290	g_1 2·32 ±0·03	g_2 2·09 ±0·03	g_3 2·25 ±0·03					+77		Ba2 52
	90	g_z 2·45 ±0·02	g_{min} (K_1K_3) 2·12 ±0·02	g_2 2·06 ±0·02					+65	39	Bl12 49

Table A (*contd.*)

Formula	T	g			A			P	ψ(°)	α(°)	Ref.
$(NH_4)_2Zn(SO_4)_2.6H_2O$ d. 50 to 2000	290	g_z 2·04 ±0·03	g_{max} (K_2K_3) 2·26 ±0·03	g_1 2·28 ±0·03					+167	32	Ba2 52
	20	g_z 2·46 ±0·02	g_x 2·12 ±0·02	g_y 2·05 ±0·02	A_z 0·0130 ±0·0005	A_x 0·0025 ±0·0005	A_y 0·0035 ±0·0005	0·0011 ±0·0001	+65	38	Bl4 55
$(NH_4)_2Cu(SeO_4)_2.6H_2O$	90	g_z 2·39 ±0·02	g_{min} (K_1K_3) 2·07₅ ±0·02	g_y 2·06₅ ±0·02					+72	37½	Bl12 49
$Rb_2Cu(SO_4)_2.6H_2O$	290	g_1 2·28 ±0·03		g_3 2·24 ±0·03					+105		Ba2 52
	90	g_z 2·45 ±0·02	g_{min} (K_1K_3) 2·11 ±0·02	g_2 2·07 ±0·02					+105	40	Bl12 49
$Rb_2Zn(SO_4)_2.6H_2O$ d. 50 to 2000	290	g_z 2·08 ±0·03	g_{max} (K_2K_3) 2·27 ±0·03	g_1 2·25 ±0·03					+15	33	Ba2 52
	20	g_z 2·44 ±0·02	g_{min} (K_1K_3) 2·12 ±0·02		A_z 0·0116 ±0·0005	A_{min} (K_1K_3) 0·0030 ±0·0005		0·0011 ±0·0001	~+105	42	‡ Bl4 55
$Rb_2Zn(SO_4)_2.6D_2O$ d. 200 to 1000	20	g_z 2·43 ±0·02	g_x 2·15 ±0·02	g_y 2·04 ±0·02	A_z −0·0110 ±0·0002	A_x <0·0020	A_y +0·0059 ±0·0004	+0·0012 ±0·0001	~+105	42	‡ Bl4 55
$Tl_2Cu(SO_4)_2.6H_2O$	90	g_z 2·40 ±0·02	g_{min} (K_1K_3) 2·08 ±0·02	g_2 2·06 ±0·02					+112	39½	Bl12 49

† $^{65}A/^{63}A = 1{\cdot}069 \pm 0{\cdot}003$, $^{63}P/^{65}P = 1{\cdot}08 \pm 0{\cdot}02$

‡ As the crystal is warmed up from 20°K, an anomalous second spectrum appears. At 90°K the intensity of the anomalous spectrum is roughly ¾ of that of the normal spectrum: the *g*-values of the two spectra differ by less than 1%.

Table B. Cu^{2+} Trigonal Crystals

Formula	T	g		A			Temp. of transition	Ref.
$Mg_3Bi_2(NO_3)_{12}.24H_2O$ C.S. 3; d. 100	90	$g_{\parallel}$ 2·219 ±0·003	$g_{\perp}$ 2·217 ±0·003	A 0·0027 ±0·0001	B 0·0026 ±0·0001			Bl5 55
	20	g_z 2·454 ±0·003	$g_{x,y}$ 2·096 ±0·003	A_z 0·0110 ±0·0001	$A_{x,y}$ 0·0017 ±0·0002			
$Cu_3La_2(NO_3)_{12}.24H_2O$ C.S. 3	290	2·22					173°K to 273°K	Bi 53
	90, 20	g_z 2·41	$g_{x,y}$ 2·10					
$Mg_3La_2(NO_3)_{12}.24D_2O$ C.S. 3; d. 500	90	$g_{\parallel}$ 2·219 ±0·003	$g_{\perp}$ 2·218 ±0·003	A 0·00290 ±0·00005	B 0·00275 ±0·00005		33°K to 45°K	Bl5 55 Bi 53
	45	2·235 ±0·005						
	20	g_z 2·470 ±0·002	$g_{x,y}$ 2·097 ±0·002	A_z −0·0113 ±0·00005	A_x +0·00190 ±0·00005	A_y +0·00123 ±0·00005		† Bl5 55
$CuSiF_6.6H_2O$ C.S. 4	(290)	2·20						Yo 54
$ZnSiF_6.6H_2O$ C.S. 4	90	$g_{\parallel}$ 2·221 ±0·005	$g_{\perp}$ 2·230 ±0·005	A 0·0021 ±0·0005	B 0·0028 ±0·0005		12°K to 50°K	Bl5 55
	20, 12	g_z 2·46 ±0·01	$g_{x,y}$ 2·10 ±0·01	A_z 0·0110 ±0·0003	$A_{x,y}$ <0·0030			
$Zn(BrO_3)_2.6H_2O$ C.S. 5; d. 100	90	$2{\cdot}21_7$ ±0·01			0·0028 ±0·0005		<7°K to 35°K	Bl5 55

† $P = +0{\cdot}00111 \pm 0{\cdot}00005$, $P' = -0{\cdot}00004 \pm 0{\cdot}00001$

Table C. Cu^{2+}

Formula	T	g			Remarks	Ref.
$Cu(NH_3)_4(NO_3)_2$	290	g_a 2·07 ±0·02	g_b 2·14 ±0·02	g_c 2·02 ±0·02	orthorhombic (?) (Groth 1908)	Ok 54
$Cu(NH_3)_4SO_4.H_2O$	290	g_a 2·02 ±0·02	g_b 2·05 ±0·02	g_c 2·15 ±0·02	orthorhombic (Groth 1908)	Ok 54
$Cu[(CH_3CO)_2CH]_2$ C.S. a	290, 90	$g_{\parallel}$ 2·28 ±0·03	$g_{\perp}$ 2·07 ±0·03		$M_m=2$	Ba1 u
$CuCl_2.2H_2O$ C.S. b	290 to 15	g_a 2·187 ±0·005	g_b 2·037 ±0·005	g_c 2·252 ±0·005	only one line observed	Ge u
	4·2 to 1·2				Antiferromagnetic below 4·3°K; spectrum described by Ub1 52	
$CuSO_4.5H_2O$ C.S. c	290	$g_{\parallel}$ 2·08 g_z 2·46	$g_{\perp}$ 2·27 $g_{x,y}$ 2·08		One line, $\tilde{\nu}\leqslant 0·8$ cm^{-1} Two lines, $\tilde{\nu}=1·2$ cm^{-1} See text	† Ba2 50b
$K_2CuCl_4.2H_2O$ / $(NH_4)_2CuCl_4.2H_2O$ C.S. d	290	$g_{\parallel(c)}$ 2·06 $g_z >2·30$	$g_{\perp}$ 2·22 $g_x <2·10_5$	$g_{y(c)}$ 2·06	One line, $\tilde{\nu}\leqslant 1·5$ cm^{-1} Two lines, $\tilde{\nu}=1·8_5$ cm^{-1} See text	Ab2 54
$Cu(CH_3COO)_2.H_2O$ C.S. e	290 90	g_z 2·34$_4$ ±0·01	g_x 2·053 ±0·005	g_y 2·093 ±0·005	$D = 0·345 \pm 0·005$, $E = 0·007 \pm 0·003$; $A_z = 0·008$, $A_{x,y} < 0·0010$; $\psi = -34°$, $\alpha=33°$; $S=1$, see text	Ab3 53b Bl3 52
$Cu(C_2H_5COO)_2.H_2O$ C.S. f		g_z 2·35	$g_{x,y}$ 2·09 –2·10		$D=0·38$, $E\sim 0$ $S=1$, see text	Ab1 53
$Cu(C_6H_4)_4(CN)_8$ C.S. g	270 to 20	$g_{\parallel}$ 2·165 ±0·004	$g_{\perp}$ 2·045 ±0·003		$\psi=+121°$, $\alpha=45°$; in crystal diluted with Zn, $A=0·020_8\pm0·001$, $B=0·003_1\pm0·001$	In2 54 Be 55

† Vi 53 show that the results are temperature dependent, with the mean g (powder) at 90°K 1% higher than at 290°K.

a. $Cu[(CH_3CO)_2CH]_2$. Cox and Webster (1935): monoclinic, $M=2$. Each Cu is surrounded by four O in a plane.

b. $CuCl_2.2H_2O$. Harker (1936): orthorhombic, $M=2$. Each Cu is surrounded by a planar array of two H_2O and two Cl. The distorted octahedron is completed by two more Cl, belonging to other Cu; these two Cl are considerably further away.

c. $CuSO_4.5H_2O$. Beevers and Lipson (1934): triclinic, $M=2$. Each Cu is surrounded by a distorted octahedron of four H_2O and two O, with tetragonal symmetry. The two tetragonal axes are nearly at right-angles to each other, and so the crystal is magnetically uniaxial; the susceptibility axis (minimum) makes angles 154°, 64°, 51° with the triclinic axes (*a*, *b*, *c*).

d. $(K, NH_4)_2CuCl_4.2H_2O$. Chrobak (1934), Wyckoff (1951): tetragonal, $M=2$. Each Cu is surrounded by four Cl in a rhomb in the *aa*-plane, of which two are considerably further from the Cu than the other two, and two H_2O on the normal. The two magnetic complexes have the same *y*-axis (*c*), but interchanged *z*, *x* axes along [110], [1$\bar{1}$0], defined with respect to Chrobak's unit cell, i.e. *z* and *x* are [100] and [010] using the morphological axes of Groth (1906).

e. $Cu(CH_3COO)_2.H_2O$. van Niekerk and Schoening (1953): monoclinic, $M=4$ of the bimolecular units. The four magnetic complexes are equivalent in pairs; description of axes as for C.S. 1. The Cu lie in close pairs (2·6 Å), and each Cu is surrounded by a distorted octahedron of four O, one H_2O and the other Cu.

f. $Cu(C_2H_5COO)_2.H_2O$. Groth (1910): monoclinic. Paramagnetic resonance shows that there are six magnetic complexes (each with two Cu) in unit cell, of which three are derived from the other three by reflection in *ac* plane. Each complex has approximate tetragonal symmetry, with axes (*z*) given by $\psi_1=106°$, $\psi_2=158°$, $\psi_3=174°$, $\alpha_1=28\frac{1}{2}°$, $\alpha_2=16°$, $\alpha_3=52°$; here ψ_i is angle between *c* and plane containing two z_i axes, and α_i is angle between *z* and *ac* plane ($i=1, 2, 3$).

g. $Cu(C_6H_4)_4(CN)_8$. Robertson (1935): monoclinic, $M=2$. Each Cu is surrounded by a square of four N. Description of axes as for C.S. 1.

Paramagnetic resonance absorption has also been observed in the following compounds, unless stated otherwise at room temperature; the *g*-values are given in brackets: $CuBr_2$ (2·23), $CuC_4H_4O_6.3H_2O$ (1·97), $Cu(C_3H_5O_3)_2.2H_2O$ (2·09), $Cu(C_5H_5N)_4(NO_3)_2.H_2O$ (2·04), $Cu[(CH_3)_3C(CO)_2CH_2C_5H_{11}]_2$ (2·04), $Cu[C_6H_5(CH_2)_3(CO)_2CH_3]_2$ (2·02), $Cu(C_7H_5O_2)_2.2H_2O$ (1·97), all La 51; $Cu(HCOO)_2.2H_2O$, $4H_2O$ (2·32 to 2·06), Ab1 53; CuF_2 (2·15), La 51; CuF_2 basic (2·08), Ra 52; $Cu(NH_3)_4Cl_2.H_2O$, Ba1 48; CuS, Ko 52; $CuSO_4$, Ba1 48; $CuSiF_6.4H_2O$, ($g_\parallel=2·40$, $g_\perp=2·10$), Yo 54; $CuWO_4.2H_2O$ (2·17), La 51; $2CuC_2O_4.H_2O$ (2·07), La 51; $Cu_3Co_2(CN)_{12}$, $T=290–12$, (2·17) Pe2 54; copper chlorophylls, $T=270, 90$, (2·05±0·01), In2 54; cupric di-o-phenanthroline persulphate, $T=290, 90, 20$ ($g_\parallel=2·3_0$, $g_\perp=2·05$), Bo5 53.

Mo^V

Formula	T		$g_\parallel$	$g_\perp$	A	B	Remarks	Ref.
$K_3[InCl_6]2H_2O$ d. 200	290 to 20	I	1·951 ±0·005	1·939 ±0·006	0·0079 ±0·0001	0·00385 ±0·00010	Two magnetically inequivalent complexes, I and II, in unit cell. Hyperfine structure from Cl nuclei also observed	Ow2 u
		II	1·959 ±0·004	1·939 ±0·006	0·0077 ±0·0001	0·00385 ±0·00010		
$K_3[Mo(CN)_8]$ p	290, 90		$\bar{g}=2·005$ ±0·005					Gr3 53

Ru^{iii}

Formula	T		g_x	g_y	g_z	A_x	A_y	A_z	Remarks	Ref.
$[Co(NH_3)_6]Cl_3$ d. 200	20	I	2·06 ±0·01	2·02 ±0·01	1·72 ±0·01	0·0048 ±0·0002	0·0048 ±0·0002	0·0049 ±0·0002	†	Gr3 53 Gr2 55
		II	1·80 ±0·01	1·90 ±0·01	2·06 ±0·01	0·0048 ±0·0002	0·0048 ±0·0002	0·0050 ±0·0002		
		III	1·15 ±0·01	1·84 ±0·01	2·66 ±0·01	0·0045 ±0·0002	0·0041 ±0·0002	0·0054 ±0·0002	$^{101}A/^{99}A=1{\cdot}09\pm0{\cdot}03$	Gr1 52b
$K_3[InCl_6]2H_2O$ d. 100	20		1·0 ±0·1	1·22 ±0·02	3·24 ±0·02					Ow2 u
$[Ru(NH_3)_6]Cl_3$, $3HgCl_2$	20		2·21	2·05	1·5 ±0·1					Gr3 53

† Monoclinic: 3 pairs of magnetically inequivalent complexes of types I, II and III. Members of each pair have reflection symmetry in *ac* plane.

Paramagnetic resonance absorption has also been observed in undiluted crystals of $[Ru(NH_3)_6]Cl_3$ and $[Ru(NH_3)_5Cl]Cl_2$ at $T=20$, Gr3 53.

Ir^{iv}

Formula	T	g	Ir h.f.s.	Cl or Br h.f.s.	Remarks	Ref.
$K_2[PtBr_6]$ C.S. 8; d. 200	20	$g_{\parallel}$ 1·60 ±0·10			3 inequivalent complexes, with axes ‖ edges of cubic unit cell	Gr1 54
		$g_{\perp}$ 1·87 ±0·04				
$K_2[PtCl_6]$ C.S. 8; d. 200	20	$g_x=g_y=g_z$† =1·78 ±0·02			All complexes equivalent	Gr3 53
$(NH_4)_2[PtCl_6]$ C.S. 8; d. 200	20	$g_x=g_y=g_z$ =1·775 ±0·001	$A_x=A_y=A_z$ =0·00265 ±0·00010	$A_1'=A_2'=A_3'$ =0·00088 ±0·00004	All complexes equivalent; x, y, z ‖ edges of cubic unit cell, and axes of Cl_6 octahedron. A' for ^{35}Cl	Gr1 54
$Na_2[PtBr_6]6H_2O$ C.S. 8; d. 200	20	g_x 2·25 ±0·02	A_x 0·00255 ±0·00010	A_1' 0·0057 ±0·0002	All complexes equivalent; x, y, z ‖ axes of Br_6 octahedron. A' mean for ^{79}Br, ^{81}Br	Gr1 54
		g_y 2·21 ±0·02	A_y 0·00255 ±0·00010	A_2' 0·0057 ±0·0002		
		g_z 0·75 ±0·10				
$Na_2[PtCl_6]6H_2O$ C.S. 8; d. 200	20	g_x 2·20 ±0·02	A_x 0·00255 ±0·00010	A_1' 0·00116 ±0·00004	All complexes equivalent; x, y, z ‖ axes of Cl_6 octahedron. A' for ^{35}Cl	Gr1 54
		g_y 2·07 ±0·02	A_y 0·00255 ±0·00010	A_2' 0·00107 ±0·00004		
		g_z 1·05 ±0·02	A_z 0·0024 ±0·0001	$A_3'<0·0005$		

† This g-value is more accurate than the value given in ref.

Nd^{3+}

Formula	T	$g_{\parallel}$	$g_{\perp}$	Isotope	A	B	Remarks	Ref.
$Mg_3La_2(NO_3)_{12}.24H_2O$ C.S. 3; d. 100	4·2	0·45 ±0·05	2·72 ±0·02	^{143}Nd	0·0052 ±0·0005	0·0312 ±0·0001		Co1 55
				^{145}Nd	0·0032 ±0·0003	0·0194 ±0·0001		
$La(C_2H_5SO_4)_3.9H_2O$ C.S. 9; d. 200	20	3·535 ±0·001	2·072 ±0·001	^{143}Nd	0·03803 ±0·00001	0·01989 ±0·00005	$^{143}A/^{145}A=1·6083±0·0012$	Bl14 54
				^{145}Nd	0·02364 ±0·00001	0·01237 ±0·00005		

Paramagnetic resonance absorption has also been reported for $Nd_2(SO_4)_3$ and $Nd_2(SO_4)_3.8H_2O$ ($T=290$, 90), Ku3 51; Nd_2O_3 ($T=290$, $g=3·2$), Ga 52a.

Sm^{3+}

Formula	T	$g_{\parallel}$	$g_{\perp}$	Isotope	A	B	Remarks	Ref.
$Mg_3Sm_2(NO_3)_{12}.24H_2O$ C.S. 3	4·2	0·76 ±0·01	0·40 ±0·05	^{147}Sm	0·0346 ±0·0005	<0·010		Co1 55
				^{149}Sm	0·0287 ±0·0005	<0·010		
$La(C_2H_5SO_4)_3.9H_2O$ C.S. 9; d. 100	4·2	0·596 ±0·002	0·604 ±0·002	^{147}Sm	0·0060 ±0·0001	0·0251 ±0·0001	$P<0·0004$	Bo4 52
				^{149}Sm	0·0049 ±0·0001	0·0205 ±0·0001	$^{147}A/^{149}A=1·222±0·008$	

Gd^{3+}

Formula	T	g	b_2^0	b_2^2	b_4^0	b_6^0	b_6^6	Ref.
$Mg_3Bi_2(NO_3)_{12}.24H_2O$ C.S. 3; d. 100	90, 20	1·992 ±0·003	+0·0124 ±0·0001		+0·00009 ±0·00001	+0·00006 ±0·00001	0·0012 ±0·0001	Tr 53
$La(C_2H_5SO_4)_3.9H_2O$ C.S. 9; d. 200	90	1·990 ±0·002	+0·0204$_7$ ±0·0002		−0·00039$_6$ ±0·00003	+0·00006$_3$ ±0·00001	+0·00035 ±0·00005	Bl14 54
	20		+0·0199$_8$ ±0·0001		−0·000391 ±0·000015	+0·000053 ±0·000005	+0·00040 ±0·00005	
$Sm_2(SO_4)_3.8H_2O$ C.S. a; d. 200	300		†(+)0·0633 ±0·0005	(+)0·038 ±0·005	(−)0·0013 ±0·0003			Bo3 54

† We are informed that the value of b_2^0 quoted in Bo3 54 is incorrect.

a. $Sm_2(SO_4)_3.8H_2O$. Zachariasen (1935): monoclinic, $M=4$, i.e. 8 Sm in unit cell. With Gd, the magnetic complexes are equivalent in fours. The axes are given by $\psi_z=28°$, $\alpha_z=\pm 35°$, $\psi_y=0°$, $\alpha_y=\pm 52°$, where ψ_i is angle between c and plane containing i axes, and α_i is angle between i axis and ac plane ($i=z, y$).

Paramagnetic resonance has also been observed with $La(NO_3)_3.6H_2O$ (d. 10), Ga 52b; $GdCl_3.6H_2O$, La 51; $Gd(BrO_3)_3.9H_2O$, Bl6 51.

References

(a) Crystallography

Astbury, W. T., 1926, *Proc. Roy. Soc.* A, **112,** 448.
Barkhatov, V., 1942, *Acta Phys.-chim. U.R.S.S.*, **16,** 123.
Barkhatov, V., and Zhdanov, H., 1942, *Acta Phys.-chim. U.R.S.S.*, **16,** 43.
Beevers, C. A., and Lipson, H., 1934, *Proc. Roy. Soc.* A, **146,** 570.
Beevers, C. A., and Schwartz, C. M., 1935, *Z. Kristallogr.*, **91,** 157.
Bokii, G. B., and Usikov, P. I., 1940, *C. R. Acad. Sci., U.R.S.S.*, **26,** 782.
Chrobak, L., 1934, *Z. Kristallogr.*, **88,** 35.
Cox, E. G., and Webster, K. C., 1935, *J. Chem. Soc.*, 731.
Fankuchen, I., 1935, *Z. Kristallogr.*, **91,** 473.
Ferrari, A., 1926, *R. C. Accad. Lincei*, **3,** 224.
Gottfried, C., and Nagelschmidt, J. G., 1930, *Z. Kristallogr.*, **73,** 357.
Groth, P., 1906, *Chemische Kristallographie* (Leipzig: Engelmann), Vol. 1; 1908, *Ibid.*, Vol. 2; 1910, *Ibid.*, Vol. 3.
Harker, D., 1936, *Z. Kristallogr.*, **93,** 136.
Hoard, J. L., and Stroupe, J. D., quoted by Dieke, G. H., and Duncan, A. B. F., 1949, *Spectroscopic Properties of Uranium Compounds*, National Nuclear Energy Series, III, 2 (New York: McGraw-Hill).
Hofmann, W., 1931, *Z. Kristallogr.*, **78,** 279.
Ketelaar, J. A. A., 1937, *Physica*, **4,** 619.
Lipson, H., 1935, *Proc. Roy. Soc.* A, **151,** 347.
Lipson, H., and Beevers, C. A., 1935, *Proc. Roy. Soc.* A, **148,** 664.
van Niekerk, J. N., and Schoening, F. R. L., 1953, *Acta Cryst., Camb.*, **6,** 227.
Pauling, L., 1930, *Z. Kristallogr.*, **72,** 482.
Pospelov, V. A., and Zhdanov, G. S., 1947, *J. Phys. Chem., Moscow*, **21,** 405.
Powell, H. M., and Wells, A. F., 1935, *J. Chem. Soc.*, 359.
Robertson, J. M., 1935, *J. Chem. Soc.*, 615.
Tutton, A. E. H., 1916, *Phil. Trans. Roy. Soc.* A, **216,** 1.
Wyckoff, R. W., 1920, *Amer. J. Sci.*, **50,** 317; 1951, *Crystal Structures* (New York: Interscience Publishers, Inc.), Vol. 2, Chap. 10.
Yu, S. H., and Beevers, C. A., 1936, *Z. Kristallogr.*, **95,** 426.
Zachariasen, W. H., 1935, *J. Chem. Phys.*, **3,** 197.

(b) Published Paramagnetic Resonance Data

Ab1 Abe, H., 1953, *Phys. Rev.*, **92,** 1572.
Ab2 Abe, H., Ono, K., Hayashi, I., Shimada, J., and Iwanaga, K., 1954, *J. Phys. Soc. Japan*, **9,** 814.
Ab3 Abe, H., and Shimada, J., 1953 a, *National Science Report*, Ochanomizu University, Vol. 4, no. 1, 77; 1953 b, *Phys. Rev.*, **90,** 316.
Abragam, A., and Pryce, M. H. L., 1951, *Proc. Roy. Soc.* A, **205,** 135.
Ar Arakawa, T., 1954, *J. Phys. Soc. Japan*, **9,** 790.
Ba1 Bagguley, D. M. S., Bleaney, B., Griffiths, J. H. E., Penrose, R. P., and Plumpton, B. I., 1948, *Proc. Phys. Soc.*, **61,** 551.
Ba2 Bagguley, D. M. S., and Griffiths, J. H. E., 1950 a, *Proc. Roy. Soc.* A, **204,** 188; 1950 b, *Ibid.*, **201,** 366; 1952, *Proc. Phys. Soc.* A, **65,** 594.
Bainbridge, K. T., and Nier, A. O., 1954, *Preliminary Report No.* 9, *Nuclear Science Series*, N. R. C. Washington, D.C.
Ba4 Baker, J. M., and Bleaney, B., 1952, *Proc. Phys. Soc.* A, **65,** 952; 1955, *Ibid.*, **68,** 257.
Ba5 Baker, J. M., Bleaney, B., and Bowers, K. D., 1955, in the press.
Be Bennett, J. E., and Ingram, D. J. E., 1955, *Nature, Lond.*, **175,** 130.
Bi Bijl, D., and Rose-Innes, A. C., 1953, *Proc. Phys. Soc.* A, **66,** 954.

Bl1 BLEANEY, B., 1950 a, *Phys. Rev.*, **78,** 214; 1950 b, *Proc. Roy. Soc.* A, **204,** 203; 1951, *Phil. Mag.*, **42,** 441.
Bl2 BLEANEY, B., BOGLE, G. S., COOKE, A. H., DUFFUS, R. J., O'BRIEN, M. C. M., and STEVENS, K. W. H., 1955, *Proc. Phys. Soc.* A, **68,** 57.
Bl3 BLEANEY, B., and BOWERS, K. D., 1951, *Proc. Phys. Soc.* A, **64,** 1135; 1952, *Proc. Roy. Soc.* A, **214,** 451.
B14 BLEANEY, B., BOWERS, K. D., and INGRAM, D. J. E., 1955, *Proc. Roy. Soc.* A, **228,** 147.
B15 BLEANEY, B., BOWERS, K. D., and TRENAM, R. S., 1955, *Proc. Roy. Soc.* A, **228,** 157.
Bl6 BLEANEY, B., ELLIOTT, R. J., SCOVIL, H. E. D., and TRENAM, R. S., 1951, *Phil. Mag.*, **42,** 1062.
B17 BLEANEY, B., and INGRAM, D. J. E., 1951 a, *Proc. Roy. Soc.* A, **205,** 336; 1951 b, *Ibid.*, **208,** 143; 1952, *Proc. Phys. Soc.* A, **65,** 953.
Bl8 BLEANEY, B., INGRAM, D. J. E., and SCOVIL, H. E. D., 1951, *Proc. Phys. Soc.* A, **64,** 601.
Bl9 BLEANEY, B., LLEWELLYN, P. M., PRYCE, M. H. L., and HALL, G. R., 1954 a, *Phil Mag.*, **45,** 992; 1954 b, *Ibid.*, **45,** 991.
Bl10 BLEANEY, B., and LOW, W., 1955, *Proc. Phys. Soc.* A, **68,** 55.
Bl11 BLEANEY, B., and PENROSE, R. P., 1948, *Proc. Phys. Soc.*, **60,** 395.
Bl12 BLEANEY, B., PENROSE, R. P., and PLUMPTON, B. I., 1949, *Proc. Roy. Soc.* A, **198,** 406.
Bl13 BLEANEY, B., and SCOVIL, H. E. D., 1952, *Phil. Mag.*, **43,** 999.
Bl14 BLEANEY, B., SCOVIL, H. E. D., and TRENAM, R. S., 1954, *Proc. Roy. Soc.* A, **223,** 15.
I BLEANEY, B., and STEVENS, K. W. H., 1953, *Rep. Progr. Phys.*, **16,** 108 (London: Physical Society).
Bl15 BLEANEY, B., and TRENAM, R. S., 1954, *Proc. Roy. Soc.* A, **223,** 1.
Bo1 BOGLE, G. S., COOKE, A. H., and WHITLEY, S., 1951, *Proc. Phys. Soc.* A, **64,** 931.
Bo2 BOGLE, G. S., DUFFUS, H. J., and SCOVIL, H. E. D., 1952, *Proc. Phys. Soc.* A, **65,** 760.
Bo3 BOGLE, G. S., and HEINE, V., 1954, *Proc. Phys. Soc.* A, **67,** 734.
Bo4 BOGLE, G. S., and SCOVIL, H. E. D., 1952, *Proc. Phys. Soc.* A, **65,** 368.
Bo5 BOWERS, K. D., 1952, *Proc. Phys. Soc.* A, **65,** 860; 1953, *Ibid.*, **66,** 666.
Br BROVETTO, P., CINI, G., and FERRONI, S., 1953, *Nuovo Cim.*, **10,** 1325.
Co1 COOKE, A. H., and DUFFUS, H. J., 1955, *Proc. Roy. Soc.* A, **229,** 407.
Co2 COOKE, A. H., DUFFUS, H. J., and WOLF, W. P., 1953, *Phil. Mag.*, **44,** 623.
Da DAVIS, C. F., KIP, A. F., and MALVANO, R., 1951, *R. C. Accad. Lincei*, **11,** 77.
EISENSTEIN, J. C., and PRYCE, M. H. L., 1955, *Proc. Roy. Soc.* A, **229,** 20.
ELLIOTT, R. J., and STEVENS, K. W. H., 1953, *Proc. Roy. Soc.* A, **219,** 387.
Ga GARAFIANOV, N. S., 1952 a, *Thesis*, Kazan University, quoted by Kozyrev, B. M., 1954, *J. Chim. Phys.*, **51,** 104; 1952 b, *Doklady Akad. Nauk.*, **84,** 923; see *Sci. Abstr.*, 1953, 5569.
Gh GHOSH, S. N., GORDY, W., and HILL, D. G., 1954, *Phys. Rev.*, **96,** 36.
Gi GIJSMAN, H. M., GERRITSEN, H. J., and VAN DEN HANDEL, J., 1954, *Physica*, **20,** 15.
Gr1 GRIFFITHS, J. H. E., and OWEN, J., 1952 a, *Proc. Roy. Soc.* A, **213,** 459; 1952 b, *Proc. Phys. Soc.* A, **65,** 951; 1954, *Proc. Roy. Soc.* A, **226,** 96.
Gr2 GRIFFITHS, J. H. E., O'BRIEN, M. C. M., OWEN, J., and WARD, I. M., 1955, to be published.
Gr3 GRIFFITHS, J. H. E., OWEN, J., and WARD, I. M., 1953, *Proc. Roy. Soc.* A, **219,** 526.
Ha1 HALLIDAY, D., and WHEATLEY, J., 1948, *Phys. Rev.*, **74,** 1712.
Ha2 HAYASHI, I., and ONO, K., 1953, *J. Phys. Soc. Japan*, **8,** 270.
He HERSCHBERGER, W. D., and LEIFER, H. N., 1952, *Phys. Rev.*, **88,** 714.
Ho HOLDEN, A. N., KITTEL, C., and YAGER, W. A., 1949, *Phys. Rev.*, **75,** 1443.
Hu1 HURD, F. K., SACHS, M., and HERSCHBERGER, W. D., 1954, *Phys. Rev.*, **93,** 373.
Hu2 HUTCHINSON, C. A., and LEWIS, W. B., 1954, *Phys. Rev.*, **95,** 1096.
Hu3 HUTCHINSON, C. A., and SINGER, L. S., 1953, *Phys. Rev.*, **89,** 256.
In1 INGRAM, D. J. E., 1953 a, *Proc. Phys. Soc.* A, **66,** 412; 1953 b, *Phys. Rev.*, **90,** 711.
In2 INGRAM, D. J. E., and BENNETT, J. E., 1954, *J. Chem. Phys.*, **22,** 1136.
It ITOH, J., FUJIMOTO, M., and IBAMOTO, H., 1951, *Phys. Rev.*, **83,** 852.
JUDD, B. R., 1955, *Proc. Roy. Soc.* A, in the press.
Ki1 KIKUCHI, C., SIRVETZ, H. M., and COHEN, V. W., 1953, *Phys. Rev.*, **92,** 109.
Ki2 KIP, A. F., DAVIS, C. F., JENNINGS, L., REINER, D., and MALVANO, R., 1951, *Nuovo Cim.*, **8,** 683.
Ko KOZYREV, B. M., SALIKHOV, S. G., and SHAMONIN, YU. YA., 1952, *J. Exp. Theor. Phys.*, **22,** 56, see *Sci. Abst.*, 1953, 3431.
Ku1 KUMAGAI, H., ONO, K., HAYASHI, I., ABE, H., SHIMADA, J., SHONO, H., and IBAMOTO, H., 1951, *Phys. Rev.*, **83,** 1077.
Ku2 KUMAGAI, H., ONO, K., HAYASHI, I., and KAMBE, K., 1952, *Phys. Rev.*, **87,** 374.
Ku3 KURENEV, V. YA. and SALIKHOV, S. G., 1951, *J. Exp. Theor. Phys.*, **21,** 864, see *Sci. Abstr.*, 1952, 5194.

La LANCASTER, F. W., and GORDY, W., 1951, *J. Chem. Phys.*, **19,** 1181; 1952, *Ibid.*, **20,** 740.
Me MEIJER, P. H. E., 1951, *Physica*, **17,** 899.
Ok OKAMURA, T., and DATE, M., 1954, *Phys. Rev.*, **94,** 314.
On1 ONO, K., 1953, *J. Phys. Soc. Japan*, **8,** 802.
On2 ONO, K., KOIDE, S., SEKIYAMA, H., and ABE, H., 1954, *Phys. Rev.*, **96,** 38.
Ow OWEN, J., 1955 a, *Proc. Roy. Soc.* A, **227,** 183; 1955 b, to be published.
Pe1 PENROSE, R. P., and STEVENS, K. W. H., 1950, *Proc. Phys. Soc.* A, **63,** 29.
Pe2 PERAKIS, N., WUCHER, J., and GIJSMAN, H. M., 1954, *C. R. Acad. Sci., Paris*, **239,** 243.
PRYCE, M. H. L., 1950, *Proc. Phys. Soc.* A, **63,** 25.
Ra RAMASESHAN, S., and SURYAN, G., 1951, *Phys. Rev.*, **84,** 593; 1952, *Proc. Indian Acad. Sci., Bangalore*, A, **36,** 211.
Sc SCHNEIDER, E. E., and ENGLAND, T. S., 1951, *Physica*, **17,** 221.
STEVENS, K. W. H., 1952, *Proc. Phys. Soc.* A, **65,** 209; 1953, *Proc. Roy. Soc.* A, **219,** 542.
Si SINGER, L. S., 1955, *J. Chem. Phys.*, **23,** 379.
Ti1 TING, Y., and WILLIAMS, D., 1951, *Phys. Rev.*, **82,** 507.
Ti2 TINKHAM, M., 1955, *Proc. Phys. Soc.* A, **68,** 258.
Tr TRENAM, R. S., 1953, *Proc. Phys. Soc.* A, **66,** 118.
Ub1 UBBINK, J., POULIS, J. A., GERRITSEN, H. J., and GORTER, C. J., 1952, *Physica*, **18,** 361.
Ub2 UBBINK, J., POULIS, J. A., and GORTER, C. J., 1951, *Physica*, **17,** 213.
Vi VITTORELLI, M. B. P., PALMA, M. U., PALEMBO, D., and SANTANGELO, M., 1953, *Ric. Sci.*, **23,** 1423.
VAN VLECK, J. H., 1932 a, *The Theory of Electric and Magnetic Susceptibilities* (Oxford: University Press); 1932 b, *Phys. Rev.*, **41,** 208; 1935, *J. Chem. Phys.*, **3,** 807; 1939, *Ibid.*, **7,** 61.
Wh WHITMER, C. A., WEIDNER, R. T., HSIANG, J. S., and WEISS, P. R., 1948, *Phys. Rev.*, **74,** 1478.
Ya YAGER, W. A., MERRITT, F. R., HOLDEN, A. N., and KITTEL, C., 1949, *Phys. Rev.*, **75,** 1630.
Yo YOKOZAWA, Y., 1954, *Monogr. Res. Inst. Appl. Elect. Hokkaido Univ.*, **4,** 95.
ZAVOISKY, E., 1945, *J. Phys., U.S.S.R.*, **9,** 211.

(c) Unpublished Paramagnetic Resonance Data

Ba1 u BAGGULEY, D. M. S., GRIFFITHS, J. H. E., and OWEN, J.
Ba2 u BAGGULEY, D. M. S., OWEN, J., and WARD, I. M.
Ba3 u BAKER, J. M., and BLEANEY, B.
Bo1 u BOGLE, G. S., and COOKE, A. H.
Bo2 u BOGLE, G. S., and OWEN, J.
Bo3 u BOWERS, K. D.
Ge u GERRITSEN, H. J., BOLGER, B., and OKKES, R. F.
Gr u GRIFFITHS, J. H. E., and WARD, I. M.
Ow1 u OWEN, J.
Ow2 u OWEN, J., and WARD, I. M.
Pa u PALMA, M. U.
Tr u TRENAM, R. S.

Index

P

Q

R

S